BASIC
INTEGRATED
CIRCUITS

BASIC

INTEGRATED CIRCUITS

MYLES H. MARKS

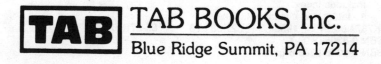
TAB BOOKS Inc.
Blue Ridge Summit, PA 17214

Also by the Author from TAB BOOKS Inc.

No. 1719   *29 Electronic Projects for Your Home, Car and Workshop*

This book is lovingly dedicated to my parents, Ben and Mildred.

FIRST EDITION

FIRST PRINTING

Copyright © 1986 by TAB BOOKS Inc.

Printed in the United States of America

Library of Congress Cataloging in Publication Data

Marks, Myles H.
    Basic integrated circuits.

    Includes index.
    1. Integrated circuits.   I. Title.
TK7874.M274   1986   621.381'73   85-27610
ISBN 0-8306-0409-X
ISBN 0-8306-0509-6 (pbk.)

Contents

Preface

It has often been said that necessity is the mother of invention. This statement was never more true than when developing the integrated circuit. The transistor was invented at Bell Laboratories in 1948 and very rapidly began to replace the vacuum tube in many applications. Even more importantly, however, transistors and semiconductor diodes began to be used in entirely new applications where vacuum tube implementation would have been impossible. One of these applications was in digital electronics. During the 1950s computers were being constructed that incorporated as many as 25,000 transistors and 100,000 diodes in each unit! The job of building a computer possessing more than 125,000 discrete components was mind boggling. During that era, transistors were of the planar type and were typically made in batches on a single wafer of semiconductor material. Each transistor would then have to be separated from each other into single units. Then, lead wires would be attached and the final unit would be packaged. These individual transistors were mounted onto printed circuit boards and soldered into place. Why not manufacture entire circuits on a single chip rather than making transistors all in a batch, separating them, and then reassembling them into circuits? This would definitely eliminate lots of tedious work!

Both Texas Instruments (TI) and Fairchild began intensive efforts to develop integrated circuits. In March, 1960, TI announced it had developed an integrated circuit for the military. Fairchild was in the process of developing its "Micrologic" product line of integrated circuits while TI was developing its 51-series logic family. Only one year later, both companies were manufacturing integrated circuits in production quantities. In October, 1961, TI delivered a small computer which had several hundred bits of semiconductor memory to the U.S. Air Force.

These early integrated circuits employed *Resistor-Transistor Logic* (RTL). The *Transistor-Transistor Logic* (TTL) types, most commonly used today, were developed by a small California company, Pacific Semiconductors, Inc. The large conglomerate, TRW Industries, later acquired Pacific Semiconductors.

Work was proceeding on the development of the field-effect transistor during this same period. The insulated gate FET (IG-FET) was developed in 1962 by two RCA engineers. Soon thereafter, RCA began to experiment with the development of integrated circuits using *Metal-Oxide Semiconductor* (MOS) technology. Using MOS technology in making integrated circuits afforded a number of advantages. They were simpler and less expensive to make and consumed less power. On the other hand, MOS circuits were slower than their bipolar counterparts. Furthermore, MOSFETs could easily be damaged by static electricity. Early production problems plagued the development of MOS integrated circuit devices. It wasn't until 1970 when some of these problems were finally resolved and the production of MOS integrated circuits skyrocketed.

The revolution which started with the development of the transistor in 1948 continues even today. Recently, IBM announced the development of a *random-access memory* (RAM) device which can store over a million bits of information on a single chip. What will be the next major breakthrough in digital electronics? No one can answer that question, of course. If the events of the past quarter-century are any indication of the future, however, there definitely will be more breakthroughs as long as there are problems waiting to be solved and intelligent people with imaginations who will provide the solutions. Who knows? After learning the basics of integrated circuits from this book, maybe you will invent the next major breakthrough in electronic technology. Go for it!

BASIC
INTEGRATED
CIRCUITS

Introduction

The primary driving force behind the widespread use of digital electronics has been the abundance of low cost, integrated circuits. Advances in integrated circuit technology have produced hundreds of excellent, low cost yet highly functional types of circuitry. These circuits are very small in size, inexpensive, and extremely reliable. Medium scale and large scale (MSI and LSI) circuits can even replace entire circuits and instruments. Electronic equipment designers recognize the availability of these devices and are taking advantage of them. Even though digital electronics and techniques have been known for many years, it was the integrated circuit that made them practical. Many equipment improvements have been made by using digital integrated circuits. Significant reductions in size, weight, cost, and power consumption usually result when analog methods are replaced with digital techniques. A few more reasons why digital integrated circuitry is so popular are:

Greater Accuracy. Digital integrated circuitry affords greater precision and resolution when representing quantities or in making measurements than do analog techniques.

Greater Stability. Digital techniques greatly minimize or completely eliminate problems such as drift and component tolerance problems which affect analog circuitry. Varying transistor biases can also cause nonlinear operation and distortion in analog circuits, which do not occur in digital methods.

Greater Dynamic Range. The difference between the upper and lower data values that can be handled properly within a system is called the dynamic range. Because of component capabilities and noise, analog systems are limited to a range less than 100,000 to 1. With digital techniques, however, almost any desired dynamic range can be attained.

Convenience. Digital integrated circuitry makes instruments and equipment much more convenient to use. For example, digital readout displays are not only more easy to read, but the possibility of errors from reading or interpolating analog meters or indicator dials is eliminated.

Automation. Many electronic processes can be fully automated when digital techniques are employed. Special control circuits or a computer can be programmed to automatically set up, control, and monitor many operations. Furthermore, data can be readily recorded, stored, and displayed.

Design Simplicity. Digital electronic equipment is relatively easy to design. The readily available integrated circuits make digital design a real pleasure. Breadboarding is mandatory in analog circuits to ensure a workable design, but digital equipment can go directly from "blue print" design to finished product in a very short time.

New Approaches. Digital techniques allow new approaches to the solution of electronic equipment design. Design problems which were impossible to solve with analog circuits are easily solved with digital integrated circuitry. In fact, digital circuits make possible some functions having absolutely no analog equivalent whatsoever!

This book is dedicated to teaching you how to become an efficient and competent digital integrated circuit designer and to take advantage of all the benefits integrated circuit technology has to offer without having to spend countless hours of classroom training and experimenting. It is also designed to take a common sense approach to this subject. You will initially refresh your memory on the basics of semiconductor devices and how they work and progress in a step-by-step manner all the way through combinational and sequential logic circuits and design.

Although this book is intended for the novice electronic enthusiast, some knowledge or exposure to electronics and basic algebra are a prerequisite for total comprehension of this text.

Chapter 1

Review of Discrete Semiconductors

C OMPREHENSION OF LOGIC CIRCUITS IS BASED ON A KNOWL-
edge of bipolar transistor operation. A thorough understanding of transistor fundamentals is a prerequisite to this book.
Therefore, this chapter is devoted to refreshing your understanding of this most important subject. Do not skip over this chapter
even if you are familiar with transistors. Your knowledge of their
operation will be greatly enhanced by building a firm foundation
of the basics. Due to the nature of the topic discussed, it is important that you read this entire chapter in one sitting rather than
breaking it up into several sessions.

HOW THE TRANSISTOR WORKS

A transistor is a semiconductor device consisting of three
elements, and it is used in electronic equipment for controlling
larger currents in proportion to variations in smaller currents. Transistors may be used as linear amplifiers and as switches.

Transistors are made from semiconductor materials such as
silicon or germanium. These materials have inherent resistances
somewhere between that or true conductors and insulators. The
resistance of silicon, therefore, is *greater* than the resistance of a
true conductor such as copper. Because the conductivity of silicon
is between that of true conductors and pure insulators such as glass
or ceramic, it is called, therefore, a *semiconductor*.

There are two types of semiconductor materials: p-type and n-type. A semiconductor such as silicon is combined with other elements to form these two different types. This process is known as *doping*. For example, pure silicon is *doped* with certain impurities to form p-type and with different impurities to form n-type semiconductors. N-type material contains an excess amount of free electrons. Therefore, the majority current carriers in an n-type semiconductor are *electrons*. Similarly, in p-type material, the majority current carriers are called *holes*. A hole is the absence of an electron in the atomic structure of p-type semiconductor material which acts like a positive charge. P-type semiconductor material has an excess amount of holes to support current flow. Therefore, in n-type material, current flow is by electrons and in p-type material, current flow is by holes.

Transistors and other semiconductor devices such as diodes and integrated circuits are made by joining n-type and p-type semiconductor materials. For example, a junction diode is formed by joining an n-type section to a p-type section as shown in Fig.1-1A. The n-type section is called the *cathode*, and the p-type section is called the *anode*. The *pn* junction thus formed possesses unilateral characteristics: Current will flow through it in *only one direction* and is blocked in the opposite direction, as shown in the schematic representation of a diode in Fig. 1-1B. A junction diode, therefore, is responsive to the direction of current flow.

If a dc voltage is applied to a junction diode, current may or

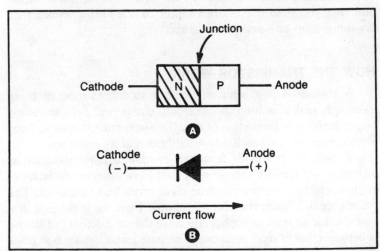

Fig. 1-1. (A) A pn junction diode. (B) Schematic symbol for a pn junction diode.

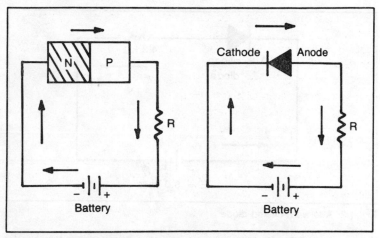

Fig. 1-2. Forward biasing a pn junction diode into conduction.

may not flow through it depending upon the *polarity* of the applied voltage. This voltage applied to a diode is called *bias*. Figure 1-2 shows a common way of biasing a junction diode. The series resistor, R, limits the current through the diode to prevent damage to it.

In Fig. 1-2, electrons flow from the negative terminal of the battery into the n-type semiconductor material of the diode. Since there is an inherent potential barrier associated with the junction of the diode, the battery voltage must be high enough to overcome this barrier and cross the junction to "fill" the holes in the p-type semiconductor material. As the holes in the p-type semiconductor are filled, they are constantly replaced with new holes as electrons are "pulled" from the p-type semiconductor by the positive terminal of the battery. This constant current flow is commonly referred to as *forward bias*. To forward bias a junction diode into conduction, therefore, it is necessary to connect the *anode* to the *positive* terminal of a power source and the *cathode* to the *negative* terminal of the same power source.

A constant voltage drop of approximately 0.7 volt exists across a silicon diode. Similarly, a constant voltage drop of approximately 0.3 volt exists across a germanium diode. This voltage drop is essentially constant regardless of the amount of current flowing through the diode as long as there is some current flowing. Figure 1-3 shows an example of how to calculate the current flowing through a diode circuit. Noted that the diode is forward biased since the polarity of the applied voltage is connected as described above. Since it is

3

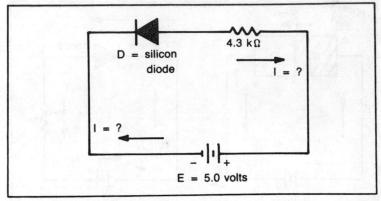

Fig. 1-3. A forward-biased diode

known that a 0.7 volt drop exists across the silicon diode, Kirchoff's Law tells us that there are (5 - 0.7) = 4.3 volts present across the 4.3 kilohm resistor, R, of the circuit. Ohm's Law tells us that the current (I) is equal to the voltage (4.3) divided by the resistance (4.3 K). The result is .001 A or 1mA. (amps multiplied by 1,000 equals milliamps.)

A forward-biased diode conducts electricity and acts as a very low resistance, permitting current to flow freely through it. If, however, the polarity of the applied voltage is reversed, as shown in Fig. 1-4, the diode is said to be reverse biased. When a diode is reverse biased, the electrons from the negative terminal of the battery fill the holes of the p-type semiconductor. Simultaneously, the excess electrons in the n-type semiconductor are drawn away by the positive terminal of the battery. This arrangement causes the current carriers (holes and electrons) to be drawn away from the

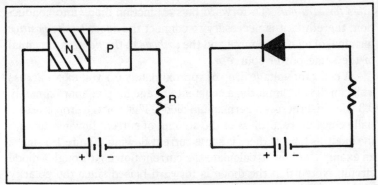

Fig. 1-4. A reverse-biased pn junction diode.

4

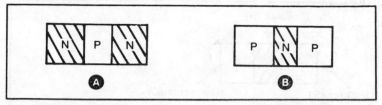

Fig. 1-5. (A) An npn bipolar transistor. (B) A pnp bipolar transistor.

junction of the two semiconductors within the diode, permitting no current to flow. The diode, therefore, acts in essence as an *open circuit*. In a practical silicon diode, however, some leakage current will flow through the junction even if it is reverse biased. This leakage current is usually very low and for all practical purposes can be considered to be negligible.

As can be seen, a diode is sensitive to applied voltage polarity and current will flow through it in only one direction: from cathode to anode.

Bipolar transistors are merely extensions of the junction diode concept. They are formed by fusing the p-type and n-type semiconductor materials to form *two* junctions. This is accomplished with three semiconductor elements as shown in Fig. 1-5. Figure 1-5A shows an *npn* transistor while Fig. 1-5B shows a *pnp* transistor. Note the physical differences between them. Figure 1-6 shows the respective schematic symbols of the two types of bipolar transistors. The distinguishing feature between the schematic designations is the direction of the arrow. Both types of transistors have two pn junctions. Each pn junction behaves exactly like the pn junction previously discussed. Each of the three elements comprising the transistor is given a specific name as shown in Fig. 1-7.

In a transistor, current flows from the *emitter* through the *base*

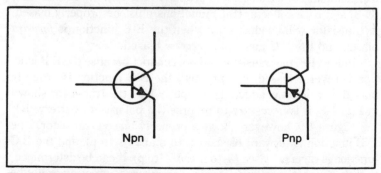

Fig. 1-6. Schematic symbols for npn and pnp transistors.

5

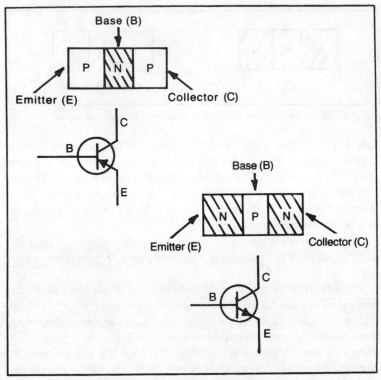

Fig. 1-7. Identifying the three elements of a bipolar transistor.

and to the *collector*. The current carriers in a pnp transistor are *holes* and the current carriers in an npn transistor are *electrons*. The amount of current flowing from the emitter to the collector is determined by the amount of current flowing through the base. Therefore, the base of a transistor can be referred to as the control element. For a transistor to properly function, the emitter-base (E-B) and base collector (B-C) junctions must be properly biased. A transistor will conduct only when the E-B junction is *forward* biased and the B-C junction is *reverse* biased.

In Fig. 1-8, the transistor will *not* conduct because the E-B junction is reverse biased. Even though the B-C junction is properly biased, it will not conduct. To properly bias the transistor shown in Fig. 1-8, it is necessary to reverse the polarity of battery, B1.

Figure 1-9, however, shows a properly-biased transistor. The E-B junction is forward biased (+ to p and − to n), and the B-C junction is reverse biased (+ to n and − to p). It can be determined, therefore, whether a transistor in a circuit is conducting or not be

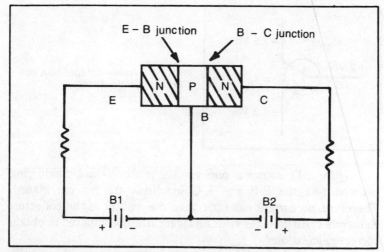

Fig. 1-8. An improperly biased pnp transistor.

merely measuring the dc voltages present at each element and noting their respective polarities. As can be seen from Fig. 1-10, the npn transistor is, in fact, conducting since the conditions for biasing a transistor to conduction are met: The E-B junction is forward biased since the base is more positive than the emitter. Likewise, the B-C junction is reverse biased since the collector is more positive than the base. Note the 0.7 volt difference between the emitter and base of the transistor. This is the same inherent voltage drop present in the conducting state of a silicon diode as previously discussed. Most contemporary solid-state devices are made from silicon.

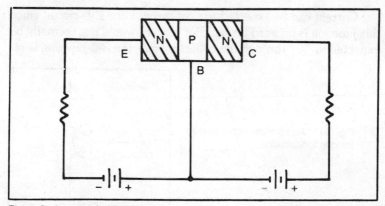

Fig. 1-9. A properly biased npn transistor.

7

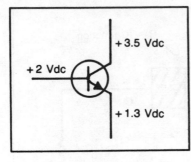

Fig. 1-10. Typical voltages on a conducting npn transistor.

+ 3.5 Vdc

+ 2 Vdc

+ 1.3 Vdc

Figure 1-11 shows a pnp transistor that is *not* conducting because *both* the E-B and E-C junctions are reverse biased. Therefore, no current can flow from the emitter to the collector. Remember: All voltages *must* be algebraically compared to obtain correct calculations!

Figure 1-12 shows the actual path of electron flow within a properly biased npn transistor. A large current (I_E) flows into and through the emitter, through the base and to the collector. A small amount of current branches off from the base. This is the forward bias current at the E-B junction which is commonly referred to as the "base current" (I_B). Its value is usually considerably less than the emitter current. The remaining current (I_C) flows through the collector.

The collector current (I_C) is usually very near the value of the emitter current (I_E). It is only slightly less in value by the amount of base current (I_B). The exact relationship can be expressed as:

$$I_C = I_E - I_B$$

Current can be expected to flow through the E-B circuit since this junction is forward biased. But current would not normally be expected to flow through the collector since the B-C junction is re-

Fig. 1-11. An npn transistor biased for nonconduction.

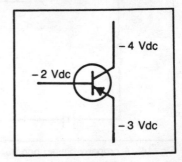

− 4 Vdc

− 2 Vdc

− 3 Vdc

8

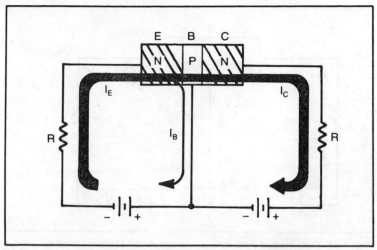

Fig. 1-12. Current flow in a properly biased npn transistor.

verse biased. Here's why: The electrons flowing through the emitter enter the base. In the base, some of the electrons combine with holes in the p-type base and create a current flow from the base. However, most of the electrons pass *through* the base and into the collector. This is because the base material is extremely thin and contains only a minimum number of current carriers to support current flow. The electrons passing through the base are subsequently attracted to the collector by the positive charge on the collector. The collector current, therefore, is about the same as the emitter current. Most of the electrons in the emitter pass through the thin base and into the collector to become collector current. A few electrons, however, combine with holes in the base to produce a small base current.

The current flow in a properly biased pnp transistor is similar to that within a npn transistor as shown in Fig. 1-13. The current carriers in a pnp transistor are *holes* rather than *electrons*. The holes flow internally from positive to negative. The transistor's external *electron* flow is indicated by the dashed lines. The internal hole currents within a pnp transistor have the same relationship as the electron currents do within an npn transistor:

$$I_C = I_E - I_B$$

The external electron flow to the transistor can be also expressed:

9

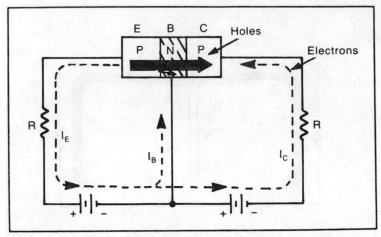

Fig. 1-13. Electron and hole flow in a properly biased pnp transistor.

$$I_E = I_C + I_B$$

The above two expressions are mathematically identical, since either one can be derived from the other by simple transposition.

To restate the above relationship: The collector current is always less than the emitter current by the amount of the base current.

The ratio of the collector current to the emitter current is approximately *one* since, in most cases, the collector current is almost equal to the emitter current. This ratio is commonly referred to as the *forward current gain* or *alpha*. The Alpha (α) can be expressed as:

$$\alpha = \frac{I_C}{I_E}$$

Practical values of α are in the neighborhood of .95 to .99. The higher the α (or gain), the better the transistor is. Even though α is *always* less than one, it is still referred to as the transistor's gain.

Figure 1-14 illustrates another approach to biasing a transistor. Since the emitter is the common element to both power sources, rather than the base as in previous examples, this configuration is known as a *common emitter* circuit.

The transistor in the common emitter circuit conducts since the E-B junction is forward biased and the B-C junction is reverse

10

biased. This reverse bias condition can be easily recognized by considering the voltage on the base: With the E-B junction forward biased, this makes the base voltage 0.7 volt more positive than the emitter. The collector is more positive than the base (with respect to the emitter) since E_2 is +5 volts. Thus, the base is less positive (or more negative) than the collector. Therefore, the B-C junction is reverse biased.

Figure 1-15 shows how current flows in a common emitter circuit. The relationship between the currents can be expressed as:

$$I_E = I_C + I_B$$

Restated, the base current and the collector current combine at the emitter to comprise the emitter current. This relationship holds true for any common emitter-biased transistor circuit.

Note that in Fig. 1-15, both power sources, E1 and E2, are positive with respect to the emitter. Therefore, they can be replaced by a *single* power source as shown in Fig. 1-16. This results in properly biasing the transistor for conduction with only one power supply instead of two! The values of resistors R_B and R_C are calculated to provide proper current levels for the transistor. The power source, labeled Vcc, is called the collector supply.

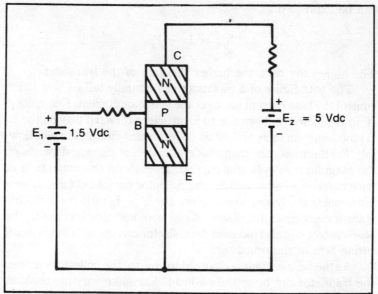

Fig. 1-14. Properly biasing a common-emitter-connected npn transistor.

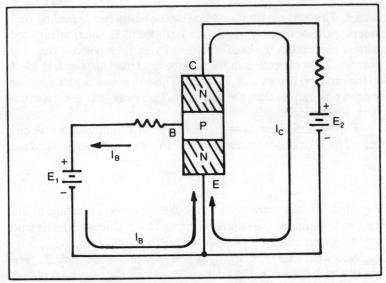

Fig. 1-15. Current flow in a common-emitter circuit.

The base current is always less than the collector current as was previously discussed. The ratio of the collector current to the base current is yet another way to define the gain of a transistor. This ratio is the dc forward current gain called *beta* (β) or h_{FE}. It can be expressed as:

$$h_{FE} = I_C \div I_B$$

The higher the beta, the higher the gain of the transistor.

The beta figure of a transistor can actually tell us how much control the base current has over the collector current. Remember: If no base current flows due to insufficient forward bias on the E-B junction, then there will be no collector nor emitter current flowing. Furthermore, the magnitude of collector current depends on the magnitude of collector current depends on the magnitude of base current. In other words, the collector current is directly proportional to the base current. Since the $I_C \div I_B$ ratio remains constant for any given transistor, it can be noted that increasing the base current will also increase the collector current by a factor equal to the beta of the transistor.

As the base current is changed to control the collector current, the transistor can be considered to behave like variable resistor: A high collector current results from a low emitter-to-collector resistance while a low collector current results from a high emitter-to-collector resistance. An increase in base current, therefore, causes the emitter-to-collector resistance to decrease.

In linear amplifier applications a small input signal to the base is all that is required to produce much larger collector currents of the same wave form or "shape" at the output of the amplifier.

The transistor can also be used to perform the function of an on-off switch. If there is no base current applied, then no collector current flows since the transistor exhibits a very high resistance. The transistor is said to be *cut off* and acts as an open switch. Likewise, if a relatively high base current is applied, then the tran-

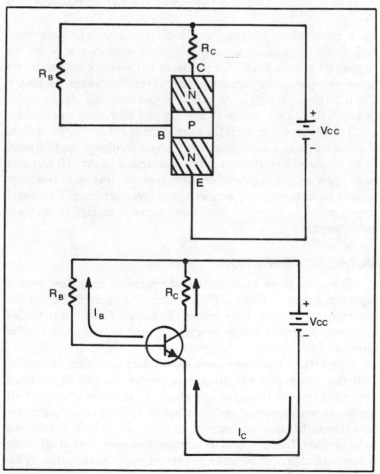

Fig. 1-16. Biasing an npn transistor from a single voltage source.

sistor conducts since it exhibits a very low resistance. The transistor is said to be *saturated* and acts like a closed switch.

THE BIPOLAR TRANSISTOR SWITCH

The basic element used in digital logic circuits is a simple switch. Most of today's digital integrated circuits use a high speed transistor switch as the primary element. The two basic types of transistor switches used in the design of digital integrated circuits are (1) the bipolar transistor, and (2) the metal oxide semiconductor field effect transistor (MOSFET). A thorough comprehension of these two devices is necessary to understand the operation, capabilities and limitations of the various types of digital integrated circuits.

A transistor switch in a digital logic circuit has a primary function of either connecting the circuit's power supply a load or disconnecting it from the load. This produces two distinct voltage levels across the load by the transistor, which represent either the binary 1 (on) on binary 0 (off) state. This transistor switch should make or break these connections as quickly and efficiently as possible.

The bipolar transistor is the most commonly used digital switch. It operates as an on/off (two-state) device in digital applications. In its off state the transistor is not conducting (is cut off) and acts as an open circuit. In its on state, however, the transistor conducts heavily (is saturated) and acts as a very low resistance. To control this operation, a two-state logic input signal is applied to the transistor switch.

MODES OF OPERATION

There are three basic modes of operation associated with a bipolar transistor: (1) cut off; (2) linear; (3) saturated. Digital circuits use all three of these modes. The cut off and linear modes are used in non-saturation modes are used in saturated bipolar circuits.

Cut Off. A transistor does *not* conduct in the cut off mode. Both the collector-base (C-B) and the emitter-base (E-B) junctions are either reverse biased or not biased at all when in the cut off mode. As was discussed earlier, when no emitter or collector current flows, the transistor acts as an open switch or is considered to be turned off. In practical transistors, however, the cut off mode is not perfect and some leakage current does, in fact, flow. This is due primarily to imperfections in different semiconductor materials from which the transistor is made. In today's transistors this leakage current is extremely low and can be neglected for most practical purposes. However, leakage current can become an important consideration where very high operating temperatures can be expected. For example, in silicon transistors, the leakage current almost doubles for each 10 °C rise in temperature!

Linear. Linear operation of transistors is used in nonsaturating digital integrated circuits. In the linear mode of operation (also referred to as the *active mode*) the emitter-base (E-B) junction is forward biased and the collector-base (C-B) junction is reverse biased. Emitter and collector current flows, so the transistor does conduct. The emitter and collector currents, however, are directly proportional to the variations of the base current. The emitter and collector currents are merely *amplified* versions of the same base current variations. The transistor functions as a variable resistor in this mode and is used to amplify analog signals.

Saturation. In the saturated mode of operation both the emitter-base (E-B) junction *and* the collector base (C-B) junction are forward biased. The transistor acts as a very low resistance and conducts heavily. The emitter to collector resistance approaches a short circuit and is analogous to a switch being in its turned on state.

When used as a switch in digital integrated circuit applications, the bipolar transistor is usually switched between its cut off mode and saturated mode. During the finite time in which it switches, however, the transistor must pass through the linear region. It is important, therefore, that bipolar transistor switches are designed to switch as quickly as possible between cut off and saturation in order to make these two states as stable as possible. Even in nonsaturating digital integrated circuit applications, speed of switching between cut off and linear modes is a paramount consideration.

SATURATED SWITCHING CIRCUITS

Figure 1-17 illustrates one of the most common forms of saturated bipolar logic switches. This circuit is called a *transistor logic inverter*. In this circuit the transistor is connected as a shunt switch. In other words, it is connected in parallel across the output load, R_L.

When the input voltage, V_I, is zero (or at ground), the transistor is in its cut off mode, and the emitter-base (E-B) junction is not forward biased. Therefore, the transistor does not conduct. Only a very small leakage current can flow through the collector in this

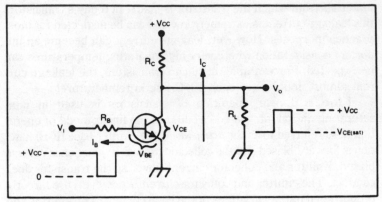

Fig. 1-17. Simple transistor switch

state. With no load connected to the output (R_L = infinity) the output voltage, V_O, is equal to the supply voltage, VCC. If, however, a resistive load, R_L, is connected to the circuit, then the output voltage, V_O, will be a value less than the supply voltage, VCC, which can be calculated by using the following formula:

$$V_O = VCC \{R_L \div (R_C + R_L)\}$$

When a sufficiently high input signal, V_I, is applied to the circuit in Fig. 1-17, the transistor will conduct since the emitter-base (E-B) junction will become forward biased. The transistor will be in either the linear or saturated mode depending upon the amplitude of the input voltage, V_I, the value of the base resistor, R_B, and the gain (β or h_{FE}) of the transistor.

Figure 1-18 illustrates typical input and output waveforms of a transistor switch circuit. When the input voltage, V_I, is *low*, the

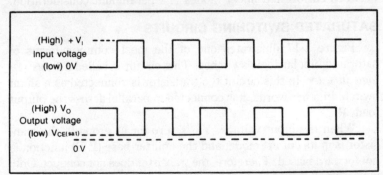

Fig. 1-18. Input and output waveforms in a shunt transistor switch.

16

transistor is in its cut off mode which results in a *high* output voltage, V_O. Similarly, when the input voltage, V_I, is high, the transistor goes into its saturation mode and acts as a low resistance which results in a low output voltage, V_O. This output voltage, V_O, is equal to the emitter-collector saturation voltage, V_{CE} *(sat)* which is typically a few tenths of a volt and can be considered to be a low (zero) for all practical purposes. As can be seen, the output voltage is high when the input voltage is low. Conversely, the output voltage is low when the input voltage is high. This is the reason for calling this circuit an *inverter*.

In a logic circuit, the amplitude of V_I and the value of R_B must be sufficient to permit enough base current to flow to drive the transistor into its saturation mode. This occurs only when the actual base current, I_B, is greater than the ratio of the collector current, I_C, to β (h_{FE}) of the chosen transistor. In mathematical terms:

$$\text{For saturation: } I_B > I_C \div h_{FE}$$

The base current, I_B, is directly proportional to the applied input voltage, V_I, and inversely proportional to the value of the base resistor, R_B. This relationship can be expressed as:

$$I_B = (V_I - 0.7) \div R_B$$

where 0.7 is the voltage drop across the forward biased emitter-base junction.

The base current, I_B, can also be calculated if the collector current, I_C, and the h_{FE}, of the transistor are known:

$$I_B = I_C \div h_{FE}$$

A transistor will saturate if the base current, I_B, is *greater* than this ratio. Therefore, both the emitter-base (E-B) and the collector-base (C-B) junctions will be forward biased. When the transistor is in this state, it will be conducting heavily and the resistance between the emitter and collector will be very low. In most switching transistors, this resistance should be between 5 and 30 ohms. Since this value is very low, the voltage drop across the emitter and collector, V_{CE} (sat), will be only a few tenths of a volt during saturation. Therefore, it can be considered to negligible for all practical purposes since it is so low as compared to the supply voltage, V_{CC}.

When a transistor is in its saturated mode, the magnitude of emitter and collector current is primarily a function of the supply voltage, VCC, and the collector resistance, R_C. Since the voltage drop across the emitter-collector of the transistor can be considered to be zero, the collector current can be calculated from the following formula:

$$I_C = VCC \div R_C$$

Remember that this relationship is only valid when there is sufficient base current to drive the transistor into its saturated mode. If the base current is less than the ratio of $I_C \div h_{FE}$, then the transistor will be operating somewhere in its linear mode. That is, even though the emitter-base junction will be forward biased, the collector-base junction will be reverse biased. As a result, the collect-emitter voltage, VCE, will be correspondingly higher.

There are two methods of determining whether a transistor is operating in its linear or saturated mode. First, you can simply measure the voltages at each of the junctions of the transistor, noting the polarity of the voltage at each element with respect to the other. From these measurements you can determine the state of the transistor.

Figure 1-19 shows typical voltages present on an npn transistor for both its linear mode (A), and its saturated mode (B). In its linear mode, Fig. 1-19(A), the emitter-base junction is forward biased since the junction voltage, VBE, is of proper polarity. Furthermore, it was discussed that a conducting silicon junction has a typical voltage drop of 0.7 volt. Moving along to the collector-base junction, you can see that the VCB is 1.3 volts with the collector more positive than the base. This indicates a reverse-biased junction.

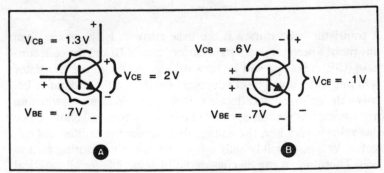

Fig. 1-19. Voltages and polarities in a conducting transistor: (A) biased for linear operation. (B) biased for saturated operation.

18

Lastly, the voltage drop across the emitter and collector, V_{CE}, is 2 volts. The voltage drops across a transistor operating in its linear mode can be expressed by the formula:

$$V_{CE} = V_{BE} + V_{CB}$$

In its saturated mode, Figure 1-19B, note that the emitter-base voltage, V_{BE}, is still 0.7 volt and the transistor is forward biased. However, note the polarity of the collector base voltage, V_{CB}. In this example, the base is more positive than the collector by 0.6 which indicates a forward-biased condition. Note, again, that the collector-emitter voltage, V_{CE}, is the *algebraic* sum of V_{CB} and V_{BE}. In this example: $0.7 + (-0.6) = 0.7 - 0.6 = 0.1$ volt. Since this is such a low voltage drop across the emitter-collector junction, it indicates that the effective resistance of the transistor must be extremely low, too. Another characteristic of a transistor operating in its saturated mode is that since there is such a low collector-emitter voltage drop, the power dissipation within the transistor is minimal, thereby reducing heat and increasing the overall efficiency of the circuit. The power dissipation can be calculated by the formula:

$$P = V_{CE} \times I_C$$

It can be noted that even though the collector current may be relatively large, the power dissipation will be kept low as a result of such a small value of the emitter-collector voltage, V_{CE}.

The alternate method of determining the state of a transistor is to measure both the base and collector currents and then determine if the base current is less than or greater than the ratio of the collector current, I_C to the h_{FE} of the transistor. As discussed earlier, if:

$$I_B > (I_C \div h_{FE}), \text{ then the}$$

transistor is saturated. On the other hand, if:

$$I_B < (I_C \div h_{FE}), \text{ then the}$$

transistor is operating in its linear mode. It should be pointed out that the *actual* value of h_{FE} depends upon many factors, among them the type of transistor being used, the magnitude of current flowing through the transistor and the operating temperature. Current gain can even vary between different transistors of the same type. This is why digital designers ensure saturation within a switching transistor by selecting a base resistor value small enough to produce a base current with a minimum logic input voltage greater than the ratio of $I_C \div h_{FE}$. This safety factor is necessary to ensure saturation under all desired conditions. However, when the base current is *greater* than the ratio of $I_C \div h_{FE}$, then the base is being overdriven; a condition which may produce excessive power dissipation and heat, and which could result in damage to the transistor.

SWITCHING SPEED

The ability to switch rapidly between logic levels (binary 0 and binary 1) is one of the most important characteristics of a logic circuit. The switching speed of a logic circuit is dependent upon the characteristics of the individual transistor, the component values of the circuit, stray inductance and capacitance, the voltage and current levels used within the circuit, and the chosen circuit configuration. When the signal changes at the input of a digital logic circuit changes from one level to the other, the output level does *not* respond to the change instantaneously. A delay time does, in fact, exist between the change in the applied input signal and the resulting change at the output of the circuit. This delay time is called *propagation delay* and is usually expressed in terms of nanoseconds (10^{-9} seconds).

The amount of base drive applied to a transistor primarily determines its turn-on time. Therefore, a heavy base current can help ensure a rapid turn on time. The turn-off time delay of a transistor is primarily determined by the characteristics of the selected transistor. When a transistor is saturated, there becomes an excess of minority carriers (electrons in a pnp transistor and holes in an npn transistor) built up near the collector-base junction. This *charge storage* keeps the transistor conducting for a period of time even after the base drive is removed. After a finite period of time, however, this charge storage leaks off and the transistor begins to come out of saturation. This charge storage time is determined by the transistor's characteristics and the amount of base drive applied to its input. By selecting the proper transistors, circuit configuration, and values of components, the switching delay times can be significantly reduced. Modern high speed switching transistors typically can change from one state to the other in only a matter of a few nanoseconds.

NONSATURATED SWITCHING CIRCUITS

As previously explained, the primary cause of slow switching speed of a bipolar transistor is the storage time associated with saturating the transistor. Since this storage time is the most significant aspect of the turn-off time, and means of minimizing it will help to increase the switching speed of the transistor. Special bipolar switching transistors are designed to have a minimum charge storage, *external circuitry*.

The simplest way to increase switching speed is to keep the transistor from saturating. This will prevent charge storage within the transistor and will permit very high switching speeds. A large number of digital logic integrated circuits have been designed which incorporate non-saturating bipolar transistor switches which switch between cut off and linear operation. Some of these ICs are capable of switching at frequencies in excess of 1 GHz.

DESIGNING A SATURATED SWITCH INVERTER

Even though modern digital equipment is implemented with integrated circuits, sometimes it becomes necessary or desirable to supplement the integrated circuit with a discrete-component circuit to accomplish a special function. Such special function could include logic level conversion, a lamp or LED driver or a relay driver. Three examples of such circuits, incorporating a saturated bipolar transistor switch, are illustrated in Fig. 1-20.

Figure 1-20 (A) is merely a logic inverter which provides an output level which may or may not be the same as its input level. This type of circuit is useful when interfacing different types of logic circuits. Figure 1-20 (B) is a LED driver. In this circuit, the LED will light when a sufficient input voltage, V_i, is applied to the circuit. The transistor acts as an on-off switch controlled by V_i. Figure 1-20 (C) shows a similar circuit which will activate relay, K1, when sufficient voltage is applied to its input. Diode, D1, is used to protect the transistor from reverse voltage which is generated when the voltage is removed from the relay coil. This reverse emf occurs when the transistor cuts off causing the magnetic field within the coil of the relay to collapse. This collapsing magnetic field can cause a very high negative voltage spike which can damage the

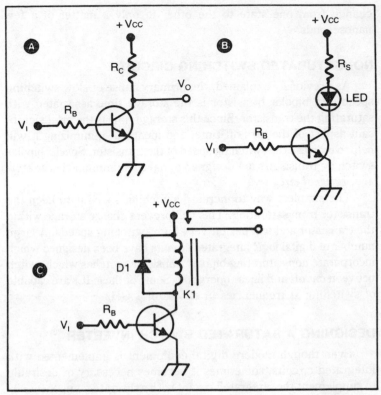

Fig. 1-20. A bipolar transistor switch used as: (A) a logic inverter, (B) an LED driver, (C) a relay driver.

transistor. This negative voltage spike causes diode, D1, to conduct which "clamps" the collector voltage to a safe level.

Since these circuits are very common with digital integrated circuitry, it is desirable, therefore, to become familiar with them and know how to design them. You should master the following procedure to reinforce your understanding of these circuits:

1. Define the parameters of the load. For lamp, LED or relay driver, the characteristics of the load should be determined. This includes the rated operating voltage, current and/or resistance. If any two of these three specifications are given, the third one an be calculated by using Ohm's law ($E = I \times R$). Similarly, if the circuit is going to be used as an inverter to supply a signal to an external load, the load voltage, current, and/or resistance must be specified.

2. Determine a supply voltage. The supply voltage, Vcc, should be equal to or greater than the operating voltage of the load. Typically, the circuit should operate from a standard power source such as +5, +9, or +12 volts.

3. Select a suitable transistor. Many types are available, and the best choice depends upon the exact requirements or application. A transistor designed for switching rather than for linear applications should be selected. The voltage and current ratings needed will be a function of the load and power supply characteristics. The voltage breakdown and collector current ratings of the transistor should be at least two times the values which will occur during operation. Switching speed and h_{FE} requirements, will depend on the application. Manufacturers' data sheets, if available, should contain all necessary information regarding exact characteristics of any given transistor.

4. Calculate the value of a series dropping resistor, if one is necessary. If the selected power supply voltage, Vcc, is greater than the required operating voltage for load device, then a series dropping resistor, R_s, will be necessary (see Fig. 1-20B). The voltage drop across this resistor will be the power supply voltage, Vcc, minus the load voltage, V_L, and minus the saturation voltage of the transistor, VCE (sat). The value of resistance, R_s, can then be calculated by using the formula:

$$R_s = [VCC - V_L - VCE (sat)] \div I_C$$

where I_C is the current of the load device and the Collector voltage, VCE (sat), is so low that it can be ignored for all practical purposes. Choose a standard resistor with a value closest to this calculation. NOTE: This step does *not* apply to calculating the value of a collector resistor used in an inverter circuit (See step 6).

5 Define an output voltage. If the circuit being designed is an inverter with a shunt load to ground, R_L, the required output voltage, V_O, should be specified. It will have to be some value less than the power supply voltage, VCC, which will depend on the values of resistors, R_C, and R_L (See Fig. 1-21). The output voltage, V_O, can thus be calculated by the formula:

$$V_O = VCC \times [R_L \div (R_C + R_L)]$$

If, however, the circuit has no shunt load (R_L) to ground, then V_O = VCC.

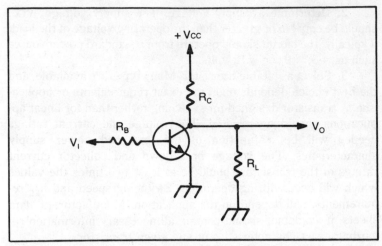

Fig. 1-21. Logic inverter with shunt load.

6. Calculate the value of the collector resistor. If the circuit being designed is an inverter with a shunt load to ground, then the value of the collector resistor, R_C, can be calculated if the power supply voltage, VCC, load resistance, R_L, and required output voltage, V_O, are known. Be rearranging the previous formula:

$$R_C = [R_L \times (VCC - V_O)] \div V_O$$

Again, choose the closest resistor value which is available.

7. Calculate the collector current. The collector current will be the current specified for the device to be driven if the circuit is to be used as a driver. However, for the inverter circuit described in the previous step, the collector current can be calculated by the formula:

$$I_C = VCC \div R_C$$

In the above expression the transistor's saturation voltage, VCE (sat), should be subtracted from the supply voltage, VCC, to be exactly correct. However, since VCE (sat) is usually only a few tenths of a volt, it can be considered to be negligible and, therefore, ignored in the above formula.

8. Calculate the base current. The base current, I_B can be found from the collector current, I_C, and the gain, h_{FE}, (from the manufacturer's data sheet) of the transistor by the formula:

$$I_B = I_C \div h_{FE}$$

The above formula is derived from transposing the expression of the definition of the gain, h_{FE}, of a given transistor. Remember:

$$h_{FE} = I_C \div I_B$$

Furthermore, to provide sufficient "overdrive" to ensure saturation, it is strongly suggested to incorporate a safety factor into the calculation by derating the minimum rated h_{FE} by *at least* 50% when using the above formula. Therefore:

$$I_B = I_C \div [h_{FE} \text{ (min.)} \div 2] = [2 \times I_C] \div h_{FE} \text{ (min)}$$

9. Calculate the base resistor. The Base resistor, R_B, can be calculated from the formula:

$$R_B = (V_i - V_{BE}) \div I_B$$

In the above formula the input voltage, V_i, should be the *lowest* expected value of base drive voltage. In other words, it is the minimum value of voltage required to produce a binary 1 (high level) for positive logic. The Base-Emitter voltage, V_{BE}, is typically 0.7 volt for silicon transistors, as was previously discussed.

If the circuit being designed is going to be driven by another inverter, as shown in Fig. 1-22, then the supply voltage and collector resistance of the driver should be considered. When transistor

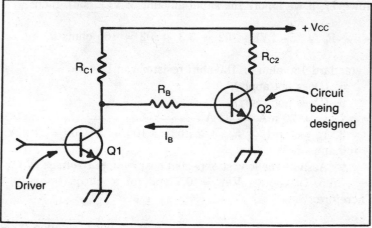

Fig. 1-22. Designing a saturated switch logic inverter.

Q1 cuts off, the circuit will be energized by base current, I_B, flowing through base resistor, R_B, and the collector resistor, R_{C1} of the driver circuit. Therefore:

$$R_B = (VCC - I_B \times R_{C1} - VBE) \div I_B$$

Choose the closest standard value of resistance for resistor, R_B.

Three practical examples for the application of this procedure will now be presented:

Sample Application #1

Design an LED driver circuit like the one shown in Figure 1-20B. (The following steps correspond to the numbers discussed in the above procedure):

1. The load is a light-emitting diode LED. Normal brilliance of an LED is obtained with 20 mA of current flowing through it. It operates with a normal voltage (V_L) of 1.7.
2. The power supply voltage (VCC) will be +5.
3. An MPSA20 silicon transistor is selected. It has a minimum h_{FE} of 100.
4. A series dropping resistor (R_S) is required since the voltage drop of the LED (V_L) is less than the power supply voltage (VCC). Therefore:

$$R_S = [VCC - V_L - VCE (sat)] \div I_C$$

However, if we ignore the small amount of VCE (sat), then:

$$R_S = (5 - 1.7) \div .02 = 3.3 \div .02 = 165 \text{ ohms } \Omega.$$

A standard 150-ohm or 180-ohm resistor can be used.

5. (Does not apply).
6. (Does not apply).
7. $I_C = 20 \text{ mA} = .02 \text{ A}$.
8. $I_B = 2 \times I_C \div h_{FE} = 2 (.02) \div 100 = .04/100 = .4 \text{ mA}$. $= 400$ amps (μA).
9. Assume the lowest expected positive input voltage (V_i) to be + 3.5. Of course, VBE = 0.7 volt for a silicon transistor. Therefore:

$$R_B = (V_i - VBE) \div I_B = (3.5 - 0.7) \div .0004 = 7,000 \ \Omega$$

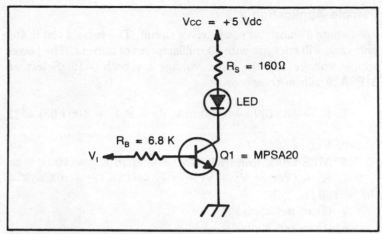

Fig. 1-23. Practical bipolar transistor LED driver.

A standard 6.8 k Ω resistor can be used. See Fig. 1-23 for the completed design of the LED driver circuit.

Sample Application 2

Design an inverter circuit like the one shown in Fig. 1-22 which will apply + 6 v (V_O) a 600 Ω load (R_L). The power supply voltage (VCC) will be + 15 and the driving signal (V_i) will be supplied from the power supply via a 1,000 Ω (1 kΩ) collector resistor.

    1. R_L = 600 Ω; V_L = + 6 V
    2. VCC = + 15 volts
    3. Select an MPSA20 silicon transistor.
    4. (Does not apply)
    5. V_O = 6 volts
    6. R_{C2} = [R_L (VCC − V_O)] ÷ V_O R_{C2} = [600 (15 − 6)] ÷ 6 = [600 (9)] ÷ 6 = 900 Ω

Use a standard 910 ohm resistor.

    7. I_C = VCC ÷ R_C = 15 ÷ 910 = .0165 A = 16.5 mA.
    8. I_B = 2 I_C ÷ h_{FE} = 2 (.0165) ÷ 100 = .00033 A = .33 mA = 330 μA
    9. R_B = (VCC − $I_B R_{C1}$ − VBE) ÷ I_B R_B = [15 − (.00033) (1000) − .7] ÷ .00033 = 13.97 ÷ .00033 = 42,333 Ω

Use a standard 39 kΩ resistor. See Fig. 1-24 for the completed inverter circuit design.

Sample Application 3

Design a transistor relay driver circuit. The relay's coil is 400 ohms and will energize with 30 milliamperes of current. The power supply voltage and the input voltage are both +15. Select an MPSA20 silicon transistor.

1. $R_L = 400 \, \Omega$; $I_L = I_C$ 30 mA; $V_L = R_L I_C = 400 \, (.03) = 12$ V

2. $V_{CC} = +15$ V

3. MPSA20 silicon transistor. Minimum $h_{FE} = 100$

4. $R_S = (V_{CC} - V_L - V_{CE}) \div I_C = (15 - 12) \div .03 = 3 \div .03 = 100 \, \Omega$

5. (Does not apply)

6. (Does not apply)

7. $I_C = I_L = 30$ mA.

8. $I_B = 2I_C \div h_{FE}$ (min.) $= 2 \, (.03) \div 100 = .06 \div 100 = .0006$ A $= 600 \, \mu$A

9. $R_B = (V1 - V_{BE}) \div I_B = (15 - .7) \div .0006 = 14.3 \div .0006 = 23,833 \, \Omega$

Use a standard 22 kΩ resistor. Figure 1-25 shows the completed design of the relay driver circuit.

MOS-FIELD-EFFECT TRANSISTORS

Another type of transistor widely used in digital integrated cir-

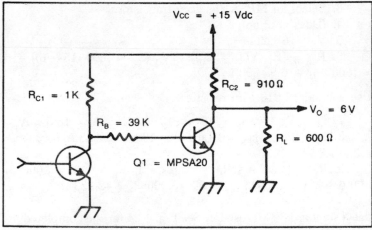

Fig. 1-24. Practical bipolar transistor inverter.

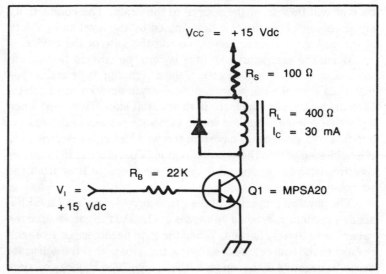

Fig. 1-25. Practical relay driver.

cuits is called the "enhancement-mode metal-oxide-semiconductor field-effect transistor" or simply MOSFET. Because of its physical design, it is also referred to as the "insulated gate field effect transistor" or IGFET. This device offers numerous advantages over the bipolar switching transistor, especially when incorporated in integrated circuits. It can be manufactured more easily and made smaller than the bipolar transistor and costs much less to produce, as well.

The N-Channel MOSFET

Figure 1-26 shows a cutaway view of the construction of an n-channel enhancement mode MOSFET. It is formed on a p-type silicon base (substrate) into which two n-type semiconductor materials are diffused. These two materials form the drain and the source of the transistor. A thin layer of silicon dioxide is diffused on top of it which acts like a glass insulator to isolate the source and drain from the remainder of the device. The insulated gate is diffused on top of the silicon dioxide layer. The gate element is merely a diffusion of metal such as aluminum or a silicon conductive material which forms a capacitor with the p-type silicon base. The silicon dioxide insulator acts as the dielectric. The area beneath the gate and between the source and drain is called the *channel*. When the drain is made positive with respect to the source, current will flow from the source to the drain. The conductivity of the channel, therefore, is determined by the level and polarity of the voltage between the source and the gate of the device.

When the gate-source voltage is zero, no current flows from the source to the drain. In effect, the alternate p-type and n-type materials between the source and the drain act like two back-to-back diodes both ot which are in their cutoff state. However, when a positive voltage is applied to the gate with respect to the source, and this voltage exceeds a certain threshold level, an electric field is established within the channel region. This electric field causes the transistor to conduct and permit electrons to flow from the source to the drain.

The physical properties of the gate-source design in a MOSFET act as a capacitor. When a voltage is applied to the gate-source the capacitor becomes charged. When the gate becomes positive with respect to the source, the area below the gate within the substrate becomes negative with respect to the source. The majority carriers (holes) in the p-type substrate will be depleted by the negative charge and, therefore, the electron density will be enhanced. This negative charge in the p-type substrate establishes a *channel* for current to flow between the two n-type regions. When the gate-source voltage is removed or if it is dropped below a certain threshold level, the conduction within the transistor will cease.

The enhancement-mode MOSFET makes an excellent switch. When the gate voltage is below the threshold level, the resistance between the source and the drain is extremely high (approaching infinity). Alternately, when the gate-source is above the threshold

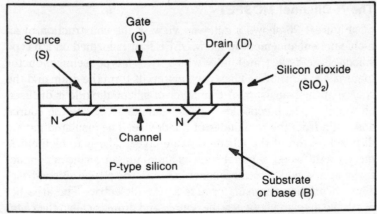

Fig. 1-26. Cutaway view of an n-channel enhancement-mode MOSFET.

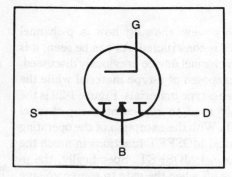

Fig. 1-27. Schematic symbol for a p-channel enhancement-mode MOSFET.

level, the transistor conducts heavily and the resistance between the drain and source approaches a short circuit (zero ohms). These properties of the enhancement-mode MOSFET make it an excellent choice for use in digital integrated circuits.

Since the input impedance between the source and the gate is extremely high in the MOSFET, which means that negligible current flows in its input, it is a far better candidate than the bipolar transistor for many applications. The typical input impedance between the source and the gate is, in fact, many thousand megohms and is effectively more capacitive than resistive. This very high input impedance minimizes the problems of loading down one logic circuit by the next one in a series of cascaded circuits. Figure 1-27 is the schematic symbol commonly used to represent the n-channel enhancement-mode MOSFET.

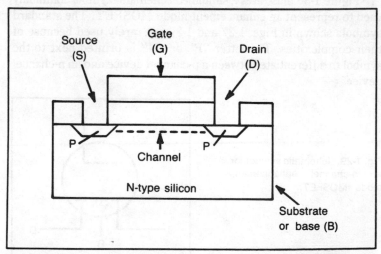

Fig. 1-28. Cutaway view of a p-channel enhancement-mode MOSFET.

The P-Channel MOSFET

Figure 1-28 is a cutaway view showing how a p-channel enhancement-mode MOSFET is constructed. As can be seen, it is very similar in design to the n-channel device previously discussed. However, the substrate is composed of n-type material while the source and drain diffusions are p-type materials. Figure 1-29 is the schematic symbol commonly used to represent the p-channel enhancement-mode MOSFET. With the exception of the operating voltage polarities, the p-channel MOSFET functions in much the same way as does the n-channel MOSFET. Specifically, the p-channel MOSFET is normally off when the gate to source voltage is below a certain threshold level. When the gate is made negative with respect to the source and is greater than the threshold level, the transistor will conduct heavily and current will flow between the source and the drain. The main difference in the p-channel MOSFET is that the current carries are holes rather than electrons.

One of the most important features of the enhancement-mode MOSFET is the variance of threshold voltages. There are two basic types of thresholds commonly used: low threshold and high threshold. Since the high-threshold devices are easier to manufacture, they are more common. This high threshold level is typically 3 to 4 volts. There are also devices available with low threshold levels in the neighborhood of 1 to 2 volts. Typically, however, p-channel MOSFETS are inherently high-threshold devices while n-channel MOSFETS are inherently low-threshold devices.

Figure 1-30 illustrates a simplified schematic symbol commonly used to represent an enhancement-mode MOSFET. The standard symbols shown in Figs. 1-27 and 1-29 are rarely used because of their complexities. The letter "P" or "N" is printed next to the symbol to differentiate between a p-channel device and an n-channel device.

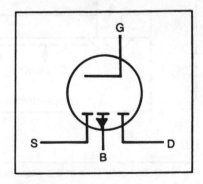

Fig. 1-29. Schematic symbol for an n-channel enhancement-mode MOSFET.

32

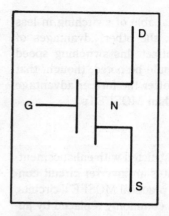

Fig. 1-30. Simplified symbol of an n-channel enhancement-mode MOSFET.

BIPOLAR TRANSISTORS VERSUS MOSFETS

The primary benefits of the MOSFET over the bipolar transistor are smaller size, simplicity of its construction, higher input impedance, and lower power consumption. However, like anything in the real world, there is a tradeoff—the major disadvantage of the MOSFET over the bipolar transistor is its slower switching speed. This slow switching speed is a result of the MOSFET's high input impedance and capacitive input characteristics, although mod-

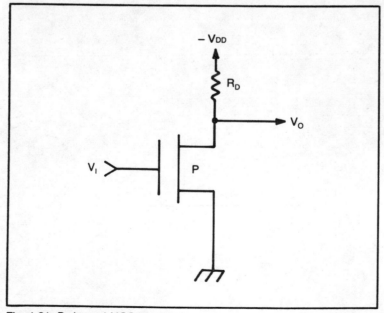

Fig. 1-31. P-channel MOS inverter.

33

ern MOSFETs have been produced capable of switching in less than 100 nanoseconds. Nevertheless, the other advantages of MOSFETs over bipolar transistors offset this switching speed drawback for most applications. It should be noted, though, that bipolar transistors are still faster and offer the further advantage of being able to handle more power than MOSFETs.

MOSFET CIRCUITS

Digital logic circuits are easily constructed with enhancement-mode MOSFETs. Figure 1-31 illustrates an inverter circuit constructed with a p-channel MOSFET. In practical MOSFET circuits, the drain resistor, R_D, is omitted. It is commonly replaced by another MOSFET which is biased on to act as a resistance. This method is used because a MOSFET is much smaller and occupies much less space in an integrated circuit than does a true resistor. Finally, it should be mentioned that a very popular type of MOS circuitry exists which combines both n-channel and p-channel devices to form what is commonly called complementary MOS or just *CMOS* logic devices.

Chapter 2

Digital Logic Circuits

E VERY PIECE OF ELECTRONIC EQUIPMENT USING DIGITAL
techniques is comprised of just a few basic types of circuitry.
Each of these circuits is called a "logic element." A logic element,
therefore, is a circuit which performs a specific logic function with
binary data.

The two basic types of digital logic circuits are decision-making
and memory. Decision-making logic elements produce outputs
based on the input status and the characteristic of the logic circuit.
Memory elements, however, serve the purpose of storing binary
data for later use.

It may be comforting to know that all digital equipment, simple or complex, is comprised entirely of these two types of logic
elements. Once it is learned how to use the basic logic elements
in their simplest forms, it will be easy to comprehend the operation of any piece of digital electronic equipment. Furthermore, by
understanding how to apply basic logic functions, you will possess
the capability to actually design your own digital electronic
equipment.

TYPES OF LOGIC CIRCUITS

As previously mentioned, the two basic types of logic circuits
are decision-making and memory. Both types produce binary outputs based on the status of their binary inputs. The output,
therefore, is a function of the input status and the characteristics

of the specific logic circuit.

Decision-making logic circuits do just exactly that: *make decisions.* The basic decision-making logic circuit is called a *gate.* A gate is comprised of two or more binary inputs and a single binary output. Figure 2-1 shows a generic symbol depicting a logic gate. Specific types of gates, however, are represented by particular symbols which represents the exact logic function of the particular gate. Each of the several types of decision-making gates has a particular symbol which clearly defines its exact operational characteristic. Each gate monitors its binary inputs and generates an appropriate binary output analogous to the decision it has made based on the status of its inputs and the logical function for which it is intended.

Although many simple logic functions can be implemented by using a gate, multiple gates are usually combined to form more sophisticated and complex decision-making logic networks called *combination circuits.* A combinational circuit is comprised of at least two gates containing two or more inputs and at least one output. Combinational circuits usually perform a unique function such as decoding, encoding, multiplexing, comparing or binary arithmetic. Figure 2-2 shows a generic block diagram of a combinational logic circuit.

The remaining type of logic element is the memory circuit. The basic memory circuit is a bistable storage device called a *flip-flop.* The flip-flop circuit can be stable in either of two states. Each state can represent either binary 1 or binary 0. The circuit can be "set" or "reset" into either state and maintain that condition thereby "remembering" the binary digit (bit) stored within it. Most memory circuits are capable of storing only a single bit of information. Therefore, it usually requires combining several memory elements to store complete binary numbers or words.

Memory elements can also be interconnected in combinational circuits to form an even-more sophisticated network called a *sequential circuit.* Figure 2-3 shows a generic block diagram of a sequential logic circuit. The inputs to the sequential circuit consist of applied binary data along with feedback signals developed within

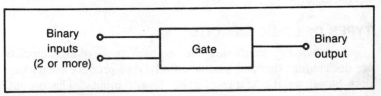

Fig. 2-1. Basic logic gate

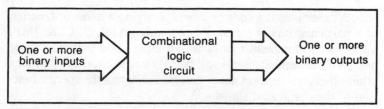

Fig. 2-2. Block diagram of a generic combinational logic circuit.

the sequential circuit itself. The outputs of the sequential logic circuit are binary signals used to control or operate other circuits or external devices. The output of this type of circuit is a function of the binary inputs, the binary data stored within the circuit itself, and the specific characteristics of the circuit in which it is used.

Sequential circuits can be used for a variety of different functions within digital electronic equipment. Common applications of sequential logic circuits are counters, timers, shift registers, sequencers and other circuits where it is desired to store and manipulate binary data at specified times.

There are three basic decision-making logic elements. They are: the *AND* gate, the *OR* gate, and the inverter or *NOT* gate. All remaining digital logic circuits are either variations or combinations of these three basic elements. Each of these three circuits accepts one or more binary inputs and generates only one binary output.

To eliminate confusion between binary input signals, and to be able to easily identify both binary inputs and outputs each signal is usually assigned a name or label. This label can be a code consisting of a letter, a word, or a *mnemonic* (pronounced: nee-MON-

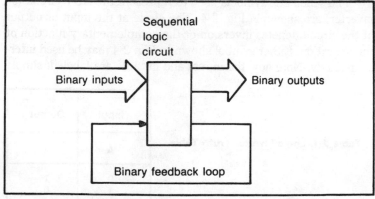

Fig. 2-3. Block diagram of a generic sequential logic circuit.

37

ick). A mnemonic is a code or label specifying a name or function of a particular binary signal. For example: A, B, C, CLK, JMP, CLR, etc. Throughout this book, all inputs and outputs will be assigned a mnemonic. Some will be only single-letter designations while others will be short abbreviations indicating the specific function of the designated signal.

THE INVERTER

The simplest digital logic element is the inverter or NOT circuit. The NOT circuit is a digital logic element which is characterized by having its output state being *always opposite* from its input state: If its input is a binary 1, then its output is a binary 0. Likewise, if its input is a binary 0, then its output is a binary 1. It is said, therefore, the inverter's output is the *complement* of its input. (Binary 1 is considered to be the complement of binary 0 and vice versa).

The operation of an inverter can be clearly defined by a simple chart called a *truth table*. A truth table is a chart which shows all possible input combinations and the resulting output states of a given circuit or gate. Table 2-1 is the truth table for the inverter. Note the input is labeled A while its corresponding output is designated $\overline{A}$ (read "A NOT" or "NOT A"). The bar over the letter A indicates the complement of A. As can be seen, the truth table shows the output state for each of the possible inputs states of the inverter. Since, however, the inverter has only a single input, there are, therefore, only two possible input combinations: 1 and 0. In each case the output is the complement (or the opposite state) of the corresponding input.

The schematic symbols used to represent the NOT circuit (or inverter) are shown in Fig. 2-4. The circle at the input or output of the circuit denotes inversion or the complementary function of the operation. Either symbol shown in Fig. 2-4 may be used interchangeably. Note how the inputs and outputs are labeled: simple

Table 2-1. Logic Inverter Truth Table.

Input	Output
A	$\overline{A}$
0 1	1 0

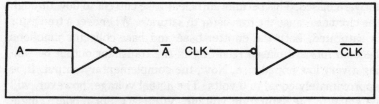

Fig. 2-4. Schematic symbol for logic inverter.

mnemonics are used instead of complicated wiring paths when possible to simplify the drawings and make them more readable. Remember, it is the function of the circuit and not circuit itself which is important when reading a logic circuit diagram.

The most common form of logic inverter is the transistor switch. Figure 2-5 shows how to construct a simple transistor switch which can be used as an inverter. This inverter operates with binary logic levels of 0 volts (ground) and a positive voltage level approximately equal to the supply voltage, + VCC. When the input, B, is 0 volts (or ground), the emitter-base junction is not forward biased and will not permit the transistor to conduct. Therefore, when the transistor is cut off, the output, $\overline{B}$, is the supply voltage, + VCC, with respect to ground as seen through collector resistor, R_C. With positive logic levels, as used here, a binary 0 input results in a binary 1 output from an inverter circuit.

Similarly, when a binary 1 (or positive voltage level approximately equal to the supply voltage + VCC) is applied to the input of an inverter, the emitter-base junction of the transistor becomes

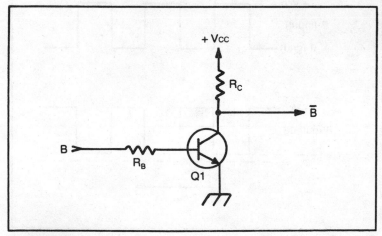

Fig. 2-5. Schematic symbol of a transistor logic inverter.

forward biased. This permits sufficient base current to flow through the circuit to cause the transistor to saturate. Whenever a transistor is saturated, both the emitter-base and base-collector junctions become forward biased resulting in the transistor output becoming a very low impedance. Now, the complementary output, $\overline{B}$, is approximately equal to 0 volts. The actual voltage, however, will be equal to the saturation voltage, V_{CE} (sat). For modern, high-speed switching transistors, this voltage is only a few tenths of a volt and can be considered negligible for all practical purposes. Again, when using positive logic levels, a binary 1 at the input of an inverter results in a binary 0 at its output. The waveforms representing the input and output operations of this circuit (versus time) are shown in Fig. 2-6. Most of today's switching transistors are capable of operating at speeds in the nanosecond range. Therefore, it is possible to design very fast circuitry operating at very high frequencies.

Figure 2-7 shows a picture of a typical 14-pin dual inline package (DIP) integrated circuit. Although most integrated circuits exhibit similar physical properties, their functions vary vastly. Therefore, to properly identify the function of a given chip, a part number is stamped on the body of each integrated circuit which identifies the chip as to its family (TTL, CMOS, Schottky, TTL etc.), and its function. For example, if the number begins with 74, such as 7400 or 7442, you know it belongs to the TTL (Transistor-

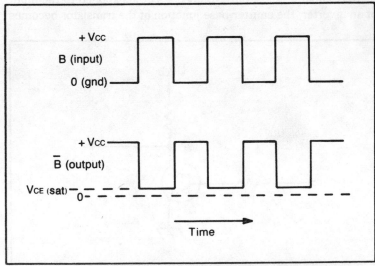

Fig. 2-6. Input and output waveforms of a transistor logic inverter.

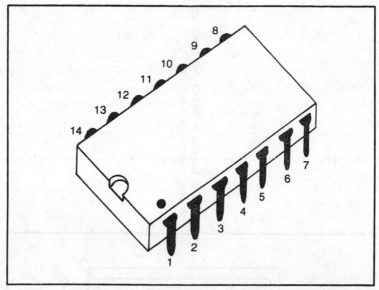

Fig. 2-7. Pinout designations of a digital IC in a 14-pin dual-in-line package (DIP).

Transistor Logic) family. Likewise, if the number begins with a 4 (4000 range), you can tell the chip is a CMOS device.

Figure 2-8 shows the logic diagram and pin out connections of the 7404 hex inverter integrated circuit. This chip contains six identical and independent logic inverters on a single substrate. The inputs and outputs are designated by pin numbers. There will be times when designing digital circuitry you will not use all six inverters contained within the 7404 chip. Unused TTL inputs are liable to pick up electrical noise which can cause unpredictable operation, and should be connected to a defined logic level. Therefore, they can be connected to either another input line or through a *pull-up* resistor to + Vcc.

DECISION-MAKING LOGIC ELEMENTS

There are two basic types of decision-making logic elements. They are the *AND* gate and the *OR* gate. These logic circuits each contain two or more inputs and have only a single output. The output state of each gate is a function of the applied input signals as well as the operation of the particular gate. The resulting output generated by the gate is the appropriate binary logic level as defined by the designer. Each of these basic gates will now be discussed in detail.

41

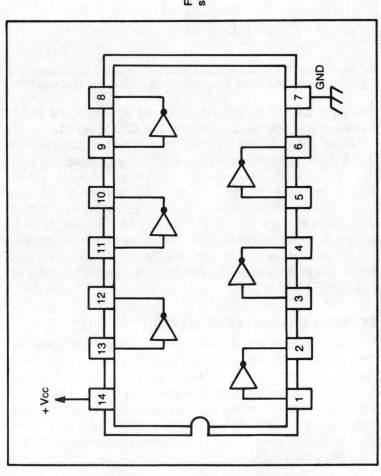

Fig. 2-8. Top view of the 7404 hex inverter IC, showing internal logic functions.

Inputs		Output
A	B	C
0	0	0
0	1	0
1	0	0
1	1	1

Table 2-2. Two-input AND Gate Truth Table.

THE AND GATE

The AND gate is a logic circuit element having two or more inputs with a single output. The gate's function is to have a binary 1 at its output *Only If All* inputs are binary 1. If any one or more of its inputs is binary 0, then the output of the AND gate will be binary 0.

Table 2-2 is the truth table for a two-input AND gate showing its logical operation. The inputs are referred to as *A* and *B*. Its output is designated *C*. The truth table shows the output status of the gate for all possible input combinations. For any given number of inputs to a gate, the total number of possible input combinations can be calculated by raising the number 2 to a power equal to the total number of inputs. For example: With two inputs (Table 2-2), each input being capable of assuming two binary states, the total number of possible input combinations is $2^2 = 4$. Note the output of the AND gate is 0 for any combination of inputs where any one or all are binary 0. By definition, the output of an AND gate is binary 1 *Only when all inputs are also binary 1.*

The standard schematic symbol used to represent a two-input AND gate is shown in Fig. 2-9. An AND gate, however, can have more than two inputs. Note how the inputs and output are labeled to correspond to the designations of the truth table in Table 2-2.

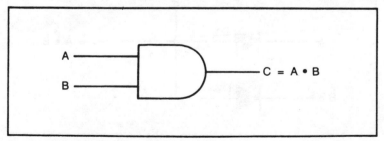

Fig. 2-9. Schematic logic symbol for AND gate.

43

It is important to point out the equation structure of the AND gate in Fig. 2-9: $C = A \bullet B$ or more simply: $C = AB$. This equation is the algebraic expression used to designate the logical AND function. The output, C, is expressed in terms of the inputs, A and B. The expression is read: "C equals A AND B." In logical equations, the AND function is represented by the dot between the input designations. The AND function, therefore, is represented in a fashion similar to the *product* of algebraic variables. (The plus sign (+) is NOT used to express the logical AND function, as would seem logical, because the plus sign (+) is used to represent the logical *OR* function which will be discussed later).

The operation of all logic circuits and gates can be expressed in algebraic equations. These expressions make it easy to analyze, design, and optimize logic circuits by using standard operations and special manipulations as defined by the rules of *Boolean* (pronounced: "BULL-yen") algebra. Boolean algebra is a special type of algebra which is useful in working with two-state binary variables. Boolean algebra will be explained in detail in Chapter 4.

Figure 2-10 shows how the logical AND gate can be implemented. Diodes, D1 and D2, and resistor, R, form an electronic circuit which produces the logical AND function when binary signals are applied to the inputs, A and B. In analyzing this circuit, we will define positive logic states of 0 volts (binary 0) and + 5 volts (binary 1). We will assume the diodes will have zero voltage drops across them when conducting and will also not have any

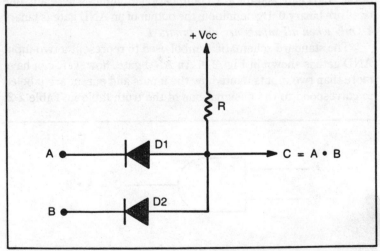

Fig. 2-10. Schematic diagram of a two-input diode AND gate.

voltage threshold before conducting. We can also define VCC to be a positive voltage higher than +5 volts.

Now, if *both* inputs are binary 0 (zero volts or ground) both diodes, D1 and D2, will conduct. Therefore, the output, *C*, will also be zero volts (remember: we are assuming the diodes to be perfect conductors). If either one of the inputs is a binary 0 while the other input is a binary 1 (+5 volts), the diode connected to the input of the binary 0 signal will still be forward biased and will still conduct thereby continuing to clamp the output, *C*, to the binary 0 state. The diode connected to the binary 1 (+5 volts) signal will be reversed biased and will be cut-off.

If, however, *both* inputs, *A* and *B*, are connected to a binary 1 (+5 volts) signal, then BOTH diodes, D1 and D2, will conduct and the output, *C*, will be +5 volts. Therefore, the only time the output of an AND gate can be binary 1, is when all inputs to the gate are also binary 1.

The characteristics and operation of the AND gate illustrated in Fig. 2-10 is detailed in the truth table, Table 2-3, and waveform timing diagram, Fig. 2-11. Note that when positive logic is implemented, the voltage truth table (Table 2-3) is identical to the logic truth table (Table 2-2). In the waveform timing diagram, Fig. 2-11 both inputs, *A* and *B*, are shown switching from binary 0 (ground) and binary 1 (+5 volts) at various times. The corresponding output, *C*, is also shown. Note that the only times when the output, *C*, is a binary 1 (+5 volts), is when *Both* inputs, *A* and *B*, are likewise, a binary 1. In other words, the output, *C*, of any AND gate is a binary 1 for the period when *all* inputs are *simultaneously (coincidentally)* binary 1s. Therefore, the AND gate is sometimes called a *coincident gate*.

Figure 2-12 illustrates a common application of the AND gate in digital circuitry. In this application one input is used for transferring data (XYZ) from the input to the output while the other input (*CTL*) controls its passage. This *CTL* "control" signal either in-

Table 2-3. Two-input Diode AND Gate Voltage Truth Table.

Inputs		Output
A	B	C
0 V	0 V	0 V
0 V	+5 V	0 V
+5 V	0 V	0 V
+5 V	+5 V	+5 V

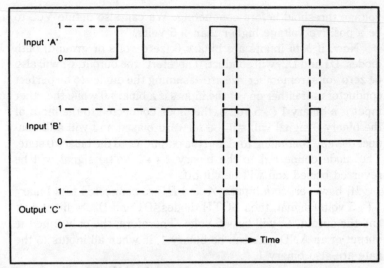

Fig. 2-11. Input and output waveforms of a diode AND gate.

hibits the passage of data, XYZ, when it is a binary 0, or enables its passage when it is a binary 1. In other words, the output of the gate is identical to the input at XYZ when and only when the *CTL* input is at binary 1. This operation can be verified by examining the waveform timing diagram of Fig. 2-12(B).

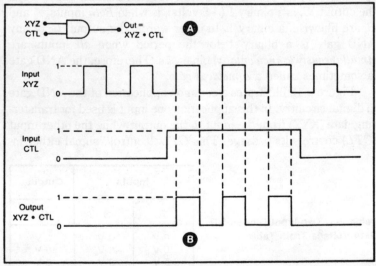

Fig. 2-12. (A) Typical AND gate application. (B) Input and output waveforms of a typical AND gate.

Inputs		Output
D	E	F
0	0	0
0	1	1
1	0	1
1	1	1

Table 2-4. Two-Input Diode OR Gate Truth Table.

It is important to remember an AND gate can have any number of inputs. Additionally, there are many different hardware configurations which can be used to implement the logical AND function. Some of these configurations will be discussed later in this chapter.

THE OR GATE

The remaining basic decision-making logic element is called the *OR* gate. The OR gate is similar to the AND gate in the respect that it, too, can have two or more inputs with a single output. However, it separation is defined that is output is a binary 1 only when any one or all of its inputs are binary 1. Conversely, the output of the OR gate is a binary 0 when and only when all of its inputs are also binary 0.

Table 2-4 illustrates the truth table and logical operation of a two-input OR gate. As explained earlier, there are 2^2 or 4 possible input combinations to any dual-input gate. The truth table in Table 2-4 exhibits all four possible combinations along with their corresponding outputs. Note the output is binary 1 only when either or both of the inputs are also binary 1. In other words, the output, F, is binary 1 if input D or input E or both inputs are binary 1.

The schematic logic symbol for the OR gate is shown in Fig. 2-13. The input designations correspond to the truth table in Table

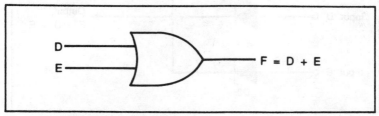

Fig. 2-13. Logic symbol for an OR gate.

2-4. Note that the output, F, is expressed as the algebraic SUM of the inputs: $F = D + E$. The plus sign (+) is used to denote the logical *OR* function.

The logical OR function can be implemented with diodes as shown in Fig. 2-14. Note the similarity between this circuit and the logical AND circuit shown in Fig. 2-10. The only difference between these two circuits is the polarity of the diodes and the power source, – Vcc. Like other logic circuits, this one operates with levels of zero and + 5 volts.

In this evaluation of the logical OR circuit, we shall assume *positive* logic assignments. Consider the condition when both inputs, D and E, are at logic level 0 (ground): Both diodes, D1 and D2, will be forward-biased and, therefore, will conduct. Assuming, again, that both diodes are perfect and will have no inherent voltage drop across them, the output, F, will also be zero. If, however, either one of the inputs, $D\ OR\ E$, is a binary 1 (+ 5 volts) while the other input remains at zero (ground), then the diode associated with the binary 1 input will raise the output level to + 5 volts (binary 1), even though it is still conducting, since the cathode is still more negative than its anode. Moreover, the diode associated with the binary 0 will be reversed-biased since its cathode will be more *positive* than its anode and will, therefore, have no effect on the circuit. Lastly, when *both* inputs are fed with a binary 1 (+ 5 volts), then BOTH diodes will conduct equally and the output will also be binary 1. Table 2-5 is the voltage truth table for the logical OR circuit, and should be carefully examined to fully understand its operation.

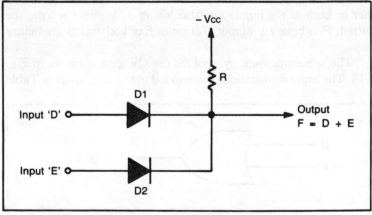

Fig. 2-14. Schematic diagram of a diode OR gate.

Inputs		Output
D	E	F
0 V	0 V	0 V
0 V	+5 V	+5 V
+5 V	0 V	+5 V
+5 V	+5 V	+5 V

Table 2-5. Two-Input Diode OR Gate Voltage Truth Table.

Figure 2-15 is a timing diagram that more clearly illustrates the operation of the logical OR gate by showing the waveforms generated at its output compared to various combinations of inputs at specific times. As can be seen, the output, F, switches to binary 1, whenever *either* input, E OR F, switches to binary 1. Be sure you completely understand this diagram before proceeding.

A typical application of the OR circuit is illustrated in Fig. 2-16. In this application a normally closed pushbutton switch, SW1, is connected to one input while a string of pulses, DAT, is connected to the other input. Power source, $+V_{CC}$, is $+5$ volts. The output, OUT, will be at binary 1 ($+5$ volts) whenever input, DAT, is binary 1 *or* whenever the pushbutton, SW1, is depressed. When the pushbutton switch, SW1, is depressed, its contacts open thereby causing input, SW1, to be $+5$ volts (binary 1) via resistor, R. The

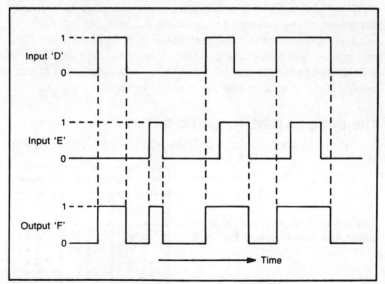

Fig. 2-15. Input and output waveforms of a diode OR gate.

49

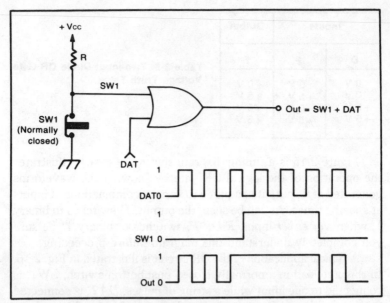

Fig. 2-16. Typical application and waveforms of the OR gate.

remaining input, DAT, is a train of binary pulses which momentarily switch between 0 and +5 volts. The algebraic expression for the output of this logical OR circuit is: $OUT = SW1 + DAT$; or $OUT = DAT + SW1$. The operation of the circuit is more clearly illustrated in the accompanying timing diagram of Fig. 2-16.

It should be kept in mind that an OR gate can have more than two inputs. Since only one method of implementing an OR gate is described here, it should be noted that many other types of electronic "hardware" can also be used to construct this gate.

THE DUAL NATURE OF LOGIC GATES

When the operation of the diode AND circuit, shown in Fig.

Table 2-6. Voltage Truth Table for Diode And Gate Circuit of Fig. 2-10.

Inputs		Output
A	B	C
0 V	0 V	0 V
0 V	+5 V	0 V
+5 V	0 V	0 V
+5 V	+5 V	+5 V

50

Input		Output
A	B	C
0	0	0
0	1	0
1	0	0
1	1	1

Table 2-7. Positive Logic Truth Table for AND Gate Circuit of Fig. 2-10.

2-10, was explained, its function was proven by considering the output voltages for each of the four possible input voltage combinations. Table 2-6(A) is the voltage truth table for the logical AND gate. When considering the operation of this circuit it is assumed that positive logic assignments are implemented. Therefore, the logic truth table can be directly translated into the table shown in Table 2-7. Careful examination of this table clearly shows the logical AND function being performed. In other words, the output, *C*, is binary 1 only when both inputs, *A AND B*, are also binary 1.

Now, what will happen to the truth table if *negative* logic level assignments are assumed? In *negative* logic levels, binary 1 is designed at 0 volts (ground) and binary 0 is designated at + 5 volts. By using the data from Table 2-6 and translating it into a logic truth table with negative logic assignments, the truth table shown in Table 2-8 is obtained. In this figure, it is obvious that the logical AND function is no longer being performed. By more careful examination, it can be determined that the logical OR function is, in fact, now being performed since the output is a logical 1 when either one or both of the inputs are a logical 1. The conclusion, therefore, must be that when *positive* logic is assigned to the circuit in Fig. 2-10, it will perform the logical AND function and when negative logic is assigned to the same circuit, the logical OR function will be performed. This phenomenon clearly shows the diode gate circuit is capable of performing either of the two basic logical

Table 2-8. Negative Logic Truth Table for AND Gate of Fig. 2-10.

Input		Output
A	B	C
1	1	1
1	0	1
0	1	1
0	0	0

51

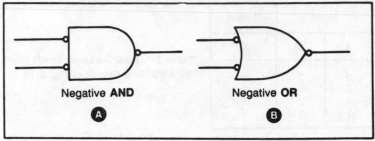

Fig. 2-17. (A) Negative AND logic gate. (B) Negative OR gate.

functions and its function is completely dependent upon the assignments of the logic levels assigned to the inputs and output.

This dual nature of logic gates applies to all logic circuits. The diode gate circuit shown in Fig. 2-14 is also dual in nature. It will perform the logical OR function with *positive* logic assignments but will also perform the logical AND function with *negative* logic assignments. This important fact is very helpful when designing, analyzing or troubleshooting digital electronic equipment. It is just as important to know what logic assignments are being used as well as the electrical function of the circuit.

Figure 2-17 shows the symbols commonly used to represent gates which perform logical AND and OR functions, respectively, with negative logic level assignments. The circles at the inputs and outputs represent the effect of reversing the logic levels from positive to negative.

NOT GATES

The majority of digital circuitry can be constructed from only three basic logic elements: AND, OR and NOT. For maximum efficiency and cost effectiveness, most of the digital equipment manufactured today implements these circuits with special versions of these elements called *NAND* and *NOR* gates. A *NAND* gate is merely an *AND* gate feeding an inverter as shown in Fig. 2-18. Similarly, a *NOR* gate is merely an *OR* gate feeding an inverter as shown in Fig. 2-19. Figures 2-18(B) and 2-19(B) are the respective schematic equivalents of the NAND and NOR gates. They are similar to their non-inverting counterparts with the exception of the circle added to their respective outputs. There are numerous advantages of the NAND and NOR gates over the simple diode gate circuits previously discussed. For example, in complex digital circuits it becomes difficult to cascade more than a few diode gate

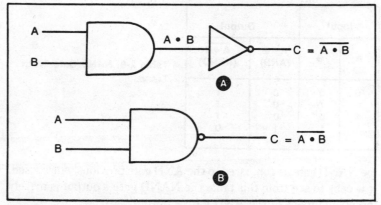

Fig. 2-18. (A) Equivalent NAND gate. (B) True NAND gate.

circuits. Furthermore, loading problems could exist that adversely affect the speed of operation between the gates, since there is no buffering in the diode gate circuit. This is why a transistor buffer is combined with a logic gate and is most commonly an inverter.

THE NAND GATE

The word *NAND* is a contraction of the term *NOT AND*. Therefore, a NAND gate is an AND gate followed by an inverter as shown in Fig. 2-18. The algebraic output term of the AND gate and the inverter is the *inverse* of the AND gate's output term. The NOT function (or inversion) is designated by the bar over the output expression.

Table 2-9 is the truth table showing the logical operation of

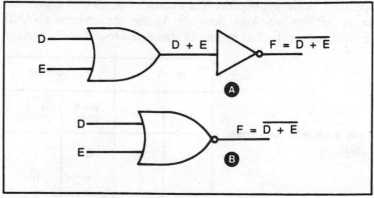

Fig. 2-19. (A) Equivalent NOR gate. (B) True NOR gate.

Input		Output	
A	**B**	**A • B** (AND)	**$\overline{A \bullet B}$** (NAND)
0	0	0	1
0	1	0	1
1	0	0	1
1	1	1	0

Table 2-9. NAND Gate Truth Table.

the NAND gate as compared to the AND gate previously discussed. It is easy to see from this table the NAND gate's output is merely the complement of the AND gate's output.

THE NOR GATE

Similar to the NAND gate, the NOR gate is a more practical logic element in implementing logic functions. The word *NOR* is a contraction of the term *NOT OR*. Therefore, by using the same logic as applied to the NAND gate, the NOR gate is merely a logic circuit combining the functions of an OR gate and an inverter. As can be seen from Fig. 2-19, the output of the NOR gate is merely the complement of the OR function and is represented by the bar over the output expression.

Table 2-10 is the truth table of the NOR gate showing its logical operation. This table also demonstrates the relationship between the OR and the NOR gates. The NOR gate's output is simply the INVERSE state of the OR gate's output.

NAND and NOR gates can have more than two inputs as specified for the application. They can also be used to implement *any* of the three basic logic elements: An inverter is merely a NAND or NOR gate with all of its inputs connected together. By further

Table 2-10. NOR Gate Truth Table.

Input		Output	
D	**E**	**D + E** (OR)	**$\overline{D + E}$** (NOR)
0	0	0	1
0	1	1	0
1	0	1	0
1	1	1	0

addition of a NAND or NOR gate to an inverter, the AND or OR function can respectively be performed.

HOW NAND AND NOR GATES ARE USED

The AND and OR logic function can be implemented by merely feeding the outputs of the NAND and NOR gates, respectively, to an inverter. This would seem logical since the NAND and NOR functions are simply the complements of the basic AND and OR functions. Therefore, we may properly assume the AND and OR functions can be achieved by merely inverting the outputs of the NAND and NOR functions. In other words, two negatives make a positive just like in ordinary multiplication. Another rule of thumb to remember is that cascading an EVEN number of inverters in a logic circuits *removes* the inversion function, while cascading an ODD number of inverters in a logic circuit will invert the logic function. Figure 2-28 illustrates how to implement the AND and OR functions with NAND and NOR gates.

It is also possible to implement the OR function with a NAND gate and the AND function with a NOR gate. As previously discussed, any of the three basic logic functions, (AND, OR and NOT) can be implemented with either a NAND or an OR gate. The AND and OR functions can be implemented by simply inverting the outputs of the NAND and NOR gates, respectively. To obtain the remaining logic functions, however, inverters must be placed on the *inputs* of the selected gate. Table 2-11 is the truth table for the NAND gate with inputs designated *A* and *B* while its output is labeled *C*. The effect of adding an inverter to each of the inputs

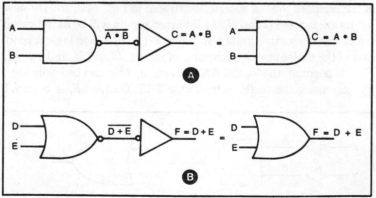

Fig. 2-20. (A) Making an AND gate using a NAND gate. (B) Making an or gate using a NOR gate.

Table 2-11. NAND Gate Truth Table.

Inverted Inputs		NAND Inputs		Output
X	Y	A	B	C
1	1	0	0	1
1	0	0	1	1
0	1	1	0	1
0	0	1	1	0

as shown in Fig. 2-21 is illustrated in Table 2-11, as well. These inverters merely complement the input signals, X and Y. Note how the inputs, X and Y, are merely the *inversion* of the inputs, A and B. Assuming the two inverters and the NAND gate in Fig. 2-21 to be a single unit, the *new* inputs become X and Y instead of A and B. Output, C, however, remains unchanged. Now, by careful examination of the truth table in Fig. 2-29, the *new* logical function can be discerned: This circuit produces a binary 1 output each time a binary 1 is applied to either *one* or *both* of the *new* inputs. This, now, is, by definition, the same operation as the OR function. As can be seen, therefore, the OR function can be implemented with a NAND gate by merely inverting the *inputs* of the NAND gate.

Similarly, by inserting inverters to the inputs of a NOR gate, the AND function can be implemented. Table 2-12 shows the truth table for the NOR gate. The inputs are designated D and E while the output is designated F. Assuming, now, inverters are placed at the *inputs* of the OR gate, as illustrated in Fig. 2-22, and the new inputs are labeled G and H, the inverted inputs will be as indicated under the respective inputs of Table 2-12. The *new* logical function of the entire circuit consisting of inputs, G and H, and output, F, now becomes the logical AND function. This can be easily seen by examining the truth table, Table 2-12. Output, F, is binary 1

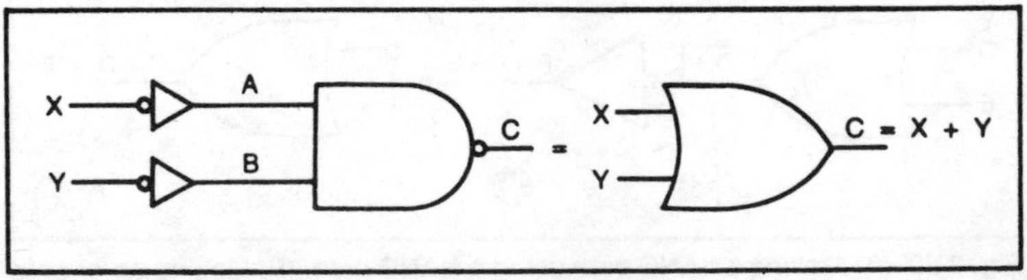

Fig. 2-21. Making an OR gate using a NAND gate.

Table 2-12. NOR Gate Truth Table.

Inverted Inputs		NOR Inputs		Output
G	H	D	E	F
1	1	0	0	1
1	0	0	1	0
0	1	1	0	0
0	0	1	1	0

when and only when both inputs, *G* and *H*, are also binary 1. Since this satisfies the definition of the logical AND function, it can be properly assumed that it is now performing the logical AND function. Figure 2-22 illustrates how a NOR gate can perform the AND function by inverting the inputs of the NOR gate.

Since we proved how the three basic logic functions can be implemented with either a NAND or NOR gate, we can further simplify things by implementing the three functions with only a single type of gate when designing digital circuitry. The choice is strictly arbitrary and at the discretion of the designer. However, there are cases when NAND and NOR gates are both used in a circuit. As will be discussed later, some cost efficiencies can be achieved in circuit design when both NAND and NOR gates are combined. The important thing to remember, however, is that *any* logic function can be constructed with only NAND or NOR gates!

PRACTICAL LOGIC CIRCUITS

There are numerous methods of electrically or mechanically obtaining a specific operational function when using logic gates. Several typical ways of implementing logic circuits will now be discussed since the overview of logic circuits previously covered was

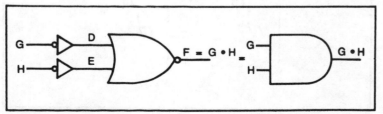

Fig. 2-22. Making an AND gate using a NOR gate.

designed with theory in mind. This section will cover the "nuts and bolts" of digital logic hardware.

RELAYS AND SWITCHES

All three basic logic functions (AND, OR and NOT) can be easily implemented with mechanical relays and switches. Figure 2-23, for example, illustrates how to construct an AND gate using two single-pole, single-throw (SPST) relays. In this example, the normally open (N.O.) contacts of the two relays, labeled A and B, are connected in *series* with a battery and a suitable lamp. As can be seen from analyzing this circuit; for any of the four possible combinations of input levels to A and B, only *one* combination will illuminate the lamp. If either one or both of the relays are *not* energized, then the lamp will not light. However, when a sufficient voltage is present at *both* inputs, A and B, then both relay contacts will close and current will flow through the lamp. It is assumed that positive logic is being used in this example and an illuminated lamp indicates a binary 1. Therefore, a series circuit usually performs the AND function.

Figure 2-24 illustrates how to implement the OR function with relays. Here, the normally open contacts of relays D and E are con-

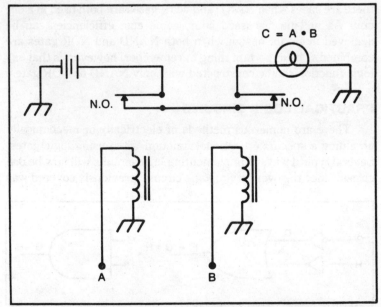

Fig. 2-23. Electromechanical relay AND gate connection.

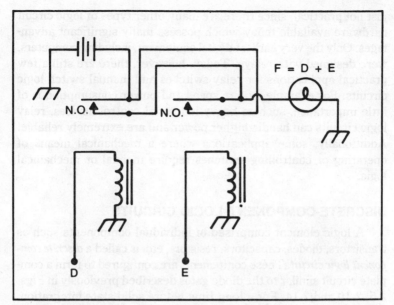

Fig. 2-24. Electromechanical relay OR gate connection.

nected in parallel. It can be seen, therefore, that when a sufficient voltage is present at either one or both of the inputs, D or E, the respective relay contacts will close, thereby supplying current flow through the lamp. It can now be concluded that parallel connected contacts usually perform the OR function.

Figure 2-25 illustrates how to implement an inverter with a relay: Instead of the normally-open contacts, the normally-closed contacts are used. As can be seen, when the relay is *de*-energized, representing binary 0, its contacts are closed, thereby supplying current from the battery through the lamp. Conversely, when the relay is energized, its contacts open, thereby cutting off the supply of current from the battery to the lamp. Therefore, when a binary 0 applied to the input, a binary 1 exists at its output. Likewise, when a binary 1 is applied to the input, a binary 0 exists at its output. By definition, it has been proven that inversion is taking place using this circuit.

The relay switching circuits just described can be combined in many different configurations to form *any* logic function. In some applications, even manually-operated switches can be substituted for the relay contacts. Relays or switches aren't used in contemporary circuit design since they are too large, slow in operation and consume an excessive amount of power. In other words, they are just not practical, since there are many other types of logic circuit hardware available today which possess many significant advantages. Only the very earliest digital equipment, including computers, were designed with relays. Today, however, there are still a few practical applications for relay switches and manual switch logic circuits. For example, where speed and power consumption is of little importance, such as heavy industrial control devices, relay logic circuits can handle higher power and are extremely reliable. Additionally, some applications where a mechanical means of operating or controlling switches require manual or mechanical logic.

DISCRETE-COMPONENT LOGIC CIRCUITS

A logic element comprised of individual components such as transistors, diodes, capacitors, resistors, etc. is called a *discrete component logic circuit*. These components are configured to form a complete circuit similar to the diode gates described previously in Figs. 2-5, 2-10 and 2-14. For a long time before solid state integration, digital logic circuits were built with discrete components. Such circuits were relatively small, performed rather well and consumed a reasonable amount of power. Today, however, discrete component logic circuits are rarely used. Just as discrete components

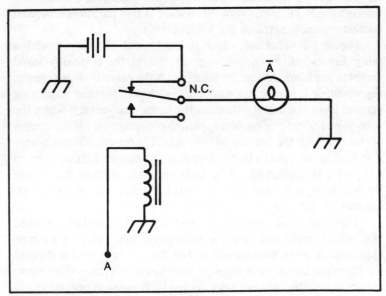

Fig. 2-25. Electromechanical relay NOT (inverter) connection.

replaced mechanical relays and switches, the integrated circuit has replaced discrete component logic circuits. Integrated circuits offer still better performance with even lower cost and improved features. Discrete component logic circuits may still be encountered in some high-power applications or in some obsolete digital equipment. However, most digital logic functions today are implemented with integrated circuits.

INTEGRATED CIRCUITS

An integrated circuit, or IC, is a semiconductor device combining transistors, diodes, resistors and capacitors in an ultra-miniature array on a single chip of silicon. Recent advances in semiconductor technology have permitted semiconductor manufacturers to design, develop and produce thousands of electronic circuits on a single wafer of silicon no larger than one-tenth of an inch square. Needless to say, these circuits are significantly smaller than their discrete-component counterparts. Since they can also be mass produced, their manufacturing costs are substantially less, as well. Many of these circuits also offer a significant savings in power consumption. The most important feature of the integrated circuit, however, is the elimination of the requirement for circuit wiring. When discrete components are used in logic circuits, each component must be properly inserted in and soldered to a printed circuit board. The finished board may then have to be interconnected to other similar circuit boards and finally tested. With an integrated circuit the entire circuitry is manufactured simultaneously. This reduces the ultimate cost of the circuit to a fraction of its discrete component counterpart while greatly improving its reliability, as well.

Integrated circuits have been around for approximately 25 years. During this time significant advances in IC technology have been made. The complexity and sophistication of the circuits has increased exponentially while the prices have continued to decline. Modern integrated circuit techniques make it possible to not only implement the basic logic elements, but also complete combinational and sequential circuits as well as fully functional devices such as oscillators, timers, amplifiers, and even computers. Integrated circuits designed for implementing the basic logic functions, such as NAND, NOR or flip-flops, are referred to as small-scale *integration* (SSI). Complete functional circuits of either combinational or sequential type are generally referred to as *medium-scale integration* (MSI). Complete circuits or systems such as a function generator, amplifier or small digital computer on a chip is produced using *large-scale integration* (LSI). Modern integrated circuit techniques have even let the designer reach near theoretical limits in package density and operating speeds by putting complete computers on a single wafer of silicon using *very large-scale integration* (VLSI).

Today, most all digital equipment is designed with integrated circuits. There are only a few applications remaining in which other forms of circuitry are required or desirable.

Chapter 3

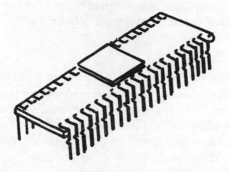

Digital Integrated Circuits

A LL OF TODAY'S DIGITAL ELECTRONIC EQUIPMENT IS BUILT with integrated circuits. Digital electronics can now be analyzed and designed from a more or less conceptual point of view as opposed to a circuit viewpoint since we have integrated circuits available to us. We can look at digital integrated circuits as "building blocks" which are used to construct digital electronic systems. Prior to the integrated circuit, designers had to not only invent the logic necessary to perform the function they desired, but they also had to create the electronic circuitry required to implement those functions. Now, however, integrated circuits make the designer's job mainly that of selecting commercially-available devices and applying them to a specific application. Very little knowledge of electronic circuit design is required to understand and use most digital electronics.

CHARACTERISTICS OF LOGIC CIRCUITS

Many different types of digital integrated circuits are available to implement digital equipment. A variety of logic circuits can be constructed with the use of saturated and unsaturated bipolar transistors as well as MOSFET devices. Each type or "family" of integrated circuits has unique capabilities and limitations. Their characteristics can vary widely and for any given application, the optimum circuit to use will depend on the specific requirements of the system.

63

Among the most important characteristics to consider when selecting digital integrated circuits are logic levels, propagation delay, power dissipation, noise immunity, and fan out. We will now examine each of these characteristics individually.

LOGIC LEVELS

The voltage values assigned to the binary 1 and binary 0 states for a given type of digital integrated circuit are the logic levels. Nominal values for these two levels are usually stated. However, the actual voltages may deviate somewhat due to factors such as internal component tolerances, power supply variations to ambient temperature. The manufacturer of the device will usually provide sufficient data regarding the minimum and maximum voltage levels which will be acceptable for determining the two logic level states.

When you are working with a specific piece of digital equipment it is important to know the logic levels so you can readily identify input and output logic states by measuring the voltages with a voltmeter or oscilloscope. Furthermore, knowledge of the logic levels will help you analyze the operation of a circuit or determine whether or not it is properly functioning.

PROPAGATION DELAY

The speed of operation of a logic circuit is its propagation delay time. This factor is one of the most important to consider when designing digital circuitry. For most applications, high speed is paramount.

Propagation delay is the length of time required for a circuit's output to respond to a change of logic state at its input. It is the sum total of all accumulated rise times, delay times, and storage times associated with a logic circuit. When an input level changes from binary 1 to binary 0, or from binary 0 to binary 1, the output of that logic circuit will respond after a finite time has elapsed.

Propagation delay is illustrated in Fig. 3-1. The top waveform is the input to a digital circuit and the bottom waveform is its corresponding output. The circuit could be an inverter, a NAND gate or a NOR gate. A binary 0 to binary 1 transition at its input causes a binary 1 to binary 0 transition at its output. Note the output transition occurs some specific time *after* the input transition. This specific time is the propagation delay. The specific propagation delay is measured from the 50% amplitude points on the curves of the corresponding input and output pulses. There are, in fact,

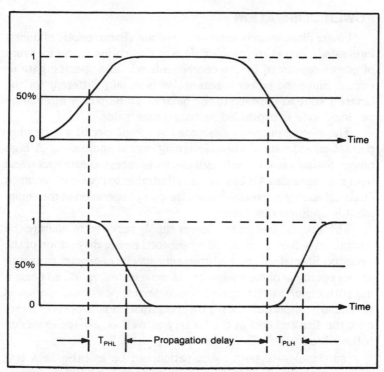

Fig. 3-1. An illustration of the concept of propagation delay.

two types of propagation delays. First is the propagation delay when the output changes from high to low, T_{PHL}. Second is the delay when the output changes from low to high, T_{PLH}. The propagation delays for the two types of level changes are different because of the characteristics of the logic circuit. Even though they are of the same order of magnitude and close in value, they are nevertheless not equal.

Propagation delays in most of today's digital integrated circuits are very short but still finite. Propagation delays less then one nanosecond are achievable, although some contemporary logic circuits have propagation delays as high as several hundred nanoseconds. Furthermore, propagation delays can vary widely from their nominal specified values due to manufacturing tolerances, circuit wiring, etc. Propagation delays are additive—they are accumulated when gates and other logic circuits are cascaded. In any digital logic system, the total propagation delay from input to output is the sum total of all propagation delays of the individual gates of the system.

POWER DISSIPATION

Power dissipation is another important characteristic of digital integrated circuits to consider. Power dissipation is the measure of power consumed by the components within a specific gate or circuit. Since the power consumption is usually different for the binary 1 state as opposed to the binary 0 state, power dissipation per logic gate is expressed as an average value.

The amount of power dissipated by a logic circuit is a very important consideration when designing digital equipment. A high power dissipation will mean high electrical energy consumption and high heat emission. Of course, it is desirable to conserve as much electrical energy as possible, since the cost of operation of the equipment is an important factor.

The size and cost of the power supply required to operate the equipment will be determined by the total power dissipation of the circuitry. Special cooling requirements may be necessary to ensure proper operation of the equipment in some instances. When designing portable or battery operated equipment, power dissipation is particularly important. Low power dissipation is necessary to reduce the size and cost of the battery as well as provide extended battery life.

Individual gate power dissipation can be as little as a few microwatts for certain MOS circuits or as high as 100 milliwatts for certain types of high-speed nonsaturated circuits.

SPEED VS. POWER

The two characteristics discussed so far, speed and power, are directly dependent upon each other. The relationship between these two characteristics is: *Speed is directly proportional to power dissipation.* In other words, the faster a logic circuit operates, the more power it will dissipate. In order to obtain high speed operation, the penalty of high power dissipation must be paid. This compromise or trade-off between speed and power dissipation is one of the most significant considerations which must be made when selecting a type of logic circuit for a given application. Almost universally, high speed digital logic circuits use nonsaturating bipolar transistors. Because these transistors do not saturate, their respective emitter-collector voltage drops are higher. Furthermore, the very low circuit resistance to minimize charge and discharge times of stray capacitance results in higher power consumption, as well.

MOS integrated circuits, on the other hand, consume very little power. Their intrinsically high impedance is mainly responsible for this. However, this characteristic coupled with its built-in capacitances give the MOS circuit very slow switching speeds. Therefore, operating frequency of MOS circuitry is severely limited. MOS circuitry, nevertheless, is extremely desirable for battery operated and portable operation where high speed is not a factor since its power consumption is only a few nanowatts per gate. Other types of logic circuits fall somewhere between the two aforementioned extremes. The speed versus power trade-off will always be an inherent compromise.

NOISE IMMUNITY

The susceptibility of a logic circuit to noise pulses on its inputs, and to what degree noise affects its output is the measure of noise immunity of a logic circuit. Noise, by definition, is any extraneous or undesired signal generated within the equipment itself or externally which is added to, or superimposed upon, the desired system logic levels. This noise can include a slowly varying dc level or very high frequency pulses. It can be either repetitive or intermittent. In any case, noise can cause a logic circuit to switch unpredictably to undesirable states.

Because of the voltage threshold levels associated with logic levels in digital circuitry, all digital logic circuits have some degree of built-in noise immunity. Most logic circuits are capable of rejecting noise spikes of relatively high magnitude. Noise immunity of most logic circuits is from approximately 10% to 50% of the power supply voltage. In other words, a noise spike will be rejected by the circuit if its amplitude is less than 10% to 50% of the voltage of the power supply. For example, a circuit with a noise immunity of 1 volt would reject noise pulses which would be 1 volt or less from the defined binary 0 or binary 1 logic levels. In some instances, noise is rejected by virtue of the slow response time of a logic circuit. Some high frequency noise, by nature, is of such short duration that the logic circuits cannot respond quickly enough to it to cause a change in logic state.

Since most digital systems generate a substantial amount of noise during operation, noise immunity is an important consideration. Additionally, much digital equipment is installed in noisy industrial environments where power line transients and other nearby electrical equipment can cause phantom triggering of logic circuits.

FAN-OUT

The characteristic of how much of a load can be connected to the output of a digital circuit before it is adversely affected is called *fan-out*. It is usually expressed in terms of the number of standard loads that a logic gate's output can accommodate and still maintain proper operation at specified logic levels, speeds, on temperatures. There is a practical limit to the number of loads which a logic circuit can accommodate because of component limitations and internal circuit configuration. For example, a logic circuit may have a fanout of ten which indicates that 10 separate gate inputs can be connected to the output of this logic gate still maintaining proper operation according to the specifications of the manufacturer.

The output of a logic circuit may be connected to a load in one of two basic ways. Some loads appear between the output of the logic circuit and the power supply while others appear between the output of the logic circuit and ground.

CURRENT-SOURCE LOGIC

The driving logic circuit functions as a current *source* when the load appears between the output of the logic circuit and ground. This type of logic is referred to as *current-source logic*. Figure 3-2A is an illustration of this type of circuit configuration. The output of the logic circuit, *Q1*, drives two similar logic circuits comprised of transistors, *Q2* and *Q3*. When transistor, Q1, is biased on, the voltage at point X is almost zero. Therefore, no base drive is applied to transistors Q2 and Q3 and they do not conduct. Now, when transistor Q1 is cut off, the supply voltage, + Vcc, passes current through the collector resistor, R_C, and base resistors, R_{B1} and R_{B2}.

As can be seen, each load is comprised of the emitter-base junction of the respective transistor and its associated base resistor connected between the output of the previous logic circuit (point X) and ground. As more loads are connected to the circuit, the total effective resistance of all the loads decreases and subsequently causes an increase in current drawn from the power supply, Vcc, through collector resistor, R_C. The voltage divider comprised of the collector resistance of transistor Q1 and all the external loads causes a *decrease* in the logic output voltage as the number of loads *increases*.

Therefore, the number of loads must be limited in order to maintain a specific minimum logic level voltage at the collector of

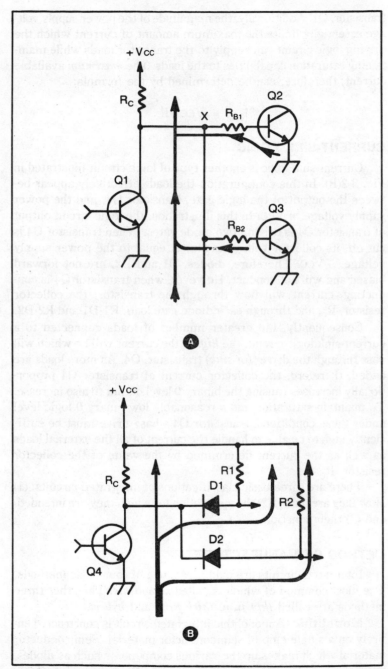

Fig. 3-2. (A) Current *source logic*. (B) Current *sink logic*.

transistor, Q1. Additionally, the magnitude of the power supply voltage essentially limits the maximum amount of current which the driving logic circuit can supply to the transistor loads while maintaining saturation capabilities to the loads. The *maximum* available current, therefore, can be determined by the formula:

$$I_{avail} = VCC \div R_C$$

CURRENT-SINK LOGIC

Current-sink logic is another type of logic circuit illustrated in Fig. 3-2(B). In this configuration the loads effectively appear between the output of the logic gate, transistor Q4, and the power supply voltage, + VCC. In this illustration, the logic circuit output of transistor Q4 is driving two diode gates. When transistor Q4 is cut off, its collector voltage is almost equal to the power supply voltage, + VCC. Therefore, diodes, D1 and D2, are not forward biased and will not conduct. However, when transistor Q4 is conducting, current will flow through the transistor, the collector resistor, R_C, and through each diode gate load, R1-D1 and R2-D2.

Consequently, the greater number of loads connected to a current-sink logic circuit, the *higher* the current will be which will pass through the driver (or *sink*) transistor, Q4. As more loads are added, therefore, the collector current of transistor Q4 proportionally increases causing the binary 0 level output to also increase. To maintain saturation and a reasonably low binary 0 logic level under these conditions, transistor Q4's base drive must be sufficiently high to be able to handle the current of all the external loads as well as the current determined by the value of the collector resistor, R_C.

There are three basic classifications of integrated circuits: (1) How they are made, (2) the application for which they are intended, and (3) their function.

METHOD OF MANUFACTURE

Integrated circuits are made from one of four basic methods. The most common of which is called *monolithic*. The other three methods are called *thin film, thick film,* and *hybrid*.

Monolithic. A monolithic integrated circuit is constructed entirely on a single chip of semiconductor material. Semiconductor material which makes up the various components such as diodes, transistors, and resistors are diffused into the basic substrate or base material. These semiconductor materials are usually deposited as gases on the substrate through a series of masking operations under very high temperatures. This results in the entire circuit being manufactured on a single base, thus the name monolithic. This technique is used to manufacture most integrated circuits.

Monolithic integrated circuits come in two basic forms: bipolar and MOS. The primary difference between these two forms is the type of transistor used to construct the circuits. Bipolar transistors can be either saturating or non-saturating and are becoming less common than MOS. The MOS circuitry is easier to manufacture and takes up less space. The component simplicity also affords a much higher manufacturing yield. The end result is that MOS circuits can be manufactured with higher density while maintaining lower cost.

Thin-and Thick-film Hybrid Circuits. Thin film and thick film integrated circuits are made by depositing metal-based materials on a non-conductive base such as ceramic. Various resistive and conductive materials are deposited on the substrate through a series of masking techniques to form conductors, resistors and inductors. Semiconductors and other components are then bonded to the resulting circuit, and connections made via thin gold wires. This technique is primarily reserved for manufacturing passive networks such as filters, attenuators, and phase-shifters; for precision instrument and operational amplifiers and for RF modules. These network devices offer nearly the same advantages over discrete component circuitry as do monolithic integrated circuits because they can be made small. Furthermore, component tolerances can be held more closely than their equivalent discrete counterparts. Thin-film and thick-film techniques are preferred, therefore, for precision circuits. The resulting circuits are often called hybrid integrated circuits. Multiple monolithic chips interconnected within a single package may also be considered to be a hybrid. Monolithic circuits combined with thin film and thick film passive networks is another example of hybrid circuitry.

A variety of different integrated circuits and components can be combined with hybrid techniques to offer special advantages not available in individual types of integrated circuits alone. Because of the very small size of a monolithic circuit, for example, power dissipation is limited. It may be necessary, therefore, to combine a low-power monolithic circuit and a power transistor mounted on a separate chip while being physically interconnected within the same package in order to handle high-power requirements. Fur-

71

thermore, high precision circuitry can be accomplished with a combination of monolithic circuitry and a highly accurate thin film network. On the other hand, hybrid circuits are much more complicated and expensive than monolithic integrated circuits because more than one type of technique is incorporated. However, they do offer a wide range of capabilities while maintaining extremely small physical size and other benefits generally associated with integrated circuits.

APPLICATION

The application of an integrated circuit is another method of classifying it. This is primarily a means of distinguishing between *digital* and *linear*. Digital integrated circuits operate with logic levels, binary data, and pulses. These devices use either bipolar transistors or MOSFETs. Linear integrated circuits, on the other hand, operate with analog signals and usually incorporate some kind of amplifier. Linear integrated circuits are made with bipolar transistors. Figure 3-3 shows the integrated circuit "Family Tree."

FUNCTION

The three basic classifications which identify the function of a digital integrated circuit are: 1) small-scale integration, 2) medium-scale integration, and 3) large-scale integration.

The simplest and most basic type of integrated circuit is the small-scale integrated (SSI) circuit. SSI circuits are amplifier or gate circuits which perform only a single basic function. These circuits require external circuitry to make complete operational circuits. A typical SSI integrated circuit may contain several logic gates or a flip-flop.

Medium-scale integrated circuits are a little more complex and contain multiple gates which are internally connected to form a complete function circuit. Most MSI circuits contain at least a dozen gates or equivalent circuitry. Typical MSI circuits can be complete functional units such as decoders, multiplexers or counters. These circuits eliminate the necessity of having to interconnect several SSI circuits to perform the same function. Consequently, MSI circuits greatly reduce the number of separate integrated circuit packages contained within a given piece of electronic equipment. This results in less cost, smaller size, reduced production time, and in some instances, less power consumption.

Large-scale integrated circuits, as the name implies, contain

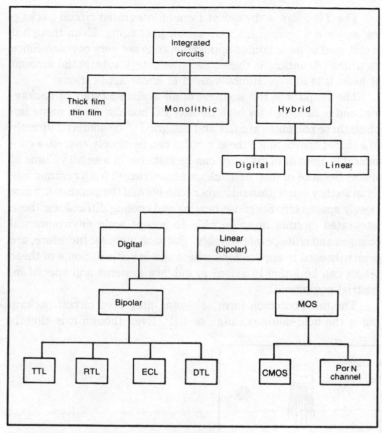

Fig. 3-3. The integrated circuit "family tree."

many more circuits than the other types. LSI circuits employ 100 or more equivalent gate circuits and can be considered to be multiple MSI circuits. This type of integrated circuit is usually a complete instrument or system. LSI circuits can be used in memory applications as well as electronic calculators, computers and testing instruments.

INTEGRATED CIRCUIT PACKAGES

The physical characteristics of packages is an important consideration to the integrated circuit user. The silicon chip can be packaged in three basic enclosures: 1) The metal-glass *TO-5* can, shown in Fig. 3-4A, 2) The *flatpack* shown in Fig. 3-4B, and 3) The dual-inline package (DIP), shown in Fig. 3-4C.

The TO-5 can is the oldest form of integrated circuit packaging and it is a spinoff from transistor packaging. Even though it is still used in some limited applications it is not very popular. Since its prime advantage is that it can dissipate a substantial amount of heat, it is more commonly used in linear applications.

The flatpack is the smallest of all available types of packaging, and is designed for high density PC boards. As its name implies, these packages are flat and designed to be soldered directly to a circuit board. Since these circuits can be closely spaced, a considerable amount of circuitry can be installed in a small volume of space. Because of this, flatpacks are constructed from ceramic material so they can withstand higher-than-normal temperatures. Since closely spaced circuits cause heating and cooling difficulties, these integrated circuits must be able to accept wide environmental changes and still operate reliably. Flatpack circuits, therefore, are primarily used in applications where size is critical. Some of these places can be found in avionics, military systems and special industrial equipment.

The most common form of digital integrated circuit packaging is the dual-inline package or DIP. Even though it is slightly

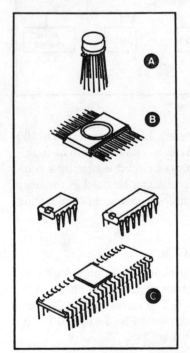

Fig. 3-4. (A) Metal-glass TO-5 package. (B) Ceramic flatpack. (C) Dual-inline package (DIP).

larger than the other forms of chip packaging, it offers many advantages. These packages are not only easy to manually mount and use, they are also designed to be used in conjunction with automatic insertion equipment on production lines. They are manufactured in various sizes from an 8-pin "mini-DIP" all the way up to a 40-pin package. Most SSI circuits are housed in 8-pin, 14-pin, or 16-pin DIPs. MSI circuits usually come in 14-pin, 16-pin, or 24-pin DIPs. Because of their larger size and complexity, LSI circuits usually require 24-pin, 28-pin, or 40-pin DIPs.

DIP packaging material can be any of several types, the most common and least expensive of which is a plastic package. In the plastic DIP, the integrated circuit chip is spot welded to a metal frame of leads and completely encapsulated in plastic by injection molding. Several types of ceramic packages are used for more critical integrated circuits. These are generally hermetically sealed to provide an extremely clean and safe environment for the circuit, and are able to withstand higher temperatures, as well.

TEMPERATURE RANGES

Most integrated circuits are also rated according to the temperature range over which they can satisfactorily operate. Manufacturers usually provide a commercial, industrial and a military grade of most circuits. The military grade circuits come packaged in ceramic flatpacks or DIPs, are hermetically sealed, and can operate at temperatures between $-55\,°C$ and $+125\,°C$.

Naturally, this type of integrated circuit is much more expensive than commercial or industrial grade components since it is designed to operate over a wide range of temperatures. They are only used, therefore, in applications involving high quality military or industrial equipment which will be operated in severe environments.

The commercial or industrial grade integrated circuit can be used for most general applications. They are usually packaged in plastic packages which are capable of operating from between $0\,°C$ to $+70\,°C$. Since other temperature ranges may sometimes be specified for different types of integrated circuits, it is always wise to consult the manufacturer's data sheet for specific information regarding temperature ranges.

TRANSISTOR-TRANSISTOR LOGIC (TTL)

Many different types of integrated circuit logic elements are used in implementing digital equipment. Even though they possess different characteristics, capabilities and limitations, they all perform the same basic logic functions. Over the years a myriad of circuits have been developed to meet special needs or requirements.

The selection of the *type* or *family* of digital logic circuit is one of the most important decisions made by the design engineer of digital equipment. This section will deal with the most popular form of bipolar logic elements: transistor-transistor logic, commonly called TTL or T²L, (pronounced: "T squared L").

The very low cost and availability of a wide variety of SSI logic elements and MSI functional circuits make the TTL type integrated circuit one of the most popular. Furthermore, its ease of use, high performance and interfacing capabilities are other desirable features. Many special types of TTL circuits are available to meet certain requirements. This type of logic circuit continues to be popular for new equipment design even though it has been in existence for over fifteen years. Its intrinsic versatility has made it the standard logic circuitry used in contemporary digital equipment.

TTL Operation

The circuit of a typical TTL NAND gate is shown in Fig. 3-5. A single +5 volt power supply is used to operate it with typical logic levels of +0.4 volt for binary 0 and +2.4 volts for binary 1. Three basic sections comprise the entire circuit: a multiple-emitter input transistor, Q1, a phase splitter transistor, Q2, and a totem-pole output circuit consisting of transistors Q3 and Q4. High-speed operation can be achieved by using the multiple-emitter input transistor along with resistor, R1, in place of individual diodes to form the diode gate.

Transistor Q2 provides complementary drive signals to the output transistors Q3 and Q4 by splitting the phase of the input signal. The output circuit, comprised of transistors Q3 and Q4 is stacked in such an arrangement to be given the name *totem-pole*. Transistor, Q4, is merely a shunt transistor switch. In this circuit, transistor Q3 acts as an active load resistor for Q4. The collector of the output transistor in some circuits is returned via a collector resistor to the power supply. In that configuration, the collector resistor is called a *pull-up* resistor because it causes the output to be "pulled-up" to the supply voltage when the output transistor cuts off. In the TTL gate of Fig. 3-5, transistor Q3 serves as an *active* pull-up resistor. This transistor supplies current to any shunt load on the

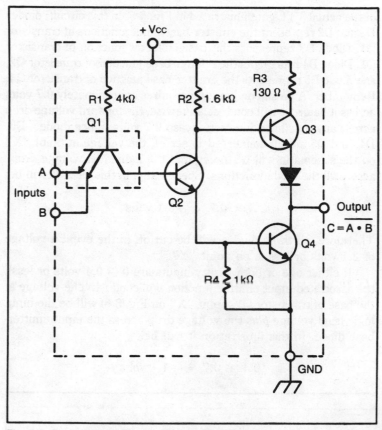

Fig. 3-5. Typical transistor-transistor-logic (TTL) gate.

output. Because this configuration provides a much lower output impedance in the binary 1 (high) state than one using an ordinary resistor, higher speed of operation can, therefore, be achieved. Conversely, in logic circuits using pull-up resistors in their outputs, any shunt output capacitance must be charged via the collector output pull-up resistor. Depending upon the amount of shunt capacitance and the value of the pull-up resistor, this length of charging time can be excessively long. By using the active pull-up transistor arrangement as shown in Fig. 3-5, however, any output capacitance can be charged very quickly through the low impedance transistor, Q3.

It is convenient to illustrate a diode equivalent of the key components of this circuit to simplify the understanding of the TTL NAND gate. Figure 3-6 shows the diode equivalent representation

77

of the actual TTL gate illustrated in Fig. 3-5. In this circuit, diodes D1 and D2 represent the emitter-base input junctions of transistor Q1. Diode D3 represents the base-collector junction of transistor Q1. Diode D4 represents the emitter-base junction of transistor Q2, and diode D5 represents the emitter-base junction of transistor Q4. Remember: A pn silicon junction requires approximately 0.7 volts across it before it will conduct. Likewise, the forward voltage drop across any pn silicon junction is also 0.7 volts. Since diodes, D3, D4, and D5 are all connected in series, the voltage at point "X" on the schematic will be the sum of the individual voltage drops across all the diode junctions. Specifically, in this case, it will be:

$$3 \times 0.7 = +2.1 \text{ volts}$$

Therefore, all three diodes will be cut off in the event a voltage of 2.1 volts or less is on point "X".

If either one or both binary inputs are 0 (+0.4 volts or less), the associated input emitter junction will conduct. The voltage at the base of transistor Q1 (point "X" on Fig. 3-6) will be the input logic level voltage *plus* the voltage drop across the input emitter-base diode. In this illustration it will be:

$$0.4 + 0.7 = +1.1 \text{ volts}$$

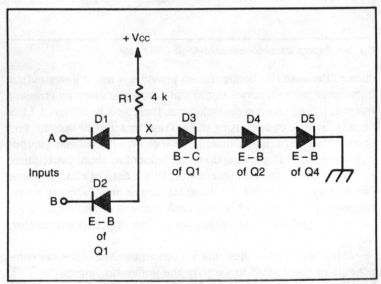

Fig. 3-6. Diode equivalent of TTL logic gate.

Current can flow through the input diode (which is low) and through the 4 kΩ pull-up resistor. Since the voltage at the base of transistor Q1 (point "X" in Fig. 3-6) is *less* than required to cause the string of three diodes, D3, D4, and D5, to conduct, the base-collector junction of transistor, Q1, will *not* conduct. Likewise, the emitter-base junctions of transistors Q2 and Q4 will not conduct and will be cut off. While transistor Q2 is cut off, base current will be supplied to transistor Q3 via resistor R2. Transistor Q3 will conduct if an output load is connected between itself and ground. At this time, the output voltage will be the power supply voltage, + VCC, minus the voltage drop across diode D1, transistor Q4, and resistor R3. A typical binary 1 output voltage level is approximately + 2.4 to + 3.6 volts. A typical binary 0 voltage level at either or both of the inputs will, therefore, produce a binary 1 output.

If, however, a binary 1 logic level is applied to *both* inputs, the input diode junctions will be reverse-biased. A typical binary 1 logic level will be at least + 2.4 volts. Since most of the inputs will be driven by other TTL outputs, these output voltages in most practical instances will, therefore, approach + 3.6 volts. While the emitter-base input diodes are reverse-biased, the diode equivalent string consisting of diodes D3, D4, and D5 in Fig. 3-6, will conduct via resistor R1. Therefore, the emitter-base junctions of transistors Q2 and Q4 will be forward-biased as well as the base-collector junction of transistor Q1. When transistor Q2, conducts, its collector voltage is lower than required to turn on transistor Q3. Base current to transistor Q3, via resistor R2, is shunted from it due to the conduction of transistor Q2. While transistor Q2 conducts, transistor Q4 will saturate. The output voltage at this time is the emitter-collector saturation voltage of transistor Q4, which will be typically less than + 0.4 volts. Therefore, when binary 1 is present on *both* inputs, the output of the circuit will be binary 0.

From this detailed circuit description, it can be concluded this circuit performs the logical NAND function using positive logic and the logical NOR function using negative logic. This conclusion can be verified by the truth tables shown in Tables 1-3. The basic characteristics of the TTL gate are summarized in Table 3-4.

TTL integrated circuits are still one of the most popular types of logic hardware available. The wide range of SSI and MSI types make TTL circuitry a most versatile line of digital integrated circuits. Texas Instruments developed the 7400 series which is the most common type of TTL circuits. There are other TTL circuits available, however. They include the 9300 series manufactured by

Inputs		Output
A	B	C
+ .4	+ .4	+ 3.6
+ .4	+ 3.6	+ 3.6
+ 3.6	+ .4	+ 3.6
+ 3.6	+ 3.6	+ .4

Table 3-1. Voltage Truth Table for TTL Logic Gate.

Fairchild and the 8000 series made by *Signetics*. Since all of these TTL circuits are compatible with each other, they may be used in any combination within any circuit design.

SPECIAL TTL VARIATIONS

All TTL integrated circuits, either SSI or MSI, sequential or combinational use the basic TTL logic gate circuit shown in Fig. 3-5. For special applications, however, there are several other variations of this design. Some of these special functions include gates for low power operation or higher speed operation as well as other special functions which will be discussed shortly.

Low Power TTL. The only difference between low power TTL circuits and the basic TTL circuit previously described is the resistor values incorporated within them. In a low power TTL circuit the resistor values are approximately ten times the values shown in Fig. 3-5. This means that power consumption will be only one-tenth of the basic design. Increasing the values of internal resistances, however, causes increased propagation delay, as well. Typical propagation delay in a low power TTL circuit is approximately 30 to 40 nanoseconds. Therefore, high speed is sacrificed for low power consumption.

High Power TTL. As with the low power TTL circuit just described, the high power TTL circuit differs from the basic design

Table 3-2. Truth Table for TTL Logic Gate Using Positive Logic (NAND).

Inputs		Output
A	B	C
0	0	1
0	1	1
1	0	1
1	1	0

Inputs		Output
A	B	C
1	1	0
1	0	0
0	1	0
0	0	1

Table 3-3. Truth Table for TTL Logic Gate Using Negative Logic (NAND).

in the values of the internal resistors. In high power TTL, resistor values are significantly *reduced* in order to obtain faster operating speed. Typical propagation delay in a high power TTL circuit is approximately 6 nanoseconds. This increase of speed, however, is achieved at the cost of increasing the power consumption by approximately 100%. Average power dissipation per gate is around 22 milliwatts in a high power TTL circuit. Therefore, most high power TTL circuits have been made obsolete by the newer Schottky TTL replacements. These Schottky TTL circuits do not only operate faster but also consume significantly less power.

Schottky TTL. TTL logic circuit transistors operate in the saturated mode. To obtain faster operating speed, therefore, non-saturating transistors must be employed. Schottky TTL circuits use transistors which do not saturate.

The primary difference between a standard TTL gate and a Schottky TTL gate is the addition of a diode connected between the collector and base of each transistor (Fig. 3-7A) to prevent them from saturating. Here is how it works: When the transistor begins to turn on, its collector voltage will quickly drop. When it reaches a certain voltage, the diode will conduct and, therefore, shunt current away from the collector-base junction (which would normally

Table 3-4. Electrical Characteristics of TTL Logic Family.

Type of logic:	current sinking
Propagation delay:	10 ns
Power dissipation:	10 mW
Fan out:	10
Noise immunity:	High
Logic levels:	binary 0 = +0.4V
	binary 1 = +3.6V
Basic gate form:	positive NAND/negative NOR
Power supply voltage (Vcc):	+5V ± 10%

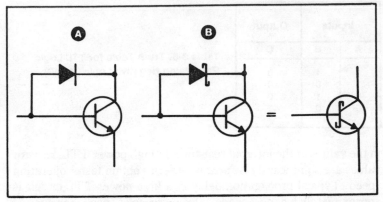

Fig. 3-7. Hot-carrier (Schottky) diodes are used to clamp the transistors used in Schottky TTL circuits to prevent saturation and increase switching speed.

conduct during saturation). The diode, in essence, "clamps" the collector at a voltage significantly high to keep the base-collector junction reverse biased. This technique permits the circuit to operate *near* saturation without actually being saturated.

The actual diode used to provide the clamping is a *hot carrier* or *Schottky* diode. Unlike other semiconductor diodes, this type does not have a pn junction. A Schottky diode is a junction of metal (such as aluminum or gold) and the n-type semiconductor material. Schottky diodes operate much faster than junction diodes since they do not possess the normal "charge storage" characteristics normally associated with pn junctions. Moreover, the forward voltage drop across this diode, as well as the voltage required for the diode to conduct, is significantly less than that of a standard pn junction diode.

Figure 3-7 (B) shows how the Schottky clamp diode is incorporated on TTL gate transistors. Note the unique symbol used to represent the Schottky diode. The equivalent Schottky-diode-clamped transistor package is also shown on the right-hand side of Fig. 3-7 (B). This symbol is used universally to represent Schottky TTL logic circuits in schematic diagrams.

Higher speed of operation is the primary advantage of Schottky TTL gates. No charge storage problems occur since these transistors do not saturate. Propagation delays as low as 3 nanoseconds per gate are possible with this type of circuit. Schottky TTL gates combine this fast switching speed with power dissipation of only about 19 milliwatts per gate. A special low power Schottky TTL gate is also available with a 10 nanosecond propagation delay and a power dissipation of only 2 milliwatts! Therefore, this type of TTL gate has one of the most favorable speed-power trade-offs of any digital integrated circuit.

TRI-STATE TTL

In tri-state TTL integrated circuits the output can assume *three* states instead of the normal two. In addition to the binary 0 and binary 1 logic levels, the tri-state TTL circuit can assume an "open" state. This open state is essentially equivalent to disconnecting the totem-pole output circuit from the output pin of the chip, since it represents a very high impedance. Tri-state TTL circuit used in digital systems incorporating multiplexed or bussed data transmissions. The following paragraphs will provide background on their applications.

Digital information or binary numbers are transferred in parallel from one point to another via a data bus. A data bus can be a group of wires, transmission lines or cables. The two basic types of data buses are unidirectional and bidirectional. As their respective names imply, a unidirectional data bus transfers data in two directions. Most digital buses are bidirectional. A common bus is used for transferring data from one place to another on a time shared basis instead of having multiple parallel paths. During data transfer other data waits until the original data transfer is complete. This concept of utilizing a single data bus to serve as a carrier of multiple signals is called *multiplexing*. In a multiplexed data bus, when circuits are not in use, they are disabled while other circuits are activated to allow them to transfer data.

A simplified diagram of a typical bidirectional digital data bus is illustrated in Fig. 3-8. In this example, only one of several identical buses is shown. This bus line is used for transmitting one bit of digital data of a multiple bit binary word. The bus line may be a cable or transmission line anywhere from several feet to several hundred feet in length. Gates 3, 4, or 5 can transmit one bit of information down the bus line to be received by gate 6. Only one of the three transmitting gates (3, 4, or 5) will be enabled at any one time. Closer examination of this illustration shows that the same data bus can be used to transmit information from either gate 7 or 8 down the line to be received by gate 1 or 2. It is important to remember that only a *single* bit of data transmission can take place at any given time. It can, however, transmit in either direction from any one of several sources to any (or all) of several destinations as desired.

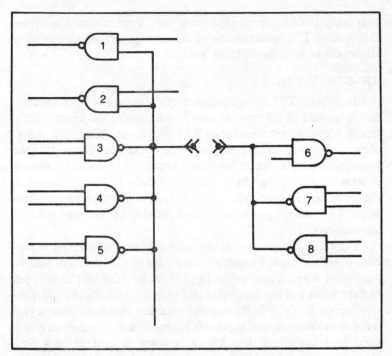

Fig. 3-8. Bidirectional digital data bus.

A digital data bus is relatively easy to implement by using collector pullup resistors contained inside logic circuits. Simply connect the outputs of the gates from which the digital data emanates as shown in Fig. 3-9. In effect, the collector resistors are paralleled by connecting their outputs directly together, thereby reducing the total resistance to one-half the value of an individual resistor. The two output transistors, therefore, share a common collector resistance. By employing this arrangement, either transistor shown in Fig. 3-9 can bring the output to binary 0. The output will rise to binary 1 (+ VCC) only when *both* transistors are cut off. Digital data, therefore, is transmitted by enabling the single gate responsible for the transmission while simultaneously disabling all remaining gates on a given data bus line. This is achieved by applying the proper input signal to the gates in order to bring their output transistors to cut-off, which permits the remaining transistor to control the state of the output signal.

Gate outputs connected in a parallel configuration as just discussed are called the *wired OR* connection. It is so named simply because either transistor, Q1 *or* Q2, can bring the state of the output to binary 0. This connection eliminates the need for an additional gate when the logical OR function is desired.

It must be noted, however, TTL circuits cannot be wired OR because the active pullup circuit in their totem pole output will cause improper operation or damage to the circuits themselves. Therefore, TTL integrated circuits cannot be used for data bus applications. However, open collector TTL integrated circuits can be used to overcome this obstacle. In open-collector TTL circuits, the active pullup totem pole is eliminated. In its place, the collector of the shunt output transistor is connected to an appropriate output pin of the chip. The user, therefore, can connect an *external* pullup resistor to this output pin. This will permit the wired OR arrangement to be implemented. By using open-collector TTL gates in the wired OR configuration (as opposed to standard TTL gates) one of the primary advantages of TTL circuitry is being eliminated—the active pullup circuit produces higher speed and lower output impedance, both of which are highly desirable from a speed standpoint as well as an improvement in noise immunity.

With the development of tri-state logic, the disadvantage of not being able to use TTL circuits in data bus applications was overcome. Tri-state logic was originally introduced by *National Semiconductor Corporation*. Tri-state logic is a special form of TTL which retains the totem pole active output circuit in the basic circuit. The

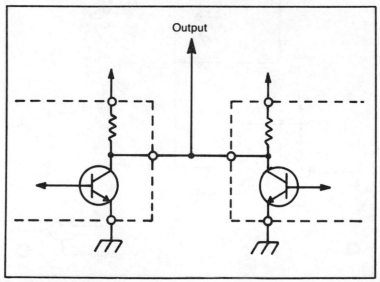

Fig. 3-9. Paralleled gate outputs sharing a common output line.

85

difference, however, is the additional circuitry to allow an optional high impedance (third state) that can essentially remove itself from any common bus line when not transmitting data.

Figure 3-10A shows a typical tri-state TTL circuit. This circuit is basically the same as the TTL circuit previously discussed. Transistor Q1 is the multiple input transistor. Transistor Q2 is the phase splitter. Transistors Q4 and Q5 form the totem pole output circuit. Transistor Q3 has been added to provide better control of output transistor Q4. These two transistors, Q3 and Q4, form a very high gain Darlington pair. The addition of diode, D1, and transistors Q6, Q7, and Q8, are to control the third state. Transistor Q6 saturates whenever the control (*CNTR*) input is low. When transistor Q6 saturates, it puts nearly the same low input level on both its collector and on the base of transistor Q7. Therefore, both transistors Q7 and Q8 are cut off and the TTL gate functions normally.

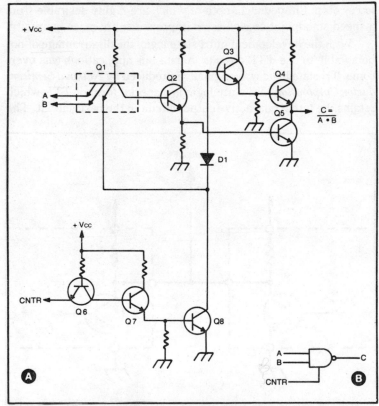

Fig. 3-10. Schematic diagram of the tri-state TTL gate.

86

When the control input (CNTR) is raised to binary 1, however, transistor Q6 cuts off. The emitter-base junctions of transistors Q7 and Q8 become forward biased via the base-collector junction of transistor Q6 and its associated base resistor. While transistor Q8 is saturated, the third input to transistor Q1 is brought to ground potential along with the cathode of diode D1. Remember: when any one or more of the inputs of a TTL gate are brought to a binary 0, its output is forced to a binary 1 level. This is usually accomplished by turning on the active pullup transistor Q4, while turning off the shunt output transistor, Q5. In this case, however, *BOTH* output transistors, Q4 and Q5, are cut off. When transistor Q8 saturates the cathode of diode D1 goes to ground. This shunts away all the base current from transistor Q3 and causes both transistors Q3 and Q4 to cut off. Now, both output transistors Q4 and Q5 are cut off which makes the output a very high impedance. Any load on this output sees essentially an open circuit because of the low leakage of its components. With this configuration, any number of tri-state TTL outputs may be paralleled in the wired OR configuration to form a common data bus line. When data is to be transmitted on such a data bus, all gates on the line which are *not* transmitting data will have their control lines (*CNTR*) held to binary 1 and, thereby, remove their respective outputs from the line. Only the single gate designated to transmit data will be enabled by bringing its control line to binary 0.

The standard logic symbol for a tri-state TTL gate is shown in Fig. 3-10B.

EMITTER-COUPLED LOGIC

The switching speed limitation of bipolar logic circuits is primarily the result of the charge storage which occurs in the base region of the bipolar transistor when both the emitter-base and base-collector junctions are forward biased (saturated). The turn off of the transistor is delayed due to the time required to remove this charge. Switching speeds can be significantly increased if this delay time is reduced or eliminated. This problem is overcome in Schottky TTL circuits because the transistors never saturate. Since this significantly increases the switching speed, non-saturating transistors, therefore, offer the best choice for fastest logic. See Table 3-5.

Emitter-Coupled Logic (ECL) is another form of logic circuit incorporating non-saturating bipolar transistors. This circuitry, also referred to as "current mode logic," is essentially a differential

Table 3-5. Electrical Characteristics of ECL Logic Family.

Type of logic:	unsaturated, current source
Propagation delay:	1 to 3 ns
Power dissipation:	40 to 60 mW
Fan out:	10 to 25
Noise immunity:	High
Logic levels:	binary 0 = −1.75V
	binary 1 = −.9V
Basic gate function:	OR/NOR
Power supply voltage (V$_{EE}$):	−5.2V

amplifier configuration which effectively prevents saturating the transistors. ECL integrated circuits are the fastest logic circuits currently available.

A typical ECL logic gate is illustrated in Fig. 3-11. Transistors, Q1, Q2, and Q3, form a differential amplifier. The inputs, *A* and *B*, are applied to transistors, Q1 and Q2 respectively. The emitters and collectors of these two transistors are in parallel to form one side of the differential amplifier circuit. If more inputs are required, additional input transistors may be paralleled. The other side of the differential amplifier is comprised of transistor Q3. Input logic level voltages are typically − 1.75 volts for binary 0 and − .9 volt for binary 1. The difference between these two voltages is the input and output swing:

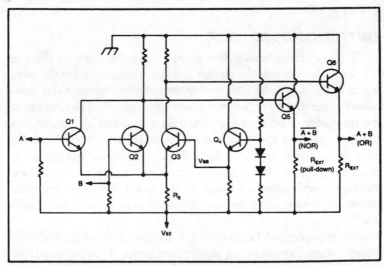

Fig. 3-11. Typical emitter-coupled logic (ECL) gate.

88

$$(-.9) - (-1.75) = .85 \text{ volts}$$

The power supply voltage, VEE, is -5.2 volts. The current source which supplies a fixed current level below the point of saturation to the transistors is formed by VEE and R_E.

The base of transistor Q3 is biased to approximately -1.3 volts by the temperature-compensated voltage source comprised of transistor Q4 and its associated components. Because of the emitter-base voltage drop, the emitter of transistor, Q3, will be about 0.7 volt more negative than its base. Therefore, the voltage on the emitters of transistors, Q1, Q2, and Q3, will be approximately:

$$(-1.3) - (.7) = -2.0 \text{ volts}$$

Assuming both logic inputs, A and B, are binary 0 (-1.75 volts), transistors Q1 and Q2 will *not* conduct because of insufficient emitter-base bias (.25 volt). The collectors of transistors Q1 and Q2 are high while the collector of transistor Q3 is low. The output emitter followers of transistors Q5 and Q6 buffer the two output logic levels and produce the desired binary 0 and binary 1 logic levels. Both the normal (OR) and complementary (NOR) functions are simultaneously available at the output.

If either one or both of the logic inputs, A or B, elevate to binary 1 ($-.9$ volt), its respective input transistor, Q1 or Q2, will conduct. The emitters of transistors Q1, Q2, and Q3, will, therefore, drop to approximately -1.6 volts. In other words, when one or more of the inputs rise to binary 1 ($-.9$ volt), the common-emitter point will also rise from -2.0 volts to -1.6 volts. This voltage level will cause transistor Q3 to cut off. The current supplied by the emitter supply voltage, VEE, and the common emitter resistor, R_E, switches from transistor Q3 to the conducting input transistor or transistors, Q1 or Q2. The collectors of transistors Q1 and Q2 will be low while the collector of transistor Q3 will be high. For positive logic assignments, this circuit performs the OR and NOR functions.

The simultaneous availability of both the normal and complementary outputs of most ECL integrated circuits is one of its major advantages. This permits both the OR and the NOR functions to be obtained without the addition of an external inverter. The emitter-follower "pull down" resistors, R_{EXT}, are usually external to the integrated circuit, thereby permitting them to be remotely located at either the end of a transmission line or other desirable location. Furthermore, it is possible to connect the OR or NOR outputs of ECL logic circuits to implement the wired OR function.

Circuit Characteristics. ECL logic circuits are easy to use, extremely versatile and are very fast. These circuits are, however, more costly and require significantly more power than other types of logic circuits. Their high speed is, therefore, the only real advantage of ECL logic circuits. Because of the cost and power requirements of ECL logic circuits, they should be used only when high speed is absolutely necessary.

METAL-OXIDE-SEMICONDUCTOR INTEGRATED CIRCUITS

Metal-oxide-semiconductor field-effect transistors (MOSFETs) offer many advantages over bipolar transistors in digital integrated circuits. Since these devices are simpler to construct, they can be made much smaller. Higher density logic networks can be designed on a single silicon chip because they occupy less space. This permits easy construction of large-scale and very-large-scale integrated circuitry. Another advantage of MOSFET technology is its intrinsic high impedance and, therefore, low power consumption. Much less power is required for MOS integrated circuits than for their bipolar counterparts.

A major disadvantage of MOS technology is its low operating speed. The low speed of MOS circuitry is the result of its high impedance and capacitive nature. MOS circuits, however, found wide applications in those areas not requiring high speed operation. Recent advances in MOS technology have helped their switching speed to approach that of bipolar circuits.

The two basic types of MOSFETs used in integrated circuits are the p-channel and the n-channel. MOSFETs used in digital integrated circuits operate in the "enhancement" mode. The transistor is normally cut off and suddenly switches on when the appropriate voltage level is applied between the source and the gate. Since these devices have an extremely high impedance when not conducting and a very low impedance when they are conducting, they are considered to be near-perfect switches.

The early MOS devices used in digital circuits were PMOS types. P-type MOSFETs are the simplest and easiest to construct. N-channel MOS devices are slightly more difficult to make but offer the advantages of smaller size and faster speed of operation. Their switching threshold is much lower thereby making them more compatible with bipolar integrated circuits. Another type of MOS technology combines both p-channel and n-channel devices on a single chip. These circuits are called complementary MOS or CMOS integrated circuits.

Because of their small size, low power consumption, and simplicity of manufacture, MOS integrated circuits are extremely attractive for many medium and large scale applications. Complete computers and test equipment can be manufactured on a single chip. Advancements in technology will eventually increase the switching speeds of MOS circuitry to acceptable limits for all but the fastest requirements.

PMOS & NMOS

When a digital integrated circuit is constructed with only p-channel MOSFETs, it is called PMOS. Conversely, digital integrated circuits constructed with n-channel enhancement-mode MOSFETs are called NMOS. The basic circuit configurations for either type of transistor are the same, however.

An n-channel MOS logic inverter circuit is illustrated in Fig. 3-12. In this circuit, transistor Q2, is a standard shunt inverter switch. Transistor Q1 is used to form a drain or load resistance since a standard integrated circuit resistor occupies substantially more space on the chip. Therefore, a MOSFET transistor Q1 is

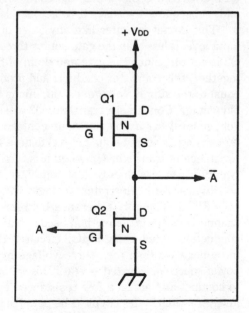

Fig. 3-12. N-channel MOS inverter.

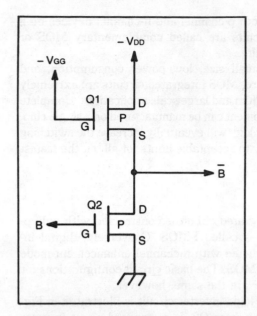

Fig. 3-13. P-channel MOS inverter.

biased into conduction to replace a fixed load resistor. This technique greatly increases the number of circuits which can be constructed on a given size silicon chip. The gate and drain of transistor Q1 are wired together which biases the transistor into conduction and, subsequently, causes it to act as a low resistance.

This circuit operates like any other inverter. When the logic input level is less than the gate-source threshold voltage, transistor Q2 is cut off. Since the gate and drain of transistor Q1 are wired together, this transistor conducts and produces an output voltage equal to the supply voltage + VDD, minus the gate-source threshold voltage. Conversely, transistor Q2 will conduct when the input voltage level *exceeds* the gate-source threshold voltage of transistor Q2 causing its output voltage level to drop to a very low level. The resistance of transistor Q2 when it is turned on is approximately twenty times less than that of transistor, Q1.

Figure 3-13 illustrates a logic inverter using p-channel MOSFETs. The only difference between this circuit and the n-channel inverter is the method used to bias the load transistor into conduction. When using PMOS circuitry, the gate voltage is made more negative than the source voltage by incorporating another power source designated – VGG. This voltage causes transistor Q1 to conduct and act as a low resistance. Transistor Q2 is a shunt inverter switch in this circuit. The power supply polarity is reversed compared to the n-channel counterpart previously described. Both circuits operate the same, however. Transistor Q2 will conduct and drop the output voltage to near zero when the gate-source threshold voltage is exceeded. Conversely, transistor Q2 will cut off and act as an open circuit when the gate-source voltage level is *less* than the threshold value. When this occurs, the output voltage is some negative value less than $-V_{DD}$. Even though this circuit configuration produces somewhat faster switching speeds than the one illustrated in Fig. 3-13, it has a disadvantage of requiring a second source of power to operate.

The two basic logic functions implemented with MOSFETS are shown in Fig. 3-14. Figure 3-14A illustrates how the n-channel devices are connected in parallel to share a common load transistor, Q3. In this arrangement, if either one or both of the input transistors are biased on, the output voltage will subsequently drop to a very low value. Conversely, when the input voltage levels are both less than the threshold value, transistors Q1 and Q2 will be cut off and allow the output voltage to rise to almost $+V_{DD}$. Therefore, using positive logic assignments, this circuit performs the NOR function.

Figure 3-14B illustrates how to implement the NAND function for positive logic assignments using MOSFETs. In this circuit, transistors Q1 and Q2 are wired in series. In order to drop the output voltage to a low level, both inputs, *A* and *B*, must be made high. If either one or both inputs are made low, the resulting output will be high. This clearly demonstrates the NAND function.

All of the aforementioned MOS logic circuits are known as *static logic circuits* since they perform logic functions with voltage levels. Another type of MOS logic, known as dynamic logic circuits, is also widely used. The main difference between these two types of circuits is that dynamic logic circuits take advantage of the capacitive nature of the MOS input devices. The input capacitance is used to temporarily store charges or logic levels. High speed clock signals are used during operation to transfer these stored charges from one circuit to another. Higher operating speed and even less power consumption is attainable by using this method.

COMPLEMENTARY MOS

As its name suggests, complementary MOS or CMOS logic circuits incorporate both p-channel and n-channel enhancement-mode MOSFETS. Figure 3-15 illustrates how to construct a logic inverter

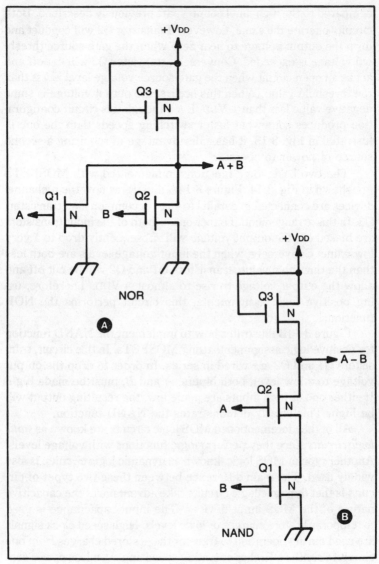

Fig. 3-14. (A) NMOS NOR gate. (B) NMOS NAND gate.

using both types of MOS devices. In this circuit, the input signal simultaneously drives the gates of both transistors. When the input voltage level is low or near zero, the gate-source threshold level for transistor Q2 is less than required for conduction and the transistor is cut off. With the input level low, however, the gate-source

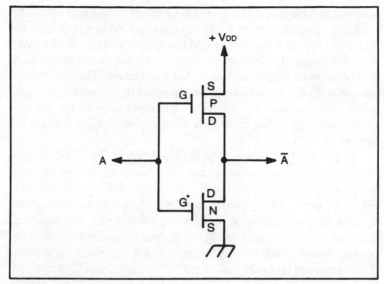

Fig. 3-15. CMOS logic inverter.

threshold level of transistor Q1 is exceeded. Since its gate is more negative than its source, the p-channel device conducts and switches the supply voltage, + VDD, to the output. See Table 3-6.

On the other hand, when the input voltage is brought to a high logic level (near the supply voltage, + VDD), the gate-source threshold level of transistor Q2 will be exceeded and the transistor will conduct. It will act as a very low resistance which will subsequently bring the output voltage to a low level. When this occurs, the gate and source of transistor Q1 are nearly equal and the threshold level is not exceeded. Therefore, transistor Q1 is cut off and logic inversion is being performed. In this type of circuit, both current

Table 3-6. Electrical Characteristics of CMOS Logic Family.

Type of logic:	current sink and current source
Propagation delay:	30 to 100 ns
Power dissipation:	.01 mW (static)
	1 mW @ 1 MHz
Fan out:	50 (minimum)
Noise immunity:	Very High (45% of VDD)
Logic levels:	binary 0 = 0 volt
	binary 1 = + VDD
Basic gate form:	positive NOR/negative NAND
Power supply voltage (+ VDD):	+3 to + 15V

sourcing and current sinking is taking place. When transistor Q2 conducts, it sinks current from the external loads which may be connected between the output and the supply voltage. When transistor Q1 conducts, however, it *supplies* current to any load which may be connected between the output and ground. The logic levels used in MOS devices are very nearly equal to the supply voltage, + VDD, and ground, due to very high input impedance and extremely low conducting resistance characteristics of the MOS transistors.

A typical CMOS logic gate is illustrated in Fig. 3-16. It consists of two p-channel series-connected transistors, Q1 and Q2, and two parallel-connected n-channel transistors, Q3 and Q4. When a binary 1 logic level is applied to either one or both inputs, A or B, the associated n-channel transistor, Q3 and Q4, will conduct. Subsequently, the output voltage will drop to nearly zero volts indicating binary 0 logic level. Whenever either input is brought high, either transistor Q1 or Q2 will be cut off. Since Q1 and Q2 are wired

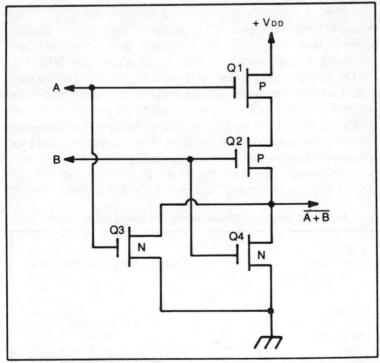

Fig. 3-16. CMOS NOR gate.

in series, the current path between the power supply, + VDD, and the output is not made complete unless *both* transistors Q1 and Q2 are in conduction.

When both inputs are brought low, however, transistors Q3 and Q4 will become cut off since their gate-source voltage is below the threshold level necessary to cause conduction. When this occurs, the gate-source voltage of transistors Q1 and Q2 will be approximately equal to the supply voltage, + VDD, and since both input transistors will be conducting, they will form a low-resistance path between the output and the supply voltage. The resulting output level, therefore, will be binary 1 (high). This clearly demonstrates that with positive logic assignments the NOR logic function is being performed by this circuit. By suitably rearranging the p-channel and n-channel devices in this circuit, any logic function (NAND, AND, or OR) can be performed.

CMOS logic offers a well-balanced combination of characteristics, making it highly desirable and versatile—one of the most perfect logic circuits for virtually all applications. Some of its features are low power dissipation, excellent noise immunity, wide range of acceptable power supply levels, high fan out, and moderately high operating speed.

CMOS circuits have low power dissipation because there is never a continuous path through any device in the circuit from the power supply to ground. A close examination of the inverter circuit shown in Fig. 3-15, or the NOR gate shown in Fig. 3-16, will reveal this characteristic. Whenever the n-channel transistors connected between the output and ground are conducting, the p-channel transistors between the output and power supply, + VDD, are cut off. Conversely, whenever the p-channel transistors between the power supply and the output are conducting, the n-channel transistors between the output and ground are cut off. The current flow which does occur between the power supply and ground is only that of which flows during the very short time when the output state switches. It is only during this instant that the p-channel and the n-channel transistors may both be on. If the switching rate is high, so is the amount of current flow. Therefore, the operating *frequency* of a CMOS circuit determines its power consumption.

The 4000 series and the 74C series of integrated circuits made by *RCA* and *National Semiconductor*, respectively, are the most popular families of CMOS integrated circuits. Both companies' lines offer a wide variety of SSI, MSI, LSI, and VLSI circuits.

THE BEST DIGITAL INTEGRATED CIRCUIT

Selecting the type of integrated circuit is the most important decision a digital designer must make. From a performance and economic standpoint, the success or failure of a design will depend directly on this choice. Therefore, careful consideration of the requirements of the intended application must be made.

Performance, economy, and reliability are the prime factors when selecting a digital integrated circuit and should be the first step in selecting one. These characteristics are specified in terms of factors such as required system speed, noise immunity and power dissipation. After all the specifications have been stated, they can then be compared with the capabilities and characteristics of the various types of available integrated circuits.

While speed (propagation delay), power consumption, and noise immunity are the three most important performance characteristics, there are also other factors to consider as well. These include cost, availability, trends and the availability of complex functions. Obviously, the lowest-cost circuits are best only if they meet all the requirements of a given application. It is also desirable to design with circuits which are available from several sources of supply.

One of the most volatile industries in the field of electronics is the semiconductor business. Some devices become quickly obsolete while others are improved because of new technological developments which occur frequently. It is very difficult for the digital designer to select an integrated circuit with a long life and stable price because these change so often. It is important, therefore, for the serious designer to keep abreast of latest technology by subscribing to manufacturers' bulletins and to review the new literature which is being published daily. Only then can anyone be successful in selecting a circuit that not only meets his or her design requirements, but that will also be cost-effective, and remain available in the future for replacement.

The availability of medium-scale integrated circuits (MSI) is a highly desirable characteristic of any IC family. A vast majority of digital equipment can be designed by simply interconnecting MSI functional circuits. It is much more economical, therefore, to incorporate MSI circuits than to attempt to implement the same functions with SSI circuitry. Not only is design time substantially reduced, but so is the quantity of components and total package size. Significant savings in power consumption and in assembly time can also be realized. It is advantageous, therefore, to use as many MSI circuits as possible when designing digital equipment.

Table 3-7. Comparison of Performance Characteristics of IC Logic Families.

Characteristic	TTL	ECL	MOS	CMOS
Fan-out	10	25	20	50 +
Cost	low	medium to high	medium to high	low to medium
Power dissipation per gate (mW)	12 to 22	40 to 60	0.2 to 10	0.01 static 1 at 1 MHz
Noise generation	high	low to medium	medium	low medium
Immunity to external noise	good	good	good	very good
Temperature range (°C)	−55 to +125 0 to 75	−55 to +125	−55° to +125 0 to 75	−55 to 125 −40 to 85
Typical supply voltage (V)	+5	−5.2	−27, −13 (PMOS) +5 (NMOS)	+1.5 to 18
Avg. propagation delay per gate (ns)	3 to 12	1 to 2	300 (PMOS) 50 (NMOS)	70
Avg clock rate (MHz)	15 to 120	200 to 1000	2 (PMOS) 5 to 10 (NMOS)	50 to 10

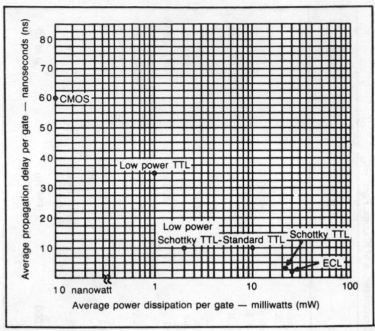

Fig. 3-17. Speed (propagation delay) versus power dissipation for common digital integrated circuits.

TRADE OFFS

All of the above factors are naturally interrelated. The final selection of integrated circuit will most often be a compromise based on application and availability. One of the most critical compromises in selecting an integrated circuit is the speed vs. power tradeoff. Noise immunity is another factor which may have to be compromised with some other characteristic depending upon what ICs are available.

Table 3-7 lists the primary characteristics of all types of logic circuits discussed in this chapter. It is intended for comparison with the requirements of an application.

Speed versus power consumption for various types of integrated circuits is shown in Fig. 3-17. In this diagram, propagation delay is plotted as a function of power dissipation for the most popular types of digital logic circuits. Obviously, the best choice of circuit is the one with the shortest propagation delay and the least amount of power dissipation. From careful examination of Fig. 3-17, it can be seen that the low-power Schottky TTL circuit generally has the most favorable speed vs. power rating.

Chapter 4

Designing Simple Logic Circuits

A LL DIGITAL CIRCUITS AND EQUIPMENT WORK WITH NUM-bers which represent specific quantities. For example, a digital voltmeter converts an analog voltage into its digital equivalent and displays a decimal value. Figure 4-1 shows in the most elementary manner how most digital circuitry processes data. The application determines the form taken by the input and output numbers. These numbers may be in either binary or decimal form and, even when digital processing is used, may be in analog form in some applications.

Decimal numbers are the most familiar type to most of us. In this system we combine the ten digits, 0 through 9, in various ways to represent specific quantities. In the binary number system, however, only two digits are used, 0 and 1. These binary digits, or bits, can also represent any decimal number when properly arranged. For example, the decimal number 52 can be represented in binary with the number 110100. The binary number system is the basis for all modern digital design.

The basis for determining a number system is called the *radix*. This "base" indicates the number of characters or digits used to represent all quantities in the particular number system. The decimal number system, therefore, has a radix of 10 since we use the 10 digits, 0 through 9, to represent any quantity. Similarly, the binary number system has a radix of 2 since only 2 digits, 0 and 1, are used to represent any quantity.

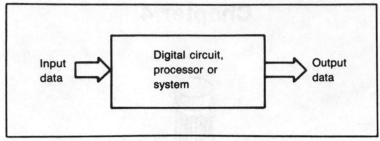

Fig. 4-1. Binary to decimal conversion.

Because most people aren't familiar with the binary number system, they tend to be intimidated by it. So far in this book we have used binary numbers to represent high and low logic states. These states can also be thought of as "true" and "false" statements. Once this simple number system is learned, however, it will seem very easy and convenient to use it, since it has special benefits when designing digital circuits.

Although digital equipment can be designed to work with decimal numbers, the binary number system is used because of its many advantages in terms of hardware design. For example, if the decimal number system were to be used, the hardware design must have *10* discrete states, each of which represents one of the ten digits, 0 through 9, used in this system. Even though many devices are available to accomplish this, such as a ten-position stepping relay or rotary switch, when the binary system is used, however, only two states need to be represented. An electronic component or circuit having only two states is significantly simpler, less expensive, more reliable and faster than a similar circuit that can have ten states. In a two-state device, each of the states (or bits) can be represented with components as simple as an on/off switch, or a transistor that is either turned on or turned off.

WEIGHTED NUMBER SYSTEMS

Both decimal and binary number systems are weighted, or positional. Each bit or digit in a number carries a particular "weight" in determining the magnitude of the particular number. For example, a decimal number has positional weights of units, tens, hundreds, thousands and so on. Each *position* has a weight which is some power of the number system's radix. In the decimal number system, these positional weights (from right to left of the decimal point) are: 10^0 = 1 (units), 10^1 (tens), 10^2 (hundreds), 10^3

(thousands), etc. The total quantity of the entire number is evaluated by considering the specific digits, the weights of their positions and adding them up. The decimal number 8743, for example, contains 3 units, 4 tens, 7 hundreds, and 8 thousands. The number can be rewritten:

$$(8 \times 10^3) + (7 \times 10^2) + (4 \times 10^1) + (3 \times 10^0) =$$
$$8000 + 700 + 40 + 3 = 8743$$

Each digit, therefore, is multiplied by the weight of its position and added together to obtain the result.

The same technique applies to binary numbers. Each digit's position carries a specific weight. The positional weights are some power of the radix (2), just as the radix (10) is used in the decimal number system. These weights are: $2^0 = 1$, $2^1 = 2$, $2^2 = 4$, $2^3 = 8$, etc. It can be seen the weight of each position is twice that of the previous position. In other words, each digit to the left is two times the value of the digit on its right. For example, the binary number 110100 can be rewritten:

$$(1 \times 2^5) + (1 \times 2^4) + (0 \times 2^3) + (1 \times 2^2) + (0 \times 2^1) + (0 \times$$
$$2^0) = 32 + 16 + 0 + 4 + 0 + 0 = 52$$

The above quantity is determined by multiplying each bit by its positional weight and adding them together.

Fractional Numbers

It is often necessary to express quantities in terms of numbers less than one, or fractional parts of a whole. Decimal fractions are positional numbers having weights which are negative powers of ten: $10^{-1} = 1/10 = .1$, $10^{-2} = 1/100 = .01$, $10^{-3} = 1/1000 = .001$, etc. The decimal point separates the fractional part of the number from the whole number. The fractional component of a number is placed to right of the decimal point and has positional weights of tenths, hundredths, thousandths, etc. For example, the number 495.87 can be rewritten:

$$(4 \times 10^2) + (9 \times 10^1) + (5 \times 10^0) + (8 \times 10^{-1}) + (7 \times 10^{-2}) =$$
$$400 + 90 + 5 + .8 + .07 = 495.87$$

In fractional binary numbers, the weights of the fractional positions are *negative* powers of

$2\text{: } 2^{-1} = 1/2 = .5, 2^{-2} = 1/4 = .25,$
$2^{-3} = 1/8 = .125, 2^{-4} = 1/16 = .0625,$ etc.

It can be noted that each positional weight is one-half the weight of the position directly to the left. Similar to the decimal point, the *binary* point separates the whole number from the fractional component.

The binary number 1101.101 can be evaluated:

$$(1 \times 2^3) + (1 \times 2^2) + (0 \times 2^1) + (1 \times 2^0) + (1 \times 2^{-1}) + (0 \times 2^{-2}) + (1 \times 2^{-3}) = 8 + 4 + 0 + 1 + .5 + 0 + .125 = 13.625$$

CONVERTING BETWEEN DECIMAL AND BINARY NUMBERS

The need for determining the decimal value of binary numbers is often required when working with digital circuitry. Additionally, it will also be necessary to be able to determine the binary equivalent of a decimal number, as well.

Binary to Decimal. Simply add together the weights of the positions in the number where binary 1s occur to convert a binary number to its decimal equivalent. Table 4-1 shows the weights of the integer and fractional positions. For example, to convert the binary number 1001 into its decimal equivalent, the following procedure should be followed. Since there is no binary point, it can be assumed the number is a whole number (without any fraction). The rightmost bit, also called the *least significant bit* or *LSB*, has the lowest integer weight of $2^0 = 1$. The leftmost bit, called the *most significant bit* or *MSB*, carries the greatest integer weight of $2^3 = 8$. To evaluate the entire number, the weights of the positions where binary 1s appear are added together. In this example there are 1s appearing at the 2^3 and 2^0 positions. The decimal equivalent, therefore, is $8 + 1 = 9$. To illustrate:

Binary						
number	1		0		0	1
Position						
weights	(8)		(4)		(2)	(1)
Decimal						
Equivalent	8	+	0	+	0	+	1	= 9

To further illustrate this procedure, here is how to convert the binary number 101.11 into its decimal equivalent:

Table 4-1. Comparison of Binary and Decimal Numbers.

					Integer									Fractional			
2^{10}	2^9	2^8	2^7	2^6	2^5	2^4	2^3	2^2	2^1	2^0		2^{-1}	2^{-2}	2^{-3}	2^{-4}
1024	512	256	128	64	32	16	8	4	2	1		.5	.25	.125	.0625
		256												.125	.0625

Binary Point

Binary number	1	0	1 .	1	1	
Position weights	(4)	(2)	(1)	(.5)	(.25)	
Decimal equivalent	4	0	1	.5	.25	= 5.75

It can be noted that the position weights where a binary 0 occur can be disregarded.

Decimal to Binary. Once you are familiar with the "weighting sequence" of binary numbers, converting a decimal number into its binary equivalent can be performed by a simple trial and error method. For example, to convert the decimal number 286 into its binary equivalent, you should first determine the *highest* positional weight that is equal to or less than the number being converted. In this case, it is 256. Now, subtract 256 from 286 and note the remainder:

$$286 - 256 = 30$$

Again, determine the highest positional weight of this remainder which does not exceed its value. In this case, it is 16. Now, determine the difference and repeat this procedure until there is no more remainder:

$$30 - 16 = 14$$

The highest positional weight less than 14 is 8:

$$14 - 8 = 6$$

The highest positional weight less than 6 is 4:

$$6 - 4 = 2$$

The highest positional weight is exactly 2:

$$2 - 2 = 0$$

Using the above information the equivalent binary number can be constructed: A binary "1" is written in the weight positions which were subtracted from the original number and the subsequent remainders. In this example, these were 256, 16, 8, 4, and 2. It can be noted that the weight positions 128, 64, 32, and 1 were not used. Therefore, these positions will be binary 0. The resulting binary equivalent of decimal 286 is, therefore, 100011110. To check the validity of this result, try converting the binary number back to its decimal equivalent by the aforementioned procedure.

An alternate method of converting decimal numbers into their binary equivalents is to keep dividing the original number and its subsequent quotients by 2 and noting the remainder. When any number is divided by 2, the remainder will *always* be either 1 or 0. This "remainder" is written to form the binary equivalent. For example, to convert decimal 286 into its binary equivalent using this technique:

REMAINDER:

286 ÷			
2	= 143	0	(LSB)
143 ÷			
2	= 71	1	
71 ÷ 2	= 35	1	
35 ÷ 2	= 17	1	
17 ÷ 2	= 8	1	
8 ÷ 2	= 4	0	
4 ÷ 2	= 2	0	
2 ÷ 2	= 1	0	
1 ÷ 2	= 0	1	(MSB)

Binary Number Sizes. Binary numbers can also be expressed in binary "words." An 8-bit binary number is equivalent to an 8-bit word. The name *byte* is also given to a binary word. Most digital systems use a fixed binary word size. The maximum magnitude and resolution of which numbers can be represented is determined by this word size. The number of bits (binary digits) used to define a word determines the total number of discrete states which can exist and the maximum quantity which can be represented.

The number of states which can be represented with a given number of bits can be calculated by the formula:

$$N = 2^n$$

Where: N = total number of states
            n = number of bits per word

For example, with a four bit word, a maximum of:

$$N = 2^n = 2^4 = 2 \times 2 \times 2 \times 2 = 16$$

can be represented.

Therefore, by using four bit positions, a total of sixteen discrete binary bit patterns or number combinations can be created. These binary bit patterns along with their decimal equivalents are listed in Table 4-2.

As Table 4-2 illustrates, the numbers 0 through 15 are represented by using only 4 bits of binary data in a weighted system. The largest decimal number which can be represented is always one less than the total number of possible states. Therefore, the largest decimal number (M) which can be represented for a given number of bits (n) can be expressed by:

$$M = 2^n - 1$$

For example, the maximum value which can be represented with an 8 bit binary number is:

$$M = 2^8 - 1 = 256 - 1 = 255$$

Binary	Decimal
0000	0
0001	1
0010	2
0011	3
0100	4
0101	5
0110	6
0111	7
1000	8
1001	9
1010	10
1011	11
1100	12
1101	13
1110	14
1111	15

Table 4-2. Binary and Decimal Equivalents of a 4-Bit Binary Word.

Likewise, by knowing the maximum decimal quantity (N) to be represented by a binary number, the required number of bits (B) can be calculated by the formula:

$$B = 3.32 \log_{10} N$$

Common logarithms can be obtained from a set of tables or a calculator having log capabilities. For example, the number of bits required to represent a maximum number of 500 is:

$$B = 3.32 \log_{10} 500$$
$$B = 3.32 \ (2.69897)$$
$$B = 8.96$$

Since, of course, fractional bits cannot be implemented, the next higher whole number should, therefore, be used. In this case, 9 bits would be required to represent the number 500. It can also be determined that with 9 bits, the maximum number which can be represented is:

$$N = 2^n - 1 = 2^9 - 1 = 512 - 1 = 511$$

Radix Identification. It is often necessary to have some way of identifying whether a number is either decimal or binary when working with both bases. This becomes particularly crucial when working with numbers using only ones and zeros. For example, the number 1010 could represent either the quantity "one-thousand ten" in decimal *or* the number 10 in binary!

To separate binary from decimal numbers, a small subscript indicating the radix (or base) of the number is usually written following the number. Some examples of this technique are:

$$1010_2 = 10_{10}$$
$$1010_{10} = 1111110010_2$$

BINARY CODES

"Coding" is the general term given to the process of converting a decimal number into its binary equivalent. A decimal number is expressed in terms of a binary code or binary number. So far, all the examples used in this book are known as the "pure" binary code. It is given this name to identify it as not being any of the special binary codes which will now be discussed.

Binary Coded Decimal

The decimal number system seems easy to use only because most of us are so familiar with it. Conversely, the binary number system seems to be less convenient since most of us are not as familiar with it. Furthermore, it is difficult to recognize the decimal equivalent of a large binary number by quickly glancing at it. For example, the binary number 10101100 represents the equivalent of decimal number 172. As can be seen, the decimal conversion can not be immediately discerned. However, by using the procedures explained earlier in this chapter, the decimal equivalent can be calculated in a short time. The amount of conversion time is a distinct disadvantage when working with this code despite the numerous hardware advantages. Therefore, a special binary code is used which is more closely compatible with the decimal number system. This special code has become accepted and widely used since so many digital devices use decimal numbers at their inputs and outputs. The name of this special code is *Binary Coded Decimal* or *BCD*. This special code combines some characteristics of both the decimal number system and the binary number system.

Using a four-bit binary code, the BCD code is a system representing the ten digits 0 through 9. This BCD code is based on the standard 8421 positional weighting system of the pure binary code. Table 4-3 shows standard 8421 BCD codes along with their decimal equivalents. The BCD numbers can be converted into their decimal equivalents by merely adding together the weights of their respective bit positions everywhere a binary 1 occurs in a manner similar to the pure binary code. It should be noted, however, there are only ten valid four-bit combinations. Therefore, the four-bit binary numbers representing decimal numbers 10 through 15 are considered to be invalid in the BCD code.

To represent a decimal number in BCD code, merely replace each decimal digit with the appropriate four-bit binary code. For example, the number 945 in BCD would be 1001 0100 0101. As can be seen, each decimal digit is represented by its equivalent 8421 four-bit code. A space is used between each digit to avoid confusing the BCD code with the pure binary code.

One of the main advantages of the BCD code is the ten code combinations are very easy to remember. With a little practice, it will be as easy to recognize a BCD number as it is to recognize

Decimal	BCD
0	0000
1	0001
2	0010
3	0011
4	0100
5	0101
6	0110
7	0111
8	1000
9	1001

Table 4-3. 8-4-2-1 Binary-coded Decimal (BCD) Code.

a decimal number. Converting decimal numbers into their BCD equivalents will be just as efficient.

Even though the BCD code helps to simplify human comprehension of digital data, it is less efficient than the pure binary code. It requires more bits to represent a given decimal number in BCD than with pure binary code. For example, the decimal number 94 in pure binary code is 1011110. In BCD code, the same number is written 1001 0100. As can be seen, it requires only 7 bits in pure binary code to represent the same number requiring 8 bits in BCD code. The inefficiency of this method stems from the fact that a certain amount of digital circuitry is required to process each bit of binary data within a digital system. Consequently, this extra circuitry costs more, increases system complexity, and consumes more power. Arithmetic manipulation using BCD numbers also consume more time and are more complex than with pure binary numbers. Remember: four bits of binary information can represent a maximum of 2^4 = 16 different states (or the decimal number equivalents of 0 through 15). In the BCD system, however, six of these states are wasted (10 through 15) since they are not used and considered to be invalid. When the BCD number system is used, some efficiency is traded off in exchange for improved communications between the equipment and the human factor.

SPECIAL BINARY CODES

The BCD number code system is the most widely used digital code next to the standard pure binary code. In most applications, either one or both of these systems will be encountered. There are, however, several other codes which are used for special applications. These include the Excess 3 Code, Gray Code, and the ASCII Code.

Excess 3 Code. The *excess 3* code is sometimes referred to as *XS3*. It is not a weighted code. In this system each four-bit number is three units greater than its standard 8421 coded number counterpart. In other words, to obtain the excess 3 code of a specific decimal number, merely add 3 to it and convert it to the corresponding 8421 binary code. For example, the excess 3 code for the decimal number 9 is the binary equivalent of 9 + 3 = 12. Therefore, the four bit excess 3 code for the number 9 is 1100. Conversely, to convert from excess 3 to decimal, merely find the decimal equivalent of each four bit group and subtract 3 from each digit. The excess 3 code was developed to simplify arithmetic operations with BCD numbers. Specifically, when used in addition, first add the binary numbers. If there is no carry-out from the four bit group, you subtract 0011 (decimal 3) from it to obtain the correct result. If, however, there is a carry-out, you *add* 0011 (decimal 3) to it to obtain the correct result.

Gray Code. The *Gray code* is another non-weighted code system which is widely used. It is sometimes referred to as the *Cyclic, Unit Distance*, or *Reflective code*, as well. The Gray code can exist in either pure binary or BCD formats. Table 4-4 shows the Gray code. It is important to note that in the Gray code only one bit changes in each digit from the previous one in the sequence. This can be seen by comparing the Gray code to the standard 8421 pure binary code also shown in Table 4-3. For example, in pure

Table 4-4. Gray Code.

Decimal	Pure Binary	Gray
0	0000	0000
1	0001	0001
2	0010	0011
3	0011	0010
4	0100	0110
5	0101	0111
6	0110	0101
7	0111	0100
8	1000	1100
9	1001	1101
10	1010	1111
11	1011	1110
12	1100	1010
13	1101	1011
14	1110	1001
15	1111	1000

binary code, the difference between 7 (0111) and 8 (1000) is the change of all four bits. In the Gray code, however, the difference between 7 (0100) and 8 (1100) is the change of only the first bit!

Because the Gray code greatly reduces the possibility of ambiguity in electronic circuits when changing from one state to the other, it is generally considered to be an error-minimizing code. In electronic circuitry, it takes a finite period of time for bits to change from one state to the other, either from 1 to 0 or 0 to 1. Since these state changes can cause timing and speed problems, the Gray code is used to minimize this effect. Because only one bit changes at a time in the Gray code, a circuit can operate at higher speed and with fewer errors using this code as opposed to the standard 8421 code whereby many bits can change at a time.

One of the big disadvantages of the Gray code, however, is its difficulty in implementing arithmetic computations. The Gray code cannot be used in operations where numbers must be added, subtracted, etc. The Gray code number, therefore, usually is converted into pure binary form when performing arithmetic operations.

ASCII code. This code, known as the *American Standard Code for Computer Information Interchange*, is a special BCD code widely used in computers and data communications equipment. It is a *seven* bit binary code used in transferring data between computers and other external peripheral devices and in communicating data via radio and telephone lines. Since the ASCII code has seven bits per word, it can represent 2^7 = 128 different states or characters. The ASCII Code, therefore, is used to represent the decimal numbers from 0 to 9, all the upper and lower case letters in the alphabet, and other special characters used for controlling various computer functions, associated peripheral devices, and communication circuits. Table 4-5 lists the standard ASCII code.

Each character, letter, number, or control function in the ASCII code is comprised of a 4-bit group and a 3-bit group. Figure 4-2 illustrates the arrangement of these groups along with their numbering sequence. The 4-bit group is on the right with bit number 1 being the Least Significant Bit (LSB). It is important to note how these groups are arranged in rows and columns as shown in Table 4-5.

To find the ASCII code for a given number or character, first locate that character in the table. Next, use the 3-bit and 4-bit codes associated with the respective column and row in which the character is located. For example, the ASCII code for the letter *M* is 1001101. It is located in column 4, row 13. The most signifi-

Table 4-5. American Standard Code for Information Interchange. (ASCII).

Row	Bits 4321	Column → 765	0 000	1 001	2 010	3 011	4 100	5 101	6 110	7 111
0	0000		NUL	DLE	SP	0	@	P	`	p
1	0001		SOH	DC1	!	1	A	Q	a	q
2	0010		STX	DC2	"	2	B	R	b	r
3	0011		ETX	DC3	#	3	C	S	c	s
4	0100		EOT	DC4	$	4	D	T	d	t
5	0101		ENQ	NAK	%	5	E	U	e	u
6	0110		ACK	SYN	&	6	F	V	f	v
7	0111		BEL	ETB	'	7	G	W	g	w
8	1000		BS	CAN	(	8	H	X	h	x
9	1001		HT	EM	)	9	I	Y	i	y
10	1010		LF	SUB	*	:	J	Z	j	z
11	1011		VT	ESC	+	;	K	[	k	{
12	1100		FF	FS	,	<	L	\	l	|
13	1101		CR	GS	-	=	M	]	m	}
14	1110		SO	RS	.	>	N	^	n	~
15	1111		SI	US	/	?	O	_	o	DEL

Explanation of special control functions in columns 0, 1, 2 and 7.

NUL	Null	DLE	Data Link Escape
SOH	Start of Heading	DCl	Device Control 1
STX	Start of Text	DC2	Device Control 2
ETX	End of Text	DC3	Device Control 3
EOT	End of Transmission	DC4	Device Control 4
ENQ	Enquiry	NAK	Negative Acknowledge
ACK	Acknowledge	SYN	Synchronous Idle
BEL	Bell (audible signal)	ETB	End of Transmission Block
BS	Backspace	CAN	Cancel
HT	Horizontal Tabulation (punched card skip)	EM	End of Medium
LF	Line Feed	SUB	Substitute
VT	Vertical Tabulation	ESC	Escape
FF	Form Feed	FS	File Separator
CR	Carriage Return	GS	Group Separator
SO	Shift Out	RS	Record Separator
SI	Shift In	US	Unit Separator
SP	Space (blank)	DEL	Delete

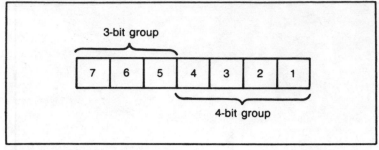

Fig. 4-2. ASCII code word format.

cant 3-bit group is 100 (column 4), and its least significant 4-bit group is 1101 (row 13).

There are also special versions of the ASCII code, each containing 6 bits or 8 bits per character. It is interesting to note that *IBM* uses another type of 8-bit encoding system called *Extended Binary Coded Decimal Interchange Code (EBCDIC)*, instead of ASCII, for the purpose of data communications and computer operations.

DATA REPRESENTATION

After becoming familiar with some binary coding systems used in digital equipment and understanding the reasons for using the binary number system, we will now consider the actual hardware involved to implement these binary numbers in greater detail. As discussed in Chapter 2, it is relatively easy to represent binary numbers with assigned voltage levels. The component used to represent a specific bit in a binary word must be capable of assuming two distinct states: one state to represent binary 0 and the other state to represent binary 1.

Electromechanical Devices. Switches and relays were once ideal for representing binary data. A closed switch or relay contact can represent a binary 1 while an open switch or contact can represent a binary 0. Conversely, if negative logic is being used, the reverse representations will apply. Even though solid-state devices replaced switches and relays for most digital functions, electromechanical devices can still be found in some places where static binary conditions are required, or very low speed and high power switching must be used.

Relays were used to represent binary numbers in the first generation digital equipment such as computers and test instruments. Vacuum tubes soon replaced relays in many applications. Each bit was represented by a separate vacuum tube which was either conducting or cut off. When the vacuum tube was conducting, it represented one binary state; when it was not conducting (cut off) it represented the other binary state. Vacuum tubes worked rather well in digital circuitry since they were able to achieve operating speeds much higher than their relay counterparts. However, because of the large physical size, high power consumption, excessive heat generation, and speed limitations, they were replaced by solid-state devices.

Transistors. The most common method of representing binary numbers in digital electronic equipment today is with a transistor. As discussed earlier, a transistor can readily assume two distinct states, saturation and cutoff. When a transistor is cut off it becomes essentially an open circuit. Conversely, when a transistor is saturated, or conducting heavily, it becomes a very low resistance and simulates a closed switch. Most of today's digital circuitry uses saturated bipolar switching transistors for data representation. In applications where high speed operation is desirable, non-saturated bipolar transistor switches are also used. Both discrete components and integrated circuit transistors are used in digital applications. The key element in MOS and CMOS integrated circuits is the enhancement-mode MOSFET which is becoming extremely widely-used.

Magnetic Cores. A magnetic core is another means of representing binary data. A magnetic core is a small piece of magnetic material, shaped like a donut which measures less than one tenth of an inch in diameter. A fine wire passing through the center of the core carries a current which magnetizes the core in either of two directions (polarization) depending upon the direction of current flow within the wire. One direction of magnetization represents binary 0 while the other direction represents binary 1. The permeability of the magnetic material permits the core to retain the applied magnetism even after the current through the wire is removed. This allows the core to store or "remember" a bit of binary data indefinitely. These cores are primarily used for data storage in many digital computers.

Logic Levels

A switch, of course, is the basic element used for representing a single bit of binary information. This switch can be mechanical, electromechanical, electronic, or magnetic. It is the on/off nature of a switch which makes it ideal for binary representation. The de-

117

fined relationship between the state of the switch and its bit representation is arbitrary. It doesn't matter, therefore, whether a transistor is on or off in a digital circuit. The important factor is that the proper bit assignment is being represented by the defined voltage level at any given point. The switching element or transistor controls these voltage levels. For example, either a binary 0 or 1 may be represented by 0 volts (ground) or $+5$ volts. Depending upon the power supplies chosen, the exact circuitry implemented, and the intended application, it is possible to use *any* voltage levels desired.

Figure 4-3 illustrates two ways to use a bipolar transistor to produce two distinct voltage levels. Figure 4-3A shows how to connect a transistor as a shunt switch. In this method, the transistor is in parallel with the output load. When the transistor is cut off (not conducting), the output voltage is $+5$ volts as seen through collector resistor, R_C. Conversely, when the transistor is saturated (conducting heavily), it acts like a very low resistance or nearly a closed switch. At this time, the output is near zero volts or at a very low positive voltage level. Of course, the switching of the transistor is controlled by the application of the appropriate base signal. With modern transistors, switching times in the nanosecond region are possible.

Figure 4-3B shows how the transistor is connected as a series switch. When the transistor is cut off, the output is near zero volts

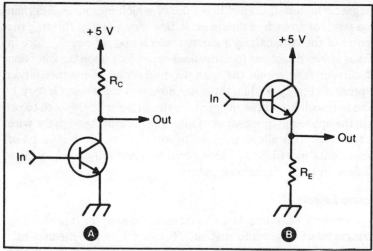

Fig. 4-3. Bipolar transistor: (A) shunt logic switch, (B) Bipolar transistor series logic switch.

Table 4-6. Positive Versus Negative Logic Voltage Levels.

Positive Logic	Negative Logic
binary 0 = +.2V binary 1 = +3.4V	binary 0 = +3.4V binary 1 = +.2V
binary 0 = -6V binary 1 = 0V	binary 0 = 0V binary 1 = -6V
binary 0 = +1V binary 1 = +15V	binary 0 = +15V binary 1 = +1V

or ground as seen through emitter resistor, R_E. Conversely, when the transistor is saturated, it acts as a very low resistance and switches the +5 volts from the supply line to the output. As in the shunt switch, the operation of this transistor arrangement is controlled by the application of the appropriate Base signal. Both shunt and series transistor switches are commonly used in digital circuits.

Positive & Negative Logic

Positive and negative logic assignments are the two basic types of logic representation. Positive logic is implemented when the more positive of the two voltage levels is assigned the binary 1 state. Conversely, negative logic is implemented when the more negative of two voltage levels is assigned the binary 1 state. Table 4-6 shows several examples of both positive and negative logic level assignments. It is important to note, however, that the voltage assignments are strictly arbitrary and are selected by the designer of the equipment at the time of conception.

PARALLEL VS. SERIAL DATA REPRESENTATION

Digital data is transmitted, processed, and manipulated in two basic ways: serial or parallel. In the serial method of data handling, each bit of information is processed in a series of one after another, one at a time. In a parallel system, however, all bits of a word or number are processed simultaneously.

Serial Data

Figure 4-4 illustrates how a binary number is represented in a serial data format. The binary number exists as a series of volt-

119

age levels representing the binary 1s and 0s, for a specific interval of time. All these voltage level changes occur at a single point or on a single line within a circuit. Each bit of information exists for a finite period of time. The bit of information located at the far left is considered to be the most significant bit (MSB), since it occurs first as time passes from left to right. It requires 8 units of time to transmit this word, because it is an 8-bit binary word. By observing the voltage levels at a specific point on the designated transmission line or data bus, and knowing positive logic assignment is being implemented, the binary number can easily be determined. This is the serial representation of binary 10110010 or the binary equivalent of decimal number 178.

Serial binary data manipulation has the primary advantage of requiring only a single line or channel for transferring information from one place to another. Additionally, only a single set of digital circuitry is usually required to process this information since each bit of data occurs separately on the line. Serial data representation, therefore, is the simpler and more economical method of the two types of manipulation. The primary disadvantage of serial data manipulation, however, is the significant amount of processing time required since each bit occurs one at a time.

Parallel Data

Parallel data handling is the other method of representing, transmitting, and manipulating digital data. In this method, all bits of a binary word or number are handled simultaneously. For this reason, a separate line or bus is necessary for each bit of a word or number. In Fig. 4-5, the 8-bit binary word, 10110010, is available at one time on eight separate output lines. Since all of the bits are simultaneously provided, there must also be sufficient digital circuitry to handle all 8 pieces of information at the same time. Paral-

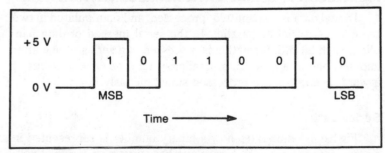

Fig. 4-4. The serial binary word: 10110010.

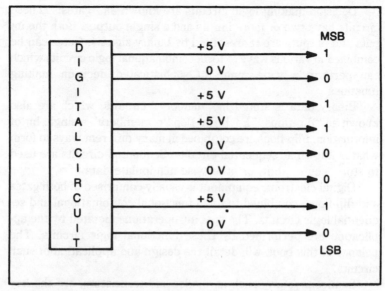

Fig. 4-5. The parallel binary word: 10110010.

lel data handling, therefore, is more complex and expensive than the serial data handling technique. However, the primary advantage of parallel data handling is that it is fast. Since all bits of a binary word or number are handled simultaneously, the time required to process this information is reduced by a factor equal to the number of bits in the word or number being processed. Parallel data handling, therefore, is preferred for high speed applications requiring rapid processing.

LOGIC CIRCUITS

The most common device used to represent binary data is the transistor. Transistors are combined with other components to form digital logic circuits. These circuits are used to manipulate or process binary information. The primary target of this book is to show how these circuits are designed and implemented in everyday usage.

The two basic types of logic circuits are: (1) *decision-making*, and (2) *memory*. The human ability to think logically requires both the capability for making decisions based on available information, *and* the ability to remember facts. This also holds true for digital circuits and equipment. Logic circuits accept information in the form of binary data, and generate binary data based upon the information and instructions provided them.

121

Decision-making logic circuits are known as "gates." These circuits have two or more inputs and a single output. Both the inputs and outputs are represented by binary signals. Gates can be combined in various ways to form combinational logic circuits which can perform a wide range of sophisticated decision making functions.

Binary data is stored in "memory" circuits, which are also known as "flip-flops." Each flip-flop "remembers" a single bit of information. Flip-flops are combined in many different ways to form what is known as sequential circuits. Sequential circuits are used to store, count, shift, or otherwise manipulate data.

Digital electronic equipment is usually comprised of both gates and flip-flops, combined to form functional combinational and sequential logic circuits. The specific operations dictated by the application are performed by these functional logic circuits. The balance of this book will detail the design and application of such circuits.

Semiconductors, such as diodes and transistors, are the key components used in digital integrated circuits. These components are combined with resistors, capacitors, and other components to form circuits used to perform the various logic functions. Today, microminiature integrated circuits, which can house complete functional instruments, are universally used to implement the majority of all digital electronic equipment. In order to fully understand the operational functions of digital integrated circuits, a knowledge of a special type of mathematics, called Boolean Algebra, is necessary.

INTRODUCTION TO BOOLEAN ALGEBRA

Boolean algebra is a system of *mathematical logic*. It is different from both ordinary algebra and the binary number system. For example, in ordinary algebra, $1 + 1 = 2$, in binary addition the result is 10, but in Boolean algebra, the result is 1. Even though there are similarities with ordinary algebra, Boolean algebra is a unique system of math.

Like the binary number system, there are only two constants within the Boolean system: 0 and 1. Each and every number is either 0 or 1 and there are no negative or fractional numbers. Therefore:

$$\text{If } X = 1, \text{ then } X \neq 0$$
$$\text{and}$$
$$\text{If } X = 0, \text{ then } X \neq 1$$

AND Laws. There are three Boolean *AND* laws that will be closely examined:

$$X \bullet 1 = X$$
$$X \bullet 0 = 0$$
$$X \bullet X = X$$

(Remember: The "$\bullet$" between terms within a Boolean expression indicates the *AND* function is being performed.) All three of the above laws can be proven by remembering the definition of the AND symbol. Consider the first equation, $X \bullet 1 = X$, and apply it to the two input AND gate shown in Fig. 4-6A. If $X = 0$ and the other input equals 1, then the output is 0. If $X = 1$ and the other input equals 1, then the output is 1. Therefore, it can be deduced that the output is always equal to the X input. In this example, it can be noted that the function of this gate is unnecessary and could be replaced with a piece of wire from the X input to the output.

Now, consider the equation, $X \bullet 0 = 0$, and apply it to a two-input AND gate as illustrated in Fig. 4-6B. Note that the output is 0 no matter what value is placed on the input X.

Finally, take the equation, $X \bullet X = X$, and apply it to the illustration in Fig. 4-6C. It can be easily seen that when the inputs,

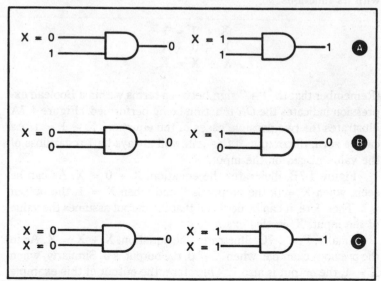

Fig. 4-6. (A) Proving X 1 = X. (B) Proving X 0 = 0. (C) Proving X X = X.

123

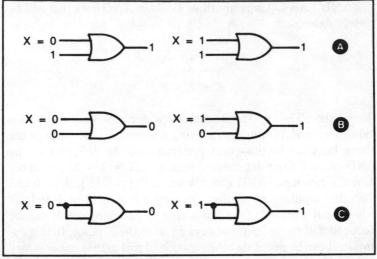

Fig. 4-7. (A) Proving X + 1 = 1. (B) Proving X + 0 = X. (C) Proving X + X = X.

X, equal 0, the output equals 0. Likewise, when the inputs, X, equal 1, the output also equals 1. Therefore, it proves the equation we are considering.

OR Laws. There are three basic *OR* laws which become apparent by examining the OR gate and the truth tables associated with its functions:

$$X + 1 = 1$$
$$X + 0 = X$$
$$X + X = X$$

(Remember that the " + " sign between terms within a Boolean expression indicates the *OR* function being performed.) Figure 4-7A illustrates the two possible cases of the equation, X + 1 = 1. As can be seen, the output of this gate will always be 1 regardless of the value placed on the input, X.

Figure 4-7B, illustrates the equation, X + 0 = X. As can be seen, when X = 0, the output is 0 and when X = 1, the output is 1. Therefore, it can be deduced that the output assumes the value of the input, X, in this example.

Finally, Fig. 4-7C, illustrates the equation, X + X = X. As in the previous example, when X = 0, the output is 0. Similarly, when X = 1, the output is also 1. Therefore, the output of this example will always assume the value of the input, X.

124

NOT Laws. When examining the inverter, there are several laws of Boolean algebra that will become apparent:

$$\overline{0} = 1$$
$$\overline{1} = 0$$
$$\text{If } X = 0, \text{ then } \overline{X} = 1$$
$$\text{If } X = 1, \text{ then } \overline{X} = 0$$

These equations can be proven by examining Fig. 4-8A. Since the NOT gate has only a single input, there are only two possible input states, 0 and 1, that X can assume. In the NOT circuit, if X = 0, then the output, $\overline{X}$, must be 1. Conversely, if the input, X, equals 1, then the output, $\overline{X}$, is 0.

Since Boolean algebra is derived from rhetorical logic, these equations can also be proven by reason. For example, the above equations can respectively be restated:

If a statement is *not* false, it *must* be true.

If a statement is *not* true, it *must* be false.

If a statement is *false*, then the *negation* of that statement is true.

If a statement is *true*, then the *negation* of that statement is false.

A fourth law of inversion which comes from the inverter is:

$$A = \overline{\overline{A}}$$

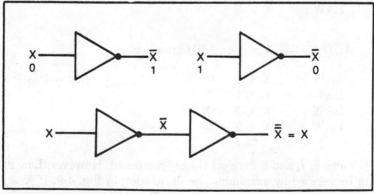

Fig. 4-8. (A) Proving NOT relationships. (B) Proving that a double negative equals a positive.

125

This law can be proven by examining Fig. 4-8B. When the input, X, on the first inverter is 0, a 1 appears at the output of the first inverter and at the input of the second inverter. The output of the second inverter, therefore, is 0. Conversely, when the input to the first inverter, X, is 1, the output of the first inverter and the input of the second inverter is 0. The output of the second inverter, therefore, is 1. We can now reason that when X is inverted TWICE, $\overline{\overline{X}} = X$ through a method of perfect induction. This statement can also be proven by means of rhetoric logic: The *double negation* of a *true* statement is also a *true* statement. In other words, if a fact is *not not* true, then it *must* be true.

BOOLEAN ALGEBRA LAWS

Boolean algebra is a unique system of mathematics. There are fundamental laws which are used to create a viable, cohesive framework upon which to build the theorems derived from these laws. Even though some of these laws have already been discussed within this chapter, they will be repeated here along with others to provide all the tools necessary for implementing Boolean expressions.

Laws of Complementation. The word "complement" is simply defined as "to invert." This means to change from 1 to 0 or from 0 to 1. The five laws of complementation are:

LAW 1 $\overline{0} = 1$
LAW 2 $\overline{1} = 0$
LAW 3   If X = 0, then $\overline{X} = 1$
LAW 4   If X = 1, then $\overline{X} = 0$
LAW 5 $\overline{\overline{X}} = X$

AND LAWS. The four AND laws are:

LAW 6 $X \cdot 0 = 0$
LAW 7 $X \cdot 1 = X$
LAW 8 $X \cdot X = X$
LAW 9 $X \cdot \overline{X} = 0$

Laws 6, 7, and 8 were previously discussed. However, Law 9 can be verified by examining the illustration in Fig. 4-9. If X = 0, then $\overline{X} = 1$. If X = 1, then $\overline{X} = 0$. The AND gate would then have *complementary* signals at its input no matter which value is

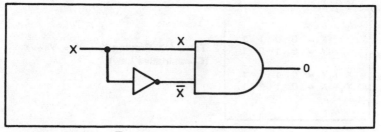

Fig. 4-9. Proving X • $\overline{X}$ = 0.

placed on X. Therefore, regardless of the value of X, X • $\overline{X}$ = 0.

OR LAWS. The four OR laws are:

LAW 10   X + 0 = X
LAW 11   X + 1 = 1
LAW 12   X + X = X
LAW 13   X + $\overline{X}$ = 1

Laws 10, 11, and 12 were previously discussed. However, Law 13 can be proven by examining the illustration in Fig. 4-10. If X = 1, then $\overline{X}$ = 0. The expression of this OR gate would be: 1 + 0 = 1. Now, if X = 0, then $\overline{X}$ = 1. The expression of the OR gate would now be: 0 + 1 = 1. It can be seen, therefore, regardless of the value of X, X + $\overline{X}$ = 1.

Commutative Laws. The commutative laws permit the AND or OR variable to be changed in position. The two commutative laws are:

LAW 14   X + Y = Y + X
LAW 15   X • Y = Y • X

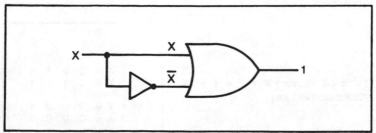

Fig. 4-10. Proving X + $\overline{X}$ = 1.

```
X = 0  0  1  1
Y = 0  1  0  1

X + Y = 0  1  1  1
Y + X = 0  1  1  1
```

Table 4-7. Proving X + Y = Y + X (Commutative Law).

Table 4-7 is the truth table proving Law 14. In every case, X + Y yields an identical result to Y + X. Therefore, Law 14 is proven.

Table 4-8, likewise, illustrates the truth table proving X • Y = Y • X.

Associative Laws. Associative laws permit the grouping of variables. The two associative laws are:

LAW 16   X + (Y + Z) = (X + Y) + Z
LAW 17   X • (Y • Z) = (X • Y) • Z

Table 4-9 is the truth table proving Law 16. ORing X and Y yields the result shown in row (X + Y). ORing Y and Z yields the result shown in row (Y + Z). The next step, ORing the row (X + Y) with Z yields the results shown in row (X + Y) + Z. It can be noted, that the result in this row is exactly the same in every case as ORing row X with (Y + Z).

Table 4-10, is the truth table proving Law 17. Similar to the above illustration, the results of (X • Y) • Z in every case are exactly the same as the results of X • (Y • Z). Therefore, this proves the law.

Distributive Laws. Distributive laws permit factoring or multiplying out expressions. Three distributive laws to be considered are:

Table 4-8. Proving X • Y = Y • X (Commutative Law).

```
X = 0  0  1  1
Y = 0  1  0  1

X • Y = 0  0  0  1
Y • X = 0  0  0  1
```

128

Table 4-9. Proving X + (Y + Z) = (X + Y) + Z (Associative Law).

X =	0	0	0	0	1	1	1	1
Y =	0	0	1	1	0	0	1	1
Z =	0	1	0	1	0	1	0	1
(X + Y) =	0	0	1	1	1	1	1	1
(Y + Z) =	0	1	1	1	0	1	1	1
(X + Y) + Z =	0	1	1	1	1	1	1	1
X + (Y + Z) =	0	1	1	1	1	1	1	1

LAW 18 $X \cdot (Y + Z) = (X \cdot Y) + (X \cdot Z)$
LAW 19 $X + (Y \cdot Z) = (X + Y) \cdot (X + Z)$
LAW 20 $X + (\overline{X} \cdot Y) = X + Y$

Table 4-11 is the perfect induction proof truth table of Law 18.
Law 19 is different from the high school algebra we learned.
This Boolean law, however, can be proven as follows:

$$X + YZ = X + YZ$$
$$= X \cdot 1 + YZ \qquad \text{Law 7}$$
$$= X(1 + Y) + YZ \qquad \text{Laws 11 \& 14}$$

Table 4-10. Proving (X • Y) • Z = X • (Y • Z) (Associative Law).

X =	0	0	0	0	1	1	1	1
Y =	0	0	1	1	0	0	1	1
Z =	0	1	0		0	1	0	1
(X • Y) =	0	0	0	0	0	0	1	1
(Y • Z) =	0	0	0	1	0	0	0	1
(X • Y) • Z =	0	0	0	0	0	0	0	1
X • (Y • Z) =	0	0	0	0	0	0	0	1

Table 4-11. Proving X • (Y + Z) = (X • Y) + (X • Z) (Distributive Law).

	X =	0	0	0	0	1	1	1	1
	Y =	0	0	1	1	0	0	1	1
	Z =	0	1	0	1	0	1	0	1

	(Y + Z) =	0	1	1	1	0	1	1	1
	(X • Y) =	0	0	0	0	0	0	1	1
	(X • Z) =	0	0	0	0	0	1	0	1
X •	(Y + Z) =	0	0	0	0	0	1	1	1
(X • Y) +	(X • Z) =	0	0	0	0	0	1	1	1

$$
\begin{aligned}
&= X + XY + YZ &&\text{Law 18}\\
&= X(1 + Z) + XY + YZ &&\text{Law 11}\\
&= XX + XZ + XY + YZ &&\text{Laws 8 \& 18}\\
&= X(X + Z) + YX + YZ &&\text{Laws 18 \& 15}\\
&= X(X + Z) + Y(X + Z) &&\text{Law 18}\\
&= (X + Z)X + (X + Z)Y &&\text{Law 15}\\
&= (X + Z)(X + Y) &&\text{Law 18}\\
X + YZ &= (X + Y)(X + Z) &&\text{Law 15}
\end{aligned}
$$

Law 20 also is a departure from standard algebra. It can be proven, however, as follows:

$$
\begin{aligned}
X + XY &= X + \overline{X}Y\\
&= X \bullet 1 + \overline{X}Y &&\text{Law 7}\\
&= X(1 + Y) + \overline{X}Y &&\text{Laws 11 \& 14}\\
&= X \bullet 1 + XY + \overline{X}Y &&\text{Law 18}\\
&= X + XY + \overline{X}Y &&\text{Law 7}\\
&= X + XY + Y\overline{X} &&\text{Law 15}\\
&= X + Y(X + \overline{X}) &&\text{Law 18}\\
&= X + Y \bullet 1 &&\text{Law 13}\\
X + XY &= X + Y &&\text{Law 7}
\end{aligned}
$$

DeMORGAN'S THEOREM

One of the most powerful tools used in Boolean algebra is DeMorgan's theorem. It provides two functions for the designer:

X =	0	0	1	1
Y =	0	1	0	1

$\overline{X}$ =	1	1	0	0
$\overline{Y}$ =	1	0	1	0
$\overline{X} \cdot \overline{Y}$ =	1	0	0	0 •

X + Y	0	1	1	1
$\overline{X + Y}$	1	0	0	0 •

Table 4-12. Truth Table Proving DeMorgan's Theorem.

1) It permits removal of individual variables from under a multi-term NOT sign. For example: $\overline{X + YZ}$ can be changed to $\overline{X}(\overline{Y} + \overline{Z})$.

2) It permits a sum-of-products form to be changed to a product-of sums form. For example:

$$X\overline{Y}Z + X\overline{Y}\overline{Z} \text{ can be changed to } \overline{(\overline{X} + Y + \overline{Z}) (\overline{X} + Y + Z)}.$$

Simply stated, DeMorgan's theorem can be expressed:

$$\text{LAW 21} \quad \overline{X} \cdot \overline{Y} = \overline{X + Y}$$

To prove this theorem, refer to Table 4-12. It should be noted that for each value assigned to X and Y, the theorem holds true. Therefore, by means of perfect induction the theorem has been proved.

Figure 4-11 shows the hardware necessary to implement this

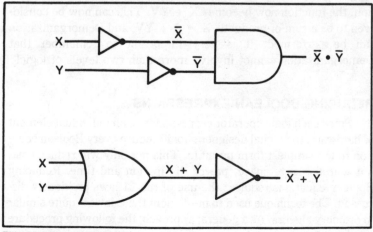

Fig. 4-11. DeMorgan logic.

131

theorem. Note that the basic logic function can be either an AND gate (Fig. 4-11A) or an OR gate (Fig. 4-11B). Since we just proved these two circuits to be exactly equal in function, it permits the designer to use either an AND gate or an OR gate (whichever is available) to perform the same task.

The transformation from one side of the theorem to the other can be accomplished in three basic steps:

1) Complement the entire function
2) Change all AND operators to OR operators
3) Complement each individual variable

This procedure is called "Demorganization."_____
For example, Demorganize the function $X\overline{Y} + Z$.

SOLUTION
Given	$X\overline{Y} + Z$
Complement function	$\overline{X\overline{Y} + Z}$
Change operators	$(X + \overline{Y})(Z)$
Complement each variable	$(\overline{X} + Y)(\overline{Z})$

This transformation can be performed on any part of a function. However, it can apply to functions involving only two levels of logic—a product of sums or a sum of products. For example, it is possible to transform the function X + Y (W + Z) *only* if the term (W + Z) were considered to be a *single* variable. Therefore, replacing the term (W + Z) with a single variable, V, in the equation, the function now becomes X + YV. This can now be considered to be a sum-of-products, X • 1 + YV, and Demorganization can be performed. It is very important to remember that Demorganization cannot involve more than two levels of logic!

REDUCING BOOLEAN EXPRESSIONS

Since each logic operator corresponds to an individual element of hardware, the digital designer should reduce every Boolean equation to the simplest form possible. This not only will reduce cost, but will also save space, power dissipation and time. Reducing Boolean equations requires the use of the 21 laws previously discussed. The technique used to implement these laws is quite similar to ordinary algebra. As a general approach, the following procedure can be followed:

132

1) Multiply all variables necessary to remove parentheses.

2) Look for identical terms. One of these terms can be dropped using Law 12.

3) Drop all terms containing a variable and its complement.

4) Drop the larger term of pairs of identical terms except for one variable (WXYZ + WXZ = WXZ).

5) If one term contains a variable and another term is identical except for containing the COMPLEMENT of the SAME variable, it should be reduced:

$$WXYZ + W\overline{X}YZ \quad = WYZ(X + \overline{X})$$
$$= WYZ \cdot 1$$
$$= WYZ$$

The preceding procedure can be used for most cases. Each expression, however, must be examined for combinations which may permit reduction.

BOOLEAN EXPRESSIONS AND LOGIC DIAGRAMS

Unless Boolean algebra can be translated into functional hardware consisting of AND, OR, and NOT gates it is useless. Likewise, the analysis of existing logic circuits can be accomplished only if the hardware can be translated into Boolean expressions. This technique can be developed only with experience and some practice should be exercised. The following sections in this chapter should help develop some of these skills.

Algebra to Logic. The best method to convert an expression into a logic diagram is to begin with the output and work toward the input. Assume, for example, the expression $\overline{X + \overline{Y}Z}$ is to be implemented. Refer to Fig. 4-12A and begin with the final expression, $\overline{X + \overline{Y}Z}$. Since this is an *inverted* function, it must be implemented with a NOT gate. Therefore, the expression $X + \overline{Y}Z$ must be inputted to a NOT gate to obtain the final expression, $\overline{X + \overline{Y}Z}$.

Next, examine the function desired at the *input* of the inverter, $X + \overline{Y}Z$. Since this is an OR function of the two terms, X and $\overline{Y}Z$, refer to Fig. 4-12B and note how to implement this function with a two-input OR gate.

Moving toward the input further, the next function necessary is the ANDing of $\overline{Y}$ and Z. Figure 4-12C shows how to implement

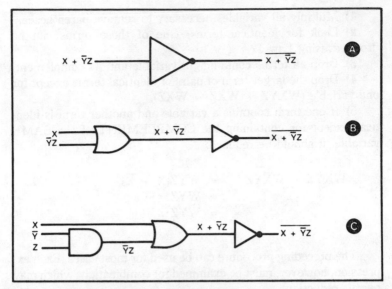

Fig. 4-12. Converting Boolean equations to logic. (A) Output inversion. (B) OR function. (C) AND function.

this function. Finally, the $\overline{Y}$ term can be left as shown, or it can be illustrated as the output of another inverter with its input, Y. However, many inputs to logic systems enter as 0-volt signals when an event similar to the $\overline{Y}$ input of this example occurs. In such a case, therefore, a Y signal never exists. This can be explained by examining the circuit in Fig. 4-13. Assume the switch is *on* when the switch is closed and *off* when the switch is open. The signal, therefore, is present when the switch sees a ground signal. If a +5

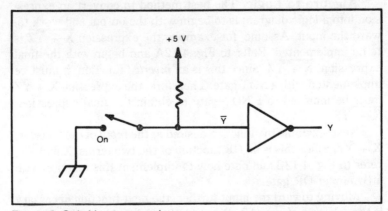

Fig. 4-13. Switching to ground.

134

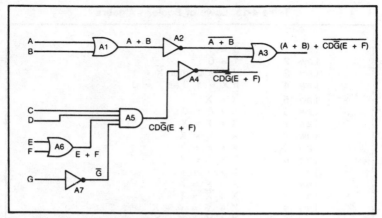

Fig. 4-14. Converting logic to Boolean algebra.

volt signal were required to indicate when the switch is *on*, the Y signal must input an inverter whose output would be $\overline{Y}$. Thus, the NOT over the Y denotes two things: 1) the signal is present only when a ground appears on the line, and 2) the signal must be inverted to obtain a high logic level.

Logic to Algebra. Logic to Algebra can be converted by beginning with the input signals and developing terms working toward the output.

For example, refer to the circuit in Fig. 4-14. Begin by labeling all inputs with mnemonics. Note that A and B input the OR gate, A1. The output of gate, A1, is, therefore, the OR of A and B. This is expressed as A + B. Similarly, E and F input the OR gate, A6, which results in the expression E + F. G is inverted in the NOT gate, A7, and results $\overline{G}$. The AND gate, A5, has inputs C, D, (E + F), and G. Therefore, ANDing these terms at the four input AND gate, A5, yields $CD\overline{G}$ (E + F). Next, this entire expression is inverted by the NOT gate, A4, resulting in $\overline{CD\overline{G}}$ (E + F). Similarly, NOT gate, A2, inverts the expression, (A + B) to obtain $\overline{(A + B)}$, providing the remaining input for the final OR gate, A3. The final result from the output of the OR gate, A3, is, therefore, $\overline{(A + B)} + \overline{CD\overline{G}(E + F)}$.

The final expression is easily obtained by using this procedure and analyzing a circuit from its input to its output.

CONVERTING CIRCUITS TO UNIVERSAL LOGIC

Most digital circuits are computed and converted into AND/OR/NOT logic. From this point, the designer selects either

Table 4-13. Laws of Boolean Algebra

Law 1	$\overline{0} = 1$
Law 2	$\overline{1} = 0$
Law 3	If $X = 0$, then $\overline{X} = 1$
Law 4	If $X = 1$, then $\overline{X} = 0$
Law 5	$\overline{\overline{X}} = X$
Law 6	$X \cdot 0 = 0$
Law 7	$X \cdot 1 = X$
Law 8	$X \cdot X = X$
Law 9	$X \cdot \overline{X} = 0$
Law 10	$X + 0 = X$
Law 11	$X + 1 = 1$
Law 12	$X + X = X$
Law 13	$X + \overline{X} = 1$
Law 14	$X + Y = Y + X$
Law 15	$X \cdot Y = Y \cdot X$
Law 16	$X + (Y + Z) = (X + Y) + Z$
Law 17	$X \cdot (Y \cdot Z) = (X \cdot Y) \cdot Z$
Law 18	$X \cdot (Y + Z) = (X \cdot Y) + (X \cdot Z)$
Law 19	$X + YZ = (X + Y)(X + Z)$
Law 20	$X + XY = X + Y$
Law 21	$\overline{XY} = \overline{X} + \overline{Y}$

NAND or NOR logic for the system. The AND/OR/NOT logic, therefore, must be converted to a universal system of either NAND or NOR logic at the discretion of the designer. This is easily accomplished by using the following procedure:

1. Draw the original circuit in AND/OR/NOT logic.
2. If NAND hardware is chosen, add a circle to the output of each AND gate and to the inputs of each OR gate.
3. If NOR hardware is chosen, add a circle to the output of each OR gate and to the inputs of each AND gate.
4. Insert or delete an inverter on each line which received a circle in step 2 or 3, above.

For example, here is how to convert the circuit in Fig. 4-15A to NAND logic: First, add inverters to the inputs of each OR gate and the output of each AND gate. Next, add inverters to lines W and X to maintain proper polarity of these lines. Note there are effectively two inverters (the actual inverter and the circle on the input of the OR gate) on each line. This maintains proper polarity of the W and X inputs. Line E is inverted by adding the circle to the AND gate. By removal of the inverter, the polarity of E remains unchanged. Lastly, since F was inverted, another inverter must be added to maintain its proper polarity. Figure 4-15B shows the completed circuit. Remember that an OR gate with inverted inputs can be replaced by a NAND gate.

Figure 4-15C demonstrates how to convert the same circuit to NOR logic. First, a circle is added to the output of each OR gate and to the inputs of each AND gate. Note there are two circles added in line Q. Since this is equivalent to a double inversion between the OR gate and the AND gate, the polarity of the signal at the input of the AND gate remains unchanged. Inverters must be added, however, on input lines Y and Z to enable the NOR gates to receive the same polarity as the original circuit. The inverter which was in line R is removed to compensate for the added circle on the AND gate. Remember: AND gates with inverted inputs can be replaced by NOR gates because they perform the same function.

Although only NAND and NOR hardware was the primary form of logic available in the 1960s, this is no longer true. Today, AND, OR and NOT logic elements are just as common, although perhaps

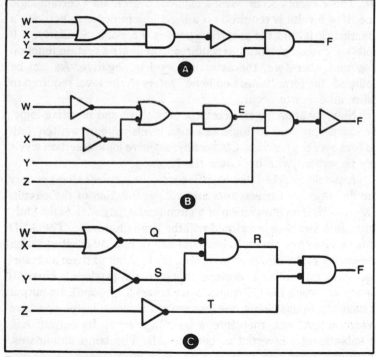

Fig. 4-15. Converting to universal logic: (A) Original circuit, (B) NAND logic, (C) NOR logic.

not as popular or inexpensive. Even though the designer may elect to implement the NAND logic, for example, as the primary element, the finished design will probably be supplemented by other logic elements in order to reduce integrated circuit package count.

Negative Logic

So far, logic levels have been defined as + 5 volts for binary 1 and 0 volts (or ground) for binary 0. This system is called positive logic since, by definition, a binary 1 is more positive than binary 0. In some systems, it is more convenient to define ground (or 0 volts) as binary 1 and + 5 volts as binary 0. This system is called NEGATIVE logic for the obvious reason.

Assertion Level

All logic circuits are designed to perform a function: a lamp illuminates, a buzzer is energized, a character is printed on a printer, etc. These events occur when a signal is present on a certain logic line. If + 5 volts is required on a logic line in order to activate a function, it is said the assertion level is + 5 volts. Similarly, if 0 volts (or ground potential) is required to activate a certain function it is said, therefore, the assertion level is negative. As can be deduced, the term "assertion level" refers to the level required to cause an event to occur.

Now, by applying this concept to positive and negative logic, we can define positive logic assertion levels as logic written with no bars over the function. Conversely, negative logic assertion levels can be written with bars over the function.

It should be noted that negative logic assignment changes only the definition of the equation and *not* the function of the circuit. Figure 4-16 is an illustration of a circuit using negative logic. Only when *both* switches are closed will the lamp illuminate. The AND gate receives low binary 1 signals, A and B. Instead of interpreting the circles at the inputs as inverters, try to think of them as assertion level indicators. Therefore, this gate will produce a binary 0 (+ 5 volts) when BOTH A and B are binary 1 (ground). Its output is then $\overline{AB}$. In this circuit, the absence of a circle indicates a positive assertion level and, therefore, a false logic level. Its output, $\overline{AB}$, is subsequently inverted to become AB. The lamp illuminates, therefore, when this level, A AND B, is grounded.

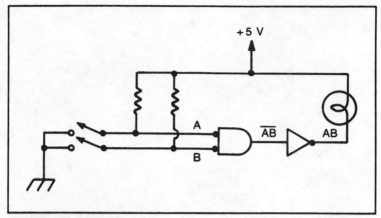

Fig. 4-16. Negative logic.

Summary

There are three basic "building blocks" used in the system: AND gates, OR gates, and NOT gates (inverters). Using only these three functions, and the rules of Boolean algebra, any logic function can be reduced to its simplest form, thereby minimizing cost of implementation. NAND and NOR logic permit a single element of hardware to perform the functions of all three building blocks. Negative logic allows the designer to define all terms relative to negative assertion levels.

Summary

Chapter 5

Flip-Flops and Registers

A FLIP-FLOP IS A DIGITAL LOGIC ELEMENT USED FOR STORING a single bit of binary data. It has two stable states: One representing binary 0 and the other representing binary 1.

Sequential circuits use the flip-flop as their basic logic element. The primary function of a sequential logic circuit is memory, and these circuits are used for a variety of storage, counting, sequencing, and timing operations. A major use of the flip-flop is in storage registers in which a multibit binary word is stored. A register is comprised of multiple flip-flops, each of which stores one bit of the entire number.

FLIP-FLOPS (BISTABLE MULTIVIBRATORS)

The basic function of the flip-flop or bistable multivibrator, is memory or storage. A flip-flop is capable of storing only a single bit of binary data. It can assume either one of the two logic states. As long as power remains applied to the flip-flop, or until it is instructed to change, it will remain in the last stable state to which it was set. A flip-flop, therefore, *remembers* to which state it was previously set. The information in the flip-flop is entered by applying appropriate logic inputs to it. The value of the bit stored in the flip-flop is determined by analyzing its output.

There are three basic types of flip-flops: the *latch*, the *D-type*, and the *J-K*. The latch is the simplest form of flip-flop. It is sometimes referred to as the *set-reset flip-flop*, and is the most

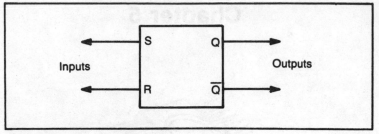

Fig. 5-1. Set-reset flip-flop.

elementary form of binary storage. The symbol used to represent this type of flip-flop is shown in Fig. 5-1. The latch has two inputs, S and R, and two outputs, Q and $\overline{Q}$. To put the latch into one of its states or the other, the appropriate logic signal must be applied to either the S or R input. The S input is used to *Set* the flip-flop while the R input is used to *Reset* the flip-flop. When the flip-flop is Set, it can be assumed to be storing a binary 1. Likewise, when the flip-flop is Reset, it can be assumed to be storing a binary 0.

Examination of the output of a flip-flop will determine the contents of data it is storing. The two outputs of the latch, Q and $\overline{Q}$, are called the *normal* and *complement,* respectively. Any letter or alphanumeric mnemonic, however, can be used to designate logic symbols as shown in Fig. 5-2. To determine the state of a given latch, the *normal* output should be examined. The logic level present on the *normal* output, therefore, tells which bit, 0 or 1, is being stored within the latch. Conversely, the *complement* output always has the *opposite* state of the normal output. If a flip-flop is reset, its normal output is a binary 0, and the complement is binary 1. The complement output, therefore, is just as useful in determining the state of a latch as long as the relationship of the two outputs is understood. Table 5-1 illustrates the relationship of the outputs of latch flip-flops as well as all other types of flip-flops.

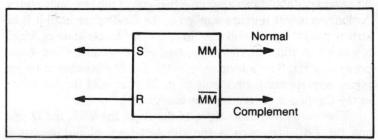

Fig. 5-2. Set-reset flip-flop with assigned output mnemonics.

Table 5-1. Relationships of Flip-flop Output States.

Flip-flop state	Outputs	
	Q	$\overline{Q}$
Set	1	0
Reset	0	1

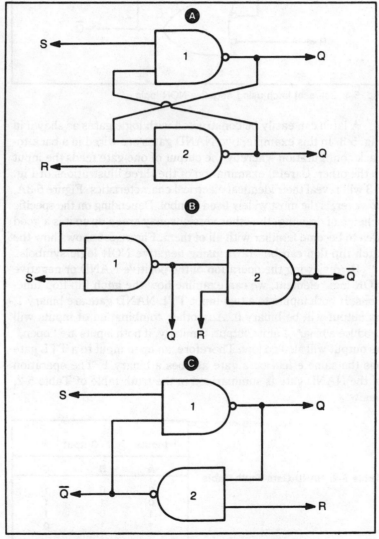

Fig. 5-3. Three variations of set-reset latch circuit.

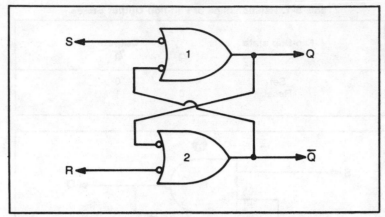

Fig. 5-4. Set-reset latch using negative NOR logic.

A latch can easily be constructed with logic gates as shown in Fig. 5-3. In this example, two NAND gates are wired in a back-to-back configuration whereby the output of one gate feeds the input to the other. Careful examination of the three illustrations of Fig. 5-3 will reveal their identical electrical characteristics. Figure 5-3A, however, is the most widely used symbol. Depending on the specific scheme of drawing, the other versions may creep up so it is a good idea to become familiar with all of them. Figure 5-4 shows how the latch flip-flop can be drawn using negative NOR logic symbols.

By reviewing the operation of the positive NAND or negative NOR logic element, we can examine how the latch flip-flop functions. If both inputs to a two-input TTL NAND gate are binary 1, its output will be binary 0. Any other combination of inputs will produce a binary 1 at its output. Similarly, if both inputs are "open," its output will also go low. Therefore, an open input to a TTL gate has the same effect on a gate as does a binary 1. The operation of the NAND gate is summarized in the truth table of Table 5-2, below:

Table 5-2. NAND Gate Truth Table

Inputs		Output
A	B	C
0	0	1
0	1	1
1	0	1
1	1	0

144

Examination of the NAND gate truth table, Table 5-2, reveals that of the four output states, only *one* of them is low. The *high* output states are created by one or more *low* inputs. It is said, therefore, that the predominant input state is low, or binary 0, for this type of gate. Now, keeping this in mind, consider the operation of the latch circuits shown in Fig. 5-5. If the S and R inputs are *both* binary 1 (or open), the circuit will simply store the previous bit of data put there, *or* it may assume *either state* upon initial application of power. This is the normal condition of this type of circuit and is sometimes called the *quiescent* state.

Assume, now, that the flip-flop is *Set*. The normal output, Q, from gate 1 will be *high* (binary 1). This output is fed back to the upper input of gate 2. Since the lower input on gate 2 is also high, the complement output, $\overline{Q}$, is made LOW (binary 0). The output

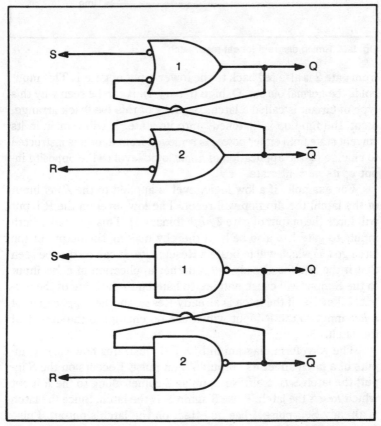

Fig. 5-5. Comparison of positive NAND and negative NOR latches.

145

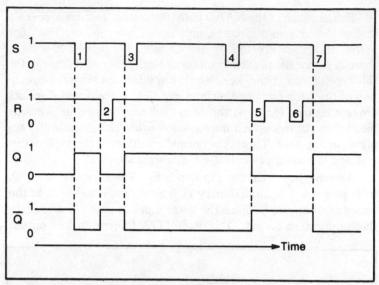

Fig. 5-6. Timing diagram for set-reset latch.

from gate 2 is also fed back to the lower input of gate 1. This input holds the normal output, Q, high (binary 1). It can be seen why this type of circuit is called a latch. Because of this feedback arrangement, the flip-flop is "latched" into its state. It will remain in its current state until either power is removed from it, or it is instructed to change by the application of a *low* logic level to the opposite input of its current state.

For example, if a low logic level is applied to the *Reset* input of the latch, the flip-flop will reset. The low level on the R input will force the output of gate 2 *high* (binary 1). This will cause both inputs to gate 1 to also be high thereby making the output of the latch go *low* which will indicate a Reset state. It can further be seen that if the latch is already Set, another application of a *low* input to the S input will cause nothing to happen to the state of the output. Likewise, if the latch is already Reset, another application of a *low* input to the R input will cause no change to the output of the latch.

The waveform diagram in Fig. 5-6 illustrates how various inputs of a latch affect its output: When pulse 1 occurs on the *S* input, the latch *Sets* itself. Next, pulse 2 comes along to the *R* input which *Resets* the latch. Pulse 3 again *Sets* the latch. Since the latch is already Set, pulse 4 has no effect on the latch's output. Pulse 5, however, comes along and *Resets* the latch. Since the latch is

146

now Reset, pulse 6 has no effect on the latch's output. Finally, pulse 7 Sets the latch, again.

Normally, both inputs should be held *high* (or open) on a NAND gate latch unless its state is being changed. The *high* inputs do not change the state of the latch whether a binary 0 or binary 1 is being stored. When the latch output is being changed, short duration input pulses that switch from *high* to *low* should be used. Refer to Fig. 5-5B and examine what happens when *both* inputs go *low* at the same time: When *both* the S and R inputs are *low*, the normal output, Q, *and* the complement output, $\overline{Q}$, will *both* be *high*. Since the outputs are no longer complementary, the true output *cannot* be determined. The latch is *neither Set* nor *Reset* and is in a state of ambiguity. This state is one of the anomalies of a latch. Care should be exercised when using a latch to avoid application of simultaneous LOW inputs. This ambiguous state of a latch actually represents a third state in which a latch can exist. It is sometimes referred to as the "limbo" state, and is generally undesirable since it can produce unwanted results from a logic circuit unless it is avoided or accounted for.

One method used to avoid the "limbo" state of a latch is to modify the circuit to one as shown in Fig. 5-7. As can be seen, *both* the normal and complement outputs are derived from gate 2. The inverter ensures that the outputs are *always* complementary even if both inputs to the latch go low at the same time.

The operation of the NAND gate latch can be summarized by examining the truth table of Table 5-3.

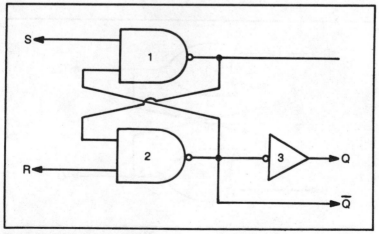

Fig. 5-7. Modified set-reset latch.

147

Table 5-3. NAND Gate Latch.

Inputs		Outputs		State
S	R	Q	$\overline{Q}$	
0	0	1	1	limbo
0	1	1	0	Set
1	0	0	1	Reset
1	1	X	X	last state (Set or Reset)

The truth table, Table 5-3, accounts for all possible input and output combinations. Note that when both inputs, S and R, are binary 1, the output state of the flip-flop is represented with an X. This X denotes a no-change condition and can be either state as determined by the previous condition of the latch.

The latches discussed so far all have been implemented with positive logic NAND gates. A similar latch can also be implemented with positive logic NOR gates as well, as illustrated in Fig. 5-8. By closely examining the operation of this flip-flop, we can determine its operation and its differences.

Recalling the operation of positive NOR gates, by analyzing the circuit in Fig. 5-8, it can be determined that this latch is either Set or Reset by binary 1 inputs. This can be proven by examining the truth table for the NOR gate.

As can be seen, a *low* binary output is produced when a *high* binary input is applied to either input. Since this relationship dif-

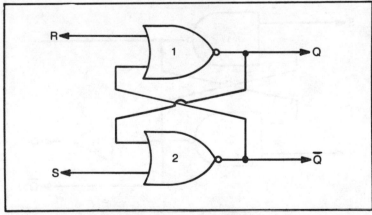

Fig. 5-8. Set-reset latch using positive NOR logic.

Inputs		Output
A	**B**	**C**
0	0	1
0	1	0
1	0	0
1	1	0

Table 5-4. NOR Gate Truth Table.

fers considerably from the NAND gate described earlier, the effective operation of the NOR gate latch will also differ considerably from the NAND gate latch.

Even though NOR and NAND latches serve the same function, they accomplish it in slightly different ways. In order to Set the NOR latch, a binary 1 (high) must be applied to the S input. Conversely, to Reset the NOR latch, a binary 1 (high) must be applied to the R input. Normally, in its quiescent state, both inputs should be held *low* (binary 0). If, however, binary 1s are simultaneously applied to both inputs, the ambiguous or "limbo" state occurs. This operation clearly states the exact opposite characteristics from the NAND latch.

Note the subtle difference between Fig. 5-8 and Fig. 5-5: The S and R inputs are reversed on the NOR gate latch from those on the NAND gate latch due to the intrinsic characteristics of the NOR gate. Application of a binary 1 to the R input of the NOR gate latch forces the output of gate 1 to go LOW. This makes the upper and lower inputs of gate 2 also LOW, producing a binary 1 (high) at its output. With this configuration, the flip-flop is clearly reset (Q = 0, $\overline{Q}$ = 1). As can be seen, the designated outputs are the same as is true for any flip-flop.

To summarize the operation of a NOR gate latch, refer to Table 5-5. The X output in Table 5-5 denotes either Set or Reset depending upon its previous state.

One of the most useful and common applications of a latch flip-flop is for switch buffering. Pushbutton switches are frequently used in digital equipment to control various operations. Most pushbuttons, however, inherently produce contact *bounce*. Contact bounce is the effect produced when a pushbutton switch is initially depressed and its contacts do not make immediate nor complete contact. A similar effect occurs when a pushbutton is released. In practice, therefore, the contacts bounce or open and close several times during a brief period as illustrated in Fig. 5-9. This waveform

Table 5-5. NOR Gate Latch Operation.

Inputs		Outputs		
S	R	Q	$\overline{Q}$	State
0	0	X	$\overline{X}$	Either Set or Reset
0	1	0	1	Reset
1	0	1	0	Set
1	1	0	0	Ambiguous

represents contact resistance. Of course, if current were being switched, this waveform would represent the voltage drop across the pushbutton switch. Instead of obtaining ideal on-off switching, series of short pulses are produced. These short pulses can trigger digital circuitry. For example, by depressing the pushbutton a single time, the expected result should be a single pulse to the circuit. Instead, however, this contact bounce produces many pulses and the circuit to which the pushbutton is connected sees multiple pushbutton depressions. This effect is usually disastrous to the performance of digital circuitry.

The circuits shown in Fig. 5-10 are two methods of supplying logic level changes. However, both of these circuits are susceptible to, and inherently produce, contact bounce. Therefore, they should be avoided when designing digital logic circuits. To overcome this problem, the switch should be combined with a latch as shown in Fig. 5-11.

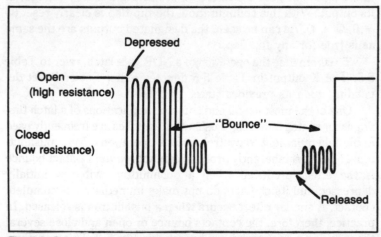

Fig. 5-9. Contact bounce in electromechanical switch.

150

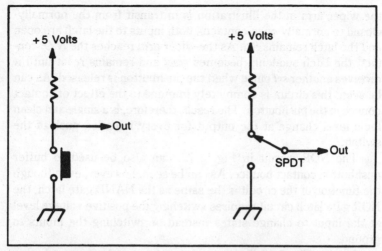

Fig. 5-10. Using pushbutton switches to produce logic level changes.

A non-shorting (break-before-make) SPDT momentary contact pushbutton switch is commonly used. When the switch is in its normal position (not depressed), the output of gate 1 is held at binary 1 (high). When the pushbutton is depressed and grounds the lower input of gate 2, the output of gate 2 is forced *high* which also applies a *high* to the lower input of gate 1, and subsequently forces its output to go *low* (binary 0). Even though the switch may bounce during this transition, it will have absolutely no effect on the operation of the latch. The effect is similar to applying a number of pulses to the *Set* input of a latch that is already set: nothing happens. As

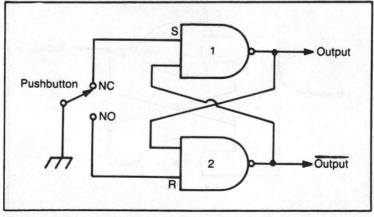

Fig. 5-11. A method of "debouncing" an electromechanical switch.

151

the wiper arm in the illustration is in transit from the normally-closed to normally-open contacts, both inputs to the latch are open and the latch remains *Set*. As the wiper arm reaches the *N.O.* contact, the latch suddenly becomes *reset* and remains reset until it receives another *set* pulse when the pushbutton is released. As can be seen, this circuit is completely immune to the effect of contact bounce in the pushbutton. The result, therefore, is a single and clean logic level change at the output for every intended push of the switch.

The NOR circuit in Fig. 5-12, can also be used to buffer pushbutton contact bounce. As can be seen, however, even though the function of the circuit is the same as the NAND gate latch, the NOR gate latch circuit requires switching the positive voltage level at the input to change states instead of switching the inputs to ground.

Finally, Fig. 5-13 illustrates how a contact buffer can be implemented using inverters. Since inverters are used, the inputs and outputs of this circuit are common. The switch normally holds the output of inverter 1 *low* thereby forcing the output of inverter 2 *high*. When the switch is depressed, the states of the two inverters are reversed. Again, the output produced is a "bounceless" logic level change.

Although the switch described in this section is a momentary type pushbutton, it can be noted that any type of switch can be used to implement this function. The important part to remember, however, is that a *non-shorting* (break-before-make), SPDT switch must be used. If any other type of switch is used, the latch would momen-

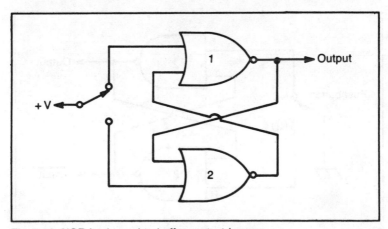

Fig. 5-12. NOR latch used to buffer contact bounce.

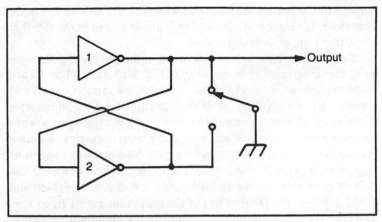

Fig. 5-13. NOT logic used to debounce switch contacts.

tarily be put into its "limbo" or ambiguous state during its transition. Use a buffer on every switch supplying logic level changes to a digital circuit!

D-TYPE FLIP-FLOPS AND REGISTERS

The D-type flip-flop is illustrated in Fig. 5-14. Like any type of flip-flop, it has two outputs which are used to determine the contents of its stored binary data. These outputs are also designated normal and complement.

Even though there are also two inputs to the D-type flip-flop, they work differently than their latch counterparts. Data is applied to the D input. The T input controls whether the flip-flop recognizes or ignores the data on the D input. As long as the T input is held *high* (binary 1), the data on the D input is stored within the flip-flop and transferred to the output, Q. When the T input is brought *low* (binary 0), the input on the D line is ignored, and the output

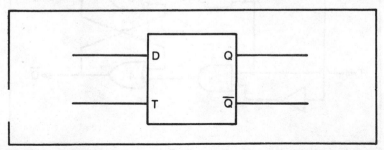

Fig. 5-14. D-type flip-flop.

153

remains in the same state as it was when the T line was last high. Therefore, the last bit of data on the D line is stored in the flip-flop when the T input is brought *low*.

To better understand the operation of the D-type flip-flop, refer to the illustration of its circuitry in Fig. 5-15. Gates 1 and 2 are *enabling* gates used to either pass or inhibit the input. Gates 3 and 4 form a latch where the bit of data can be stored. The inverter at the input of gate 2 ensures that the S and R inputs are always complementary to prevent any ambiguity from occurring. Assume that a binary 1 is applied to the D input. Nothing will happen as long as the T input is held to binary 0 (LOW). When, however, the T input goes high (binary 1), both gates, 1 and 2, are enabled and the binary 1 on the D input forces the output on gate 1 to go low. The inverter puts a low on the input to gate 2, maintaining its output high. The low output of gate 1 *sets* the latch and causes it to store the binary 1 data. When the T input is returned to a low logic level (binary 0), the D input is disabled but the previous binary 1 input data is retained.

Carefully examine the timing diagram waveforms of the D-type flip-flop shown in Fig. 5-16 to fully understand its operation. As can be seen, the output, Q, is identical to the D input as long as the T input is held *high*. When the T input goes *low*, however, the flip-flop stores the *last* bit it sees on the D input before the T input goes *low*.

The configuration illustrated in Fig. 5-17 is another method of implementing the D-type flip-flop. Similar to the circuit in Fig. 5-15, gates 1 and 2 control the input while gates 3 and 4 form the storage latch. It should be noted, however, that no separate inverter

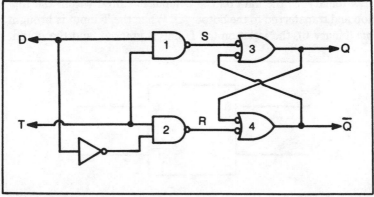

Fig. 5-15. Implementation of a D-type flip-flop.

154

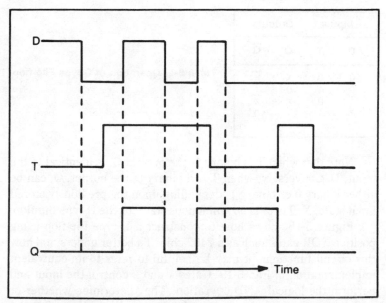

Fig. 5-16. Timing diagram for D-type flip-flop.

is used in this circuit. Although this circuit is more economical to implement, its operates in exactly the same way as does the previously-described version, and can be easily constructed from a single quad 2-input NAND chip such as a 7400.

The complete operation of a D-type flip-flop can be described by a truth table. Below is the truth table summarizing the D-type flip-flop:

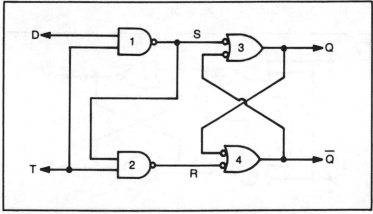

Fig. 5-17. Alternate method of D-type flip-flop implementation.

155

Inputs		Outputs	
D	**T**	**Q**	**Q̄**
0	0	X	X̄
0	1	0	1
1	0	X	X̄
1	1	1	0

Table 5-6. Operation of D-type Flip-flop.

Note that when T is binary 1, the output, Q, is identical to the input, D. Conversely, when T is a binary 0, the output, Q, can be either binary 0 or binary 1, depending upon the previously stored input state, X. There is no ambiguous state for the D-type flip-flop.

Figure 5-18 shows how to construct a D-type flip-flop using positive NOR gates such as a 7402 chip. To better understand how this circuit functions, it may be helpful to refer to its equivalent implementation in Fig. 5-19. Gates 1 and 2 control the input and perform the logical AND operation. They determine whether or not to transfer the input data to the storage latch. Gates 3 and 4 comprise the storage latch which can be either *Set* or *Reset* by the inputs controlled by gates 1 and 2.

The NOR flip-flop, however, does NOT perform in the same way as does the NAND flip-flop, although both circuits store one bit of binary data and the recognition of the D input is determined by the state of the T input in both circuits. Unlike the NAND flip-flop, the NOR flip-flop's T input must go *low* to recognize the D input. Conversely, bringing the T input *high* disables the D input in the NOR flip-flop. The last D input to the flip-flop is stored in the latch prior to the T input going *high*.

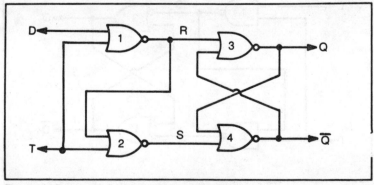

Fig. 5-18. D-type flip-flop using positive NOR gates.

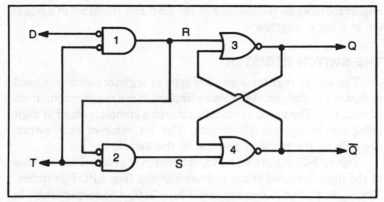

Fig. 5-19. Equivalent circuit of positive NOR gate D-type flip-flop.

The D-type flip-flop is most commonly used as a storage register element. Since each flip-flop can store a single bit of a data word or digit, a register is comprised of a group of flip-flops used to store a complete binary word. To store a complete BCD digit consisting of four bits of data, for example, a storage register consisting of four flip-flops is needed.

Figure 5-20 shows a four-bit register. Each flip-flop is labeled with its own mnemonic. In this illustration, A through D is used for identification, and the state of each flip-flop is also shown. Generally, the least significant bit (LSB) is designated with the lowest letter of the alphabet or the lowest number if digits are used for designations. Therefore, if A is defined as the LSB in the example shown in Fig. 5-20, then the number stored in this four bit register is 0101. If, however, the LSB is D in this example, then the number stored in the register is 1010. As can be seen, it is most

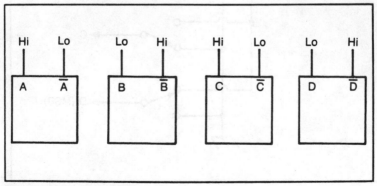

Fig. 5-20. Four-bit register.

157

important to know the identity of the LSB and the MSB of a register in a logic diagram.

THE SWITCH REGISTER

The switch register is another type of register commonly used in digital applications. As its name implies, it is a register comprised of switches. The group of switches stores a complete word or digit using one switch per bit of data. The bit value of each switch depends on the physical position of the switch.

Figure 5-21 illustrates a four-bit switch register. The bit value of the digit is stored in the positions of the four SPDT switches. The A, B, C, and D outputs are +5, +5, 0, +5, respectively, in this example. Since bit A is defined to be the LSB, the number stored in this register is 1011 (assuming positive logic assignments). This translates into decimal 11. The contents of a switch register can be determined by observing its electrical outputs. A visual identification may also be used to identify the contents of a switch register since, in most applications, the switches are mounted adjacent

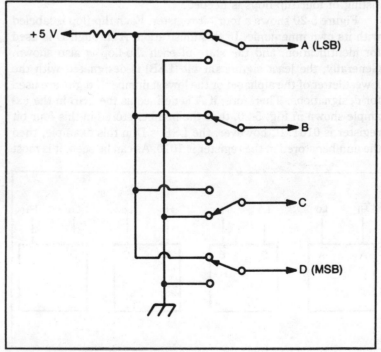

Fig. 5-21. Four-bit switch register.

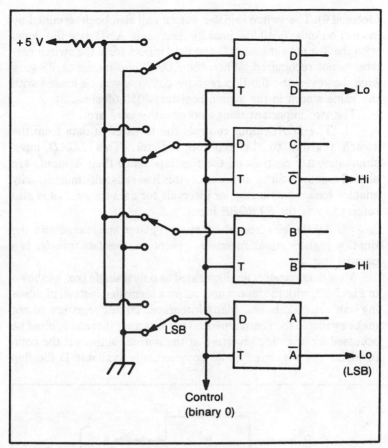

Fig. 5-22. How data is transferred between registers.

to each other in a logical pattern with the LSB switch located in the right-most position. Usually, toggle switches are implemented with the UP position indicating a binary 1 and the DOWN position indicating a binary 0.

In digital equipment a frequent operation is the transfer of data from one register to another. Figure 5-22 shows how data can be transferred from a switch register to a register comprised of D-type flip-flops. The wiper outputs from the switches are fed to the D inputs of the flip-flops. Since all the T inputs of the flip-flops are tied together, they form a common control line to the register.

Since the data provided in this example shows the outputs from the *complements* of the flip-flops, the actual value of the contents of the register would be the *complement of the complements*, or 1001

159

(decimal 9). The switch register output can also be determined by inspection to be 0010 (decimal 2). Assuming AND gate flip-flops, with the T inputs at binary 0, the data inputs from the switch register is not recognized. When the *LOAD* line momentarily goes *high*, however, the flip-flop register contents will be loaded with the value stored in the switch register, 0010 (decimal 2).

The two important things noteworthy here are:

1. The *LOAD* input controls the transfer of data from the switch register to the flip-flop register. This *LOAD* input simultaneously controls all the flip-flops since their T inputs are all tied together. Since, in practice, this line is usually momentarily enabled (or *strobed*) at regular intervals for data transfer, it is also referred to as the *STROBE* input.

2. All the bits from the switch register are loaded into the flip-flop register simultaneously. Therefore, the data transfer is a parallel transfer.

Most data registers are illustrated as only a single box, as shown in Fig. 5-23, with the inputs and outputs identified instead of drawing four separate boxes. Many integrated circuit registers do not make available the complemented outputs and, therefore, must be accessed by inserting inverters at the normal outputs if the complements are required. Some commercially-available D flip-flop

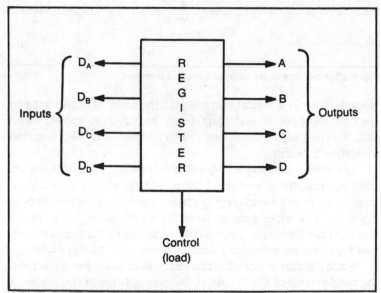

Fig. 5-23. A self-contained four-bit register.

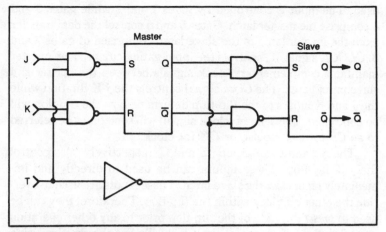

Fig. 5-24. J-K flip-flop circuit.

registers have a single *RESET* line which, when activated, will clear all the flip-flops to 0000 simultaneously without having to load 0000 into the register.

J-K FLIP-FLOPS

The most versatile type of binary storage element in common use is the J-K flip-flop. In addition to performing all the functions of the R-S and D-type flip-flops, it is capable of doing many other things. Since it is more complex and, therefore, more expensive, it should only be used where simpler circuits aren't adequate.

The J-K flip-flop is actually two flip-flops in a single package, and consists of two cascaded latches with appropriate input gating on each as illustrated in Fig. 5-24. This configuration is called a *master-slave* J-K flip-flop. The input circuit is designated the master flip-flop since logic signals applied to the J and K inputs either *set* or *reset* the master latch. The slave flip-flop is the latch from which the outputs from the master latch are taken. Both latches are controlled by *CLOCK* pulses at a common T input. Now, since there are *two* places in which to store data n a J-K flip-flop, it is possible, therefore, for the master and slave latches to be identical or for them to be complementary. Only the *slave* latch, however, is responsible for the state of the entire J-K flip-flop. If the slave flip-flop is *set*, then the J-K flip-flop is storing binary 1. The master flip-flop *controls* the state of the slave flip-flop, but the *slave output determines the state of the flip-flop*. This can be understood by examining the logic diagram of Fig. 5-25. Positive NAND gates are used. The input is controlled by gates 1 and 2 while gates 3 and 4 comprise the master latch. Gates 5 and 6 control the data transfer from the master latch to the slave latch comprised of gates 7 and 8. *CLOCK* signal, T, controls the input gating circuit. The inverter maintains complementary clock signals between the master and slave input gates. The *Clock* signal controls the J-K flip-flop while the J and K inputs to the flip-flop determine how the flip-flop will be controlled. The T input (clock signal) will sometimes be referred to as *CP* for clock pulse or *CK* for clock.

The *Set* and *Clear* inputs, S and C, respectively, also control the J-K flip-flop. These inputs can be used to directly and immediately *set* or *clear* the slave latch. These inputs are used to override the other circuitry within the flip-flop. Therefore, they can be used to *preset* the state of the flip-flop prior to any other operation involving the J-K inputs or the Clock. To Set the flip-flop using these inputs, the S input should be *low* and the C input should be *high*. This forces the normal output, Q, *high* (binary 1) indicating the latch is *Set*. Conversely, to *Reset* the flip-flop using these inputs, the S input should be held *high* while the C input is brought *low*. Normally, when these inputs are not being used to preset the flip-flop they are *both* held high as is done with the NAND latch.

Refer to Fig. 5-25 to examine the effect of the J, K, and T (clock) inputs on the J-K flip-flop. During the time when the T input is low, gates 1 and 2 will be inhibited. Therefore, the J and K inputs cannot control the state of the master latch. When the

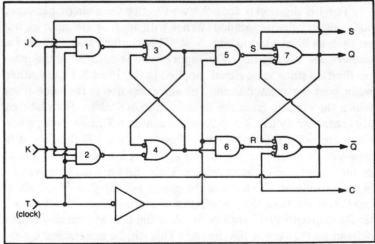

Fig. 5-25. Typical implementation of a J-K flip-flop.

T input goes *high*, however, gates 1 and 2 will be enabled and the output of the inverter will inhibit gates 5 and 6. Therefore, the J and K inputs can change the state of the *master* latch but will have no control over the inhibited *slave* latch. Simultaneously, however, both outputs, Q and $\overline{Q}$, will also determine the state of the master latch, since they are fed back to the input of gates 1 and 2 as well. For example, if both inputs, J and K, are held *low*, the outputs of gates 1 and 2 will be held *high*. Therefore, no change in the state of the master latch can occur. If, however, both inputs, J and K, are held *high*, or open, then the state of the master latch will be determined solely by the state of the outputs, Q and $\overline{Q}$. Specifically, if the slave latch is *Set*, the master latch will be *Reset*. Conversely, if the slave latch is *Reset*, the master latch will be *Set*.

This flip-flop operation occurs because of the interaction between the outputs of the slave latch and inputs to the master latch. As can be seen, the output of gate 7 is fed back to the input of gate 2. Likewise, the output of gate 8, is fed back to the input of gate 1. This intercrossing of latches causes the entire flip-flop to be controlled by the outputs, Q and $\overline{Q}$, when the J, K, and T inputs are all held *high*.

Consider, now, the effect of the *J* and *K* inputs. These inputs can be considered to be analogous to the *Set* and *Reset* inputs on a simple latch. If input, J, is 1 and input K, is 0, the master latch will be *Set*. Conversely, if input, J, is 0 and input, K, is 1, the master latch will be *Reset* as long as the input, T, line is held *high*.

By definition, the state of the J-K flip-flop is determined by the state of the *slave* latch. The state of the slave latch is determined by the state of the master latch. The state of the master latch is determined by the J and K inputs as well as the outputs of the flip-flop. Finally, the input, T, determines *when* each of these latches will be controlled. When the input, T, is *high*, only the master latch can be affected. The inverter on the clock line prevents any change from occurring to the slave latch via gates 5 and 6. The state of the master latch is transferred to the slave latch, therefore, only when the clock line, T, switches from *high* to *low*. This is called the *trailing edge* of the clock pulse. For example, if both inputs, J and K, are left open (or held *high*), the state of the flip-flop will change each time the clock input, T, switches from *high* to *low*. The effect can be illustrated by examining the timing diagram, Fig. 5-26, which represents a normal output of a J-K flip-flop with both inputs, J and K, held *high*. As can be seen, when the clock switches from *high* to *low*, the state of the flip-flop changes. It should

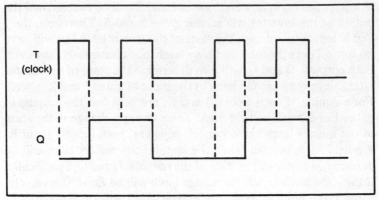

Fig. 5-26. Timing diagram for typical J-K flip-flop.

be noted there is *no* effect when the clock switches from *low* to *high* (leading edge).

Keeping the above information in mind, refer to Fig. 5-27 and note the relationship between the output, Q, and the clock input, T: The output, Q, has a frequency of exactly one-half the input frequency of the clock pulse, T. This is simply because the flip-flop changes state on only the trailing edge of the clock pulse and ignores the leading edge. Therefore, when the J-K flip-flop is operated in this mode (called *toggling mode*), it can be used as a divide-by-two frequency divider. In other words, it *halves* any input frequency applied to the clock input, T, of the flip-flop. For example, if a 60-Hz signal is applied to the T input, the output, Q, will be 30 Hz in the toggling mode. It can further be seen that frequency division by *any* factor of 2 can be accomplished by cascading J-K flip-flops. This frequency ratio division can be expressed as 2^n where n equals the number of flip-flops being cascaded.

Now that all modes of operation of the J-K flip-flop have been discussed, they will be summarized as follows:

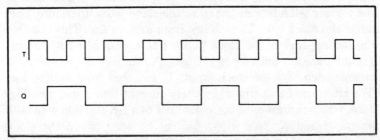

Fig. 5-27. Timing diagram for output of a J-K flip-flop.

Inputs		Outputs	
S	C	Q	$\overline{Q}$
1	1	X	$\overline{X}$
0	1	1	0
1	0	0	1
0	0	1	1

Table 5-7. Effect of S and C Inputs on the J-K Flip-flop.

The effect of the S and C inputs can be expressed by the truth table in Table 5-7. The truth table is identical to that of the NAND latch.

As can be seen, the J-K flip-flop does have an ambiguous state. When both inputs, S and C, are held *low*, both outputs, Q and $\overline{Q}$, will be *high*. Therefore, care should be exercised to prevent this from occurring.

The *Set* and *Clear* inputs (S and C, respectively) are used to PREset the flip-flop to some desirable condition prior to any subsequent operation. The most common PREset is to REset the flip-flop. Therefore, some types of J-K flip-flops provide only a C input without the S input.

When the S and C inputs are used, it is referred to as the *asynchronous* mode of operation. The state of the flip-flop changes immediately upon application of either the S or C input signal without the necessity for other conditions to exist. This effect is not true, however, for the J and K inputs since their effect is dependent upon the state of the clock signal at the T input. Therefore, when the J and K inputs are used, it is referred to as the *synchronous* mode of operation because the effect of their input states are transferred to the output only on the occurrence of specific clock transitions that are in *synchronism* with the master clock.

The synchronous mode of operation of the J-K flip-flop is summarized in Table 5-8. Note that only one output, Q, is shown. There

Table 5-8. Synchronous Operation of J-K Flip-flop.

Inputs		Outputs	
J	K	Q(t)	Q(t + 1)
0	0	X	X
0	1	X	0
1	0	X	$\frac{1}{X}$
1	1	X	$\overline{X}$

are two designations for it, however. In the third column, output, Q, is established *prior* to a clock pulse, (t). In the fourth column, output, Q is established *following* a clock pulse, (t + 1). The output state, X, can represent either Set (1) or Reset (0).

From Table 5-8, it can be determined that to *Reset* the J-K flip-flop, a binary 0 (low) must be applied to the J input and a binary 1 (high) must be applied to the K input and then a clock pulse, t, must be applied. Similarly, to *Set* the J-K flip-flop, a binary 1 (high) must be applied to the J input and a binary 0 (low) must be applied to the K input and then a clock pulse, t, must be applied. Note that nothing happens to change the state of the flip-flop when *both* the J and K inputs are at binary 0 (LOW). No matter how many clock pulses are applied to it, the flip-flop will retain the last bit stored in it as long as both inputs, J and K, are held LOW. This is called the *inhibit mode*.

When the J and K inputs are both at binary 1 (high), the flip-flop toggles or complements itself each time the clock pulse switches from 1 to 0. The flip-flop, therefore, acts as a 2 to 1 frequency divider, since no change of state occurs during the 0 to 1 clock pulse switch. Some of the new variety of ECL flip-flops can switch at rates as high as the gigahertz range. The standard logic symbol for the J-K flip-flop is shown in Fig. 5-28.

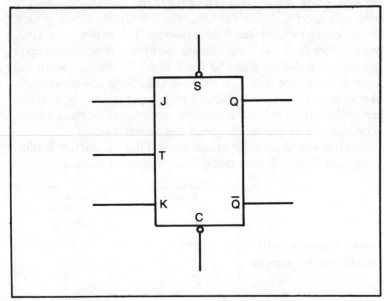

Fig. 5-28. Standard logic diagram symbol for J-K flip-flop.

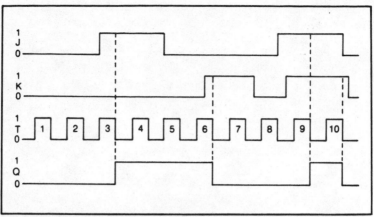

Fig. 5-29. Timing diagram for J-K flip-flop.

Figure 5-29 is a timing diagram of a typical J-K flip-flop application. To reinforce your understanding of it, examine this diagram carefully before proceeding to the next chapter.

The normal output of the flip-flop is *low* prior to the first clock pulse, T. Since both the J and K inputs are *low*, the flip-flop is inhibited and no state change takes place during the first two clock pulses. The J input then goes *high*. The flip-flop *Sets* on the trailing edge of the next (third) clock pulse, therefore. The output of the flip-flop remains *high* for the duration of the next two clock pulses since the J input remains *high*. On the *fifth* clock pulse, however, the J input goes *low* but the output remains *high* since both inputs, J and K, are *low*, and the flip-flop is in the inhibit mode. On the *sixth* clock pulse, the K input goes *high* and the output of the flip-flop *Resets* on the trailing edge of this clock pulse. The flip-flop remains in this state until the *ninth* clock pulse at which time both the J and K inputs go *high*. Since this satisfies the conditions for the flip-flop to go into its toggle mode, the output complements itself on the trailing edge of each of the following two clock pulses. Finally, preceding the eleventh clock pulse, both the J and K inputs go *low*, again, which puts the flip-flop in its inhibit mode. Therefore, no change in its output occurs during the eleventh clock pulse.

Because the J-K flip-flop is an extremely versatile device, it is widely used as a storage register, frequency divider, and counter. These applications will be discussed in greater detail in succeeding chapters of this book.

Chapter 6

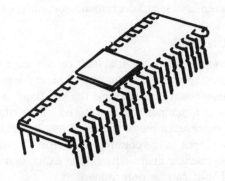

Sequential Logic Circuits

S EQUENTIAL LOGIC CIRCUITS ARE USED FOR A VARIETY OF timing, sequencing, and storage functions. The prime characteristic of sequential logic circuits is memory. The output of a sequential logic circuit, therefore, is a function of both the input states applied to it and the result of previous operations which are stored within the circuit itself.

Flip-flops are the main elements comprising sequential logic circuits. Binary data is stored within these flip-flops. Their states can be changed by applying logic input signals to them at appropriate times according to the information stored within them. Complete synchronism of sequencing is accomplished by a single periodic logic signal called a *clock*. This clock is an oscillator that generates square wave pulses at a fixed frequency.

Almost an infinite number of different sequential logic circuits can exist. In practice, however, only a few types are actually employed on a regular basis. Two of the most common types are *counters* and *shift registers*. The operation and applications of these two types of circuits, therefore, will be emphasized in this chapter. Most commonly used sequential logic circuits are available as complete functional devices on a single MSI chip.

COUNTERS

Several different types of counters are used in digital circuits, the most common of which is the binary counter. The binary counter counts in the standard pure binary code. BCD counters are also widely used, since they count in the standard 8421 code. Counters can also be developed to count in any of the special binary or BCD codes. Both incrementing and decrementing counters are available.

BINARY COUNTERS

A binary counter is a sequential logic circuit, comprised of flip-flops, that is used to count the number of binary input pulses applied to it. These count pulses cause the flip-flops in the counter to change state in a manner that the stored binary number within the counter is representative of the exact number of count pulses occurring at the input to the counter. Therefore, by observing the contents of the counter at its output, the exact number of input pulses applied to it can be determined.

Binary counters use the standard pure binary code. They can be constructed with JK flip-flops cascaded in a manner illustrated in Fig. 6-1. Both the J and K inputs to all of the flip-flops are open or high. The normal output of each flip-flop is fed to the toggle (T) input of the succeeding flip-flop. The "count" pulses are applied to the toggle (T) input of the first (A) flip-flop.

To examine the operation of this counter, first remember that when both the J and K inputs are held high, a JK flip-flop changes state or toggles each time the trailing edge of a pulse occurs at the T input. The flip-flops, therefore, will change state each time the normal output of the previous flip-flop switches from binary 1 (high) to binary 0 (low). Assuming the counter is initially reset, all the outputs will be at binary 0. When the first input pulse occurs at the T input of the first flip-flop, the "A" flip-flop will become set (binary 1 or high). The binary number now stored within the counter represents the number of pulses which have occurred at the input and is, therefore, read at the outputs of the flip-flops. In this in-

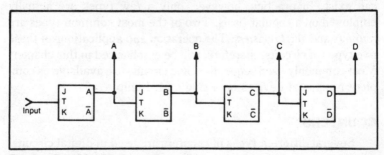

Fig. 6-1. Four-bit binary counter.

stance the binary number is read from right to left (DCBA) since the A flip-flop is the least significant bit (LSB) of the binary word. After the first input pulse, the contents of the counter becomes 0001 indicating that only a single pulse has occurred at the input.

When the second input pulse occurs, the "A" flip-flop toggles and now becomes reset. As it resets, its normal output switches from binary 1 to binary 0. Since this output is also connected to the T input of the "B" flip-flop, all the conditions are met to enable the "B" flip-flop to become set. Now, by observing the new output state of the counter, the binary number 0010 can be observed indicating that two input pulses have occurred at the input.

Next, when the third input pulse occurs at the input, the first flip-flop again becomes set. The normal output of the "A" flip-flop switches from binary 0 to binary 1 and no other changes take place. This transition is ignored by the T input of the "B" flip-flop, since it only recognizes trailing pulses (from binary 1 to binary 0). The new number now stored within the counter is 0011. This is decimal 3, which represents the three input pulses which have occurred at the input.

When the fourth input pulse occurs, the "A" flip-flop becomes reset. Since its normal output switches from binary 1 to binary 0, it also causes the "B" flip-flop to toggle. This resets the "B" flip-flop to binary 0. Since the normal output of the "B" flip-flop switches from binary 1 to binary 0, as well, it causes the third flip-flop to subsequently toggle. Therefore, the "C" flip-flop now becomes set. Observing the contents of the counter reveals the new number stored within is now 0100 or decimal 4 representing the four input pulses occurring at the input.

The aforementioned process continues as long as the pulses occur at the input to the counter. This count sequence is the standard four bit binary code as illustrated in Fig. 6-2. An important consideration to note in this description is the operation of the circuit when the counter is storing binary 1111 (decimal 15). Since this is the maximum number a four-bit counter can hold the counter is said to be filled-up and upon application of the *next* input pulse to the counter, all flip-flops change state and become reset to 0000. Therefore, it can be determined that when the maximum number of pulses a counter can hold is reached, the counter simply resets itself to 0000 and begins the count sequence all over again.

The complete system operation of a four-bit binary counter is shown in the timing diagram of Fig. 6-3. The upper waveform represents the series of input pulses to be counted. They are il-

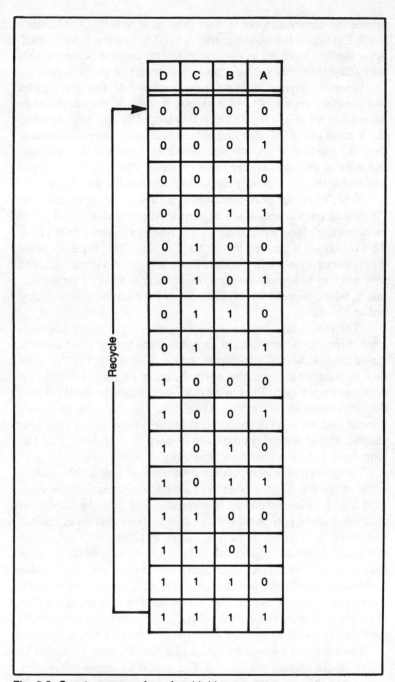

D	C	B	A
0	0	0	0
0	0	0	1
0	0	1	0
0	0	1	1
0	1	0	0
0	1	0	1
0	1	1	0
0	1	1	1
1	0	0	0
1	0	0	1
1	0	1	0
1	0	1	1
1	1	0	0
1	1	0	1
1	1	1	0
1	1	1	1

Recycle

Fig. 6-2. Count sequence for a four-bit binary counter.

172

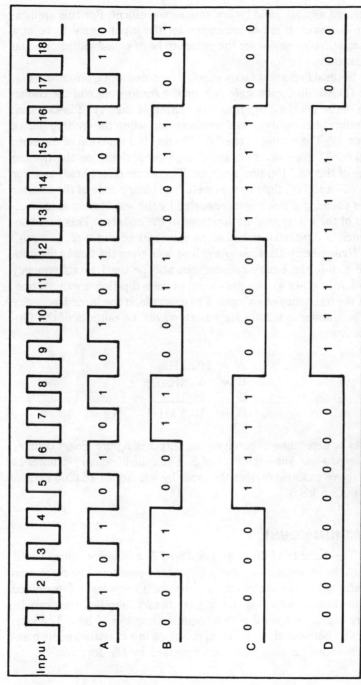

Fig. 6-3. Timing diagram for a four-bit binary counter.

lustrated as a periodic binary square waveform. For this application, however, it is not necessary for the input signal to be at a constant frequency or for the pulses to be of equal widths or equal separations.

Several important factors should be noted while observing Fig. 6-3: (1) All flip-flops toggle only on the *trailing* edge of the transition of the previous flip-flop. The output of the "A" flip-flop can, therefore, be readily traced by observing when the trailing pulses occur. (2) The output of the "B" flip-flop is a function of the state of the "A" flip-flop. Its state change occurs only on the trailing edge of the "A" flip-flop's output. This same effect holds true for the "C" and "D" flip-flops, as well. The binary code of the counter after each input pulse is represented by the waveforms at the outputs of the corresponding flip-flops of the counter. This count sequence is illustrated in the sequence chart of Fig. 6-2.

Frequency Divider. As can be seen from the timing diagram of Fig. 6-3, the binary counter can also be used as a frequency divider. In other words, the output of each flip-flop is exactly one-half the frequency of its input. For example, if the input frequency to the counter is a 200 kHz square wave, the outputs of the flip-flops are:

$$A = 100 \text{ kHz}$$
$$B = 50 \text{ kHz}$$
$$C = 25 \text{ kHz}$$
$$D = 12.5 \text{ kHz}$$

It can be determined, therefore, the output of a pure binary counter is *always* some sub = multiple of 2. The four-bit binary counter in the above example divides the input by a factor of 16 (200 kHz ÷ 16 = 12.5 kHz).

MAXIMUM COUNT

The number of flip-flops employed in a binary counter determines the maximum count capacity of the counter. The maximum number a binary counter can hold before it recycles is determined in the same way as is the largest binary number that can be represented by a word with a specified number of bits. The relationship between the number of flip-flops in a counter and its maximum count capability can be expressed by the formula:

$$N = 2^n - 1$$

Where N is the maximum number that occurs before the counter recycles and n is the number of flip-flops employed. For example, the maximum number that can be contained within a counter employing five flip-flops is:

$$N = 2^5$$
$$= 32 - 1$$
$$= 31 \text{ (binary 11111)}$$

Conversely, to determine the number of flip-flops required to comprise a counter with a specified count capacity, use the formula:

$$n = 3.32 \log_{10} N$$

For example, to construct a counter capable of counting to the decimal number 100:

$$n = 3.32 \log_{10} N$$
$$= 3.32 \, (2)$$
$$= 6.64$$
$$n = 7$$

(The next whole number is used since there is no such thing as a fractional part of a flip-flop.) A counter comprised of 7 flip-flops, therefore, has a maximum count capacity of:

$$2^7 - 1 = 127$$

When the binary counter is used as a frequency divider, the factor by which the counter divides is also a function of the number of flip-flops employed and can be expressed by the formula:

$$N = 2^n$$

Where N is the factor by which the counter will divide and n is the number of flip-flops employed. For example, if a binary counter is comprised of seven flip-flops, an applied input signal would be divided by:

$$N = 2^n$$
$$= 2^7$$
$$= 128$$

In other words, the output of the seventh flip-flop will be 1/128 the frequency of the input signal. The frequency division ratio of a binary counter is always some power of 2. It is possible, however, to implement frequency dividers that can divide a frequency by *any* integer value. These methods will be discussed later.

DOWN COUNTERS

It is also possible to construct a counter whereby the input pulses cause the binary number stored within to decrease by one. In this application, the input pulses are said to *decrement* the counter. This is the exact opposite operation of the previously-discussed counter in which the application of an input pulse increased (or *incremented*) the counter's contents by one.

A four-bit binary down counter is illustrated in Fig. 6-4. The only difference between this configuration and the one shown in Fig. 6-1 is the use of the complement outputs of the flip-flops in place of the normal outputs used in the up counter's circuit. This modification to the circuit causes the exact reverse count sequence of the up counter to occur. The count sequence of the down counter is illustrated in Fig. 6-5. The corresponding waveforms of the flip-flops' outputs are illustrated in the timing diagram of Fig. 6-6. It is important to remember that even though the complementary outputs of the flip-flops are used to cascade them, the contents of the counter are still observed from the *normal* outputs of the flip-flops in a down counter. Assuming the counter is initially reset to 0000, the application of an input pulse will cause all four flip-flops to

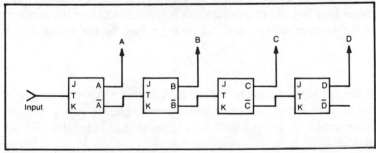

Fig. 6-4. A four-bit binary down counter.

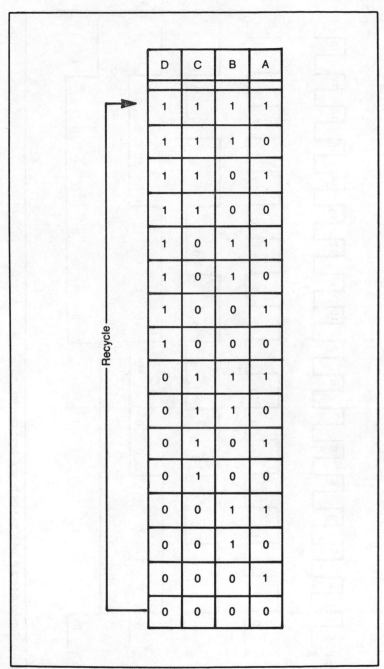

Fig. 6-5. Count sequence of the four-bit binary down counter.

177

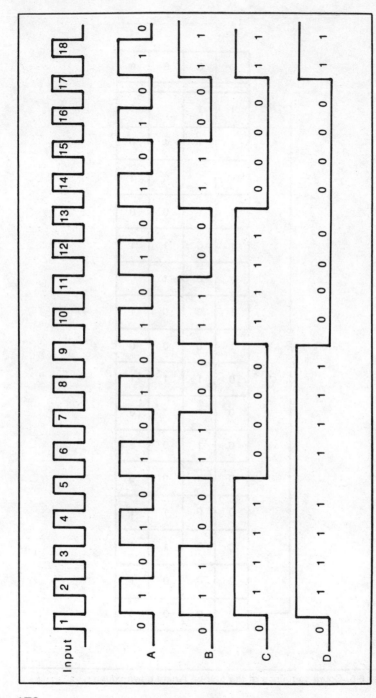

Fig. 6-6. Timing diagram for a four-bit binary down counter.

178

become set (1111)—when the "A" flip-flop is reset, its complement output is high. Following the first input pulse, the "A" flip-flop will be set and its complement output will switch from high to low (binary 1 to binary 0). This transition of the complement output of "A" flip-flop will cause the "B" flip-flop to also toggle and become set. The complement output of the "B" flip-flop switches from binary 1 to binary 0 (high to low) and causes the same effect to occur on the "C" flip-flop which, in turn, causes the "D" flip-flop to change state, as well. The ultimate result of this initial input pulse changes the state of the entire counter from 0000 to 1111.

Upon application of the next input pulse, the "A" flip-flop will again become reset and its complement output will go high. The "B" flip-flop ignores this transition and no further state change takes place. The resulting contents of the counter now becomes 1110 and is decremented from decimal 15 (1111) to decimal 14 (1110).

Application of another input pulse to the counter will again toggle the "A" flip-flop to set it. As it sets, its complement output switches from high to low which causes the "B" flip-flop to reset. As it resets, the complement output of the "B" flip-flop switches from low to high which is ignored by the "C" flip-flop. No further state change, therefore, takes place and the new contents of the counter again decrements by one and now becomes 1101 or decimal 13. The count sequence of the down counter can be completely traced by examining Fig. 6-5 and its associated timing diagram, Fig. 6-6.

UP/DOWN COUNTER

Now that the operation of both the up counter and down counter has been explained, Fig. 6-7 illustrates how *both* of these functions can be implemented within a single circuit. As can be seen, the flip-flops are coupled via AND and OR gates. The normal output of each flip-flop is connected to gate #1. The complement output of each flip-flop is connected to gate #2. The respective states of these gates determine whether the normal or complement output signals will toggle the succeeding flip-flop. The *UP/DN control* line signal controls the operation of the counter—a binary 1 on this line will enable all the #1 gates. The normal outputs of the flip-flops will be coupled to the inputs of the succeeding flip-flops via the #3 OR gates and all #2 gates will be inhibited. The circuit will, therefore, function as an *up* counter. Conversely, a binary 0 on this control line will enable all #2 gates and simultaneously inhibit all #1 gates.

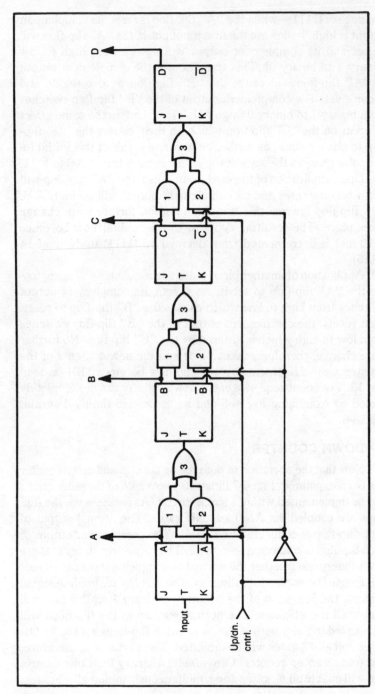

Fig. 6-7. Up/down binary counter.

The complement outputs of the flip-flops will be coupled to the succeeding flip-flops via the #3 OR gates and the circuit will function as a *down* counter.

SYNCHRONOUS COUNTERS

So far, all the counters discussed are known as *ripple counters* or *asynchronous counters*. The term *ripple* is derived from the fact that since the flip-flops are cascaded in series, the input count, in effect, *ripples* through the flip-flops from the first element through the last one. The term *asynchronous* comes from the fact that the flip-flops are *not* controlled by a single clock pulse. Synchronous digital circuits, on the other hand, are locked in synchronism by a master timing pulse called a clock.

Simplicity is the primary advantage of the ripple counter. Its operation is limited primarily by its counting speed. Since the counting speed of a binary counter is limited by the propagation delay of the flip-flops, a ripple counter's propagation delay is equal to the sum of the propagation delays of all the flip-flops comprising the counter. It can take a significant amount of time, therefore, for a pulse to ripple through all the flip-flops within a binary ripple counter, since each flip-flop is triggered by the preceding flip-flop. Furthermore, when all the flip-flops within a ripple counter change state on the same input pulse, such as from 1000 to 0111, the worst case condition occurs, because the circuit's delay is the total delays of *all* the flip-flops within the counter. For example, if each flip-flop in a four-bit counter has a propagation delay of 25 nanoseconds, it will take $4 \times 25 = 100$ nanoseconds for the four-bit counter to change state in order to count that single input pulse. On the other hand, if only the first bit of the binary counter has to change state, such as from 0000 to 0001, only $1 \times 25 = 25$ nanoseconds are required for the counter to change state. Therefore, should the input pulses occur at a rate faster than 100 nanoseconds, it is *unlikely* that the number stored within the binary counter will be the actual number of input pulses which have occurred because the counter's state will lag the input signal. The upper frequency limit (f) of a ripple counter can be expressed:

$$f = (1 \div n \bullet t) \times 10^9$$

where n is equal to the number of flip-flops in the counter and t is equal to the propagation delay time (in nanoseconds) of each flip-flop. For example, with flip-flops having a propagation delay of 35 nanoseconds in a four bit counter, the fastest counting speed will be:

$$f = 1 \div (4 \bullet 35) \times 10^9$$
$$= 7.1428 \text{ MHz}$$

This means that this counter can count up to around 7 MHz without any counting errors. Should the count pulses occur much faster, the states of the flip-flops will not keep pace with the more rapid input pulses and counting errors will probably be encountered.

It is possible, however, to reduce propagation delay within a counter and thereby increase its operating speed by incorporating a special circuit technique known as a *synchronous* counter. A synchronous counter is one in which all the flip-flops are triggered simultaneously by a single clock pulse or signal being counted. Since all the flip-flops change state at the same time (and on the same pulse), the total propagation delay time for the entire circuit is essentially equal to that of a single flip-flop. Much higher counting speeds can be obtained with this arrangement since the propagation delay times are not additive.

Figure 6-8 illustrates a typical synchronous binary counter. Note how all the T inputs of the flip-flops are connected together to a common *count input* line. This connection distinguishes this circuit as being synchronous. In other words, all the flip-flops are *synchronized* to the input count signal. The states of the JK flip-flops control the operation of the flip-flops. Up to this point, it has always been assumed the J and K inputs were either open (not connected) or held high (binary 1 logic level). This essentially enabled the flip-flop to be toggled each time the trailing edge of a pulse occurred at the T input of it. If, however, the J and K inputs are brought to binary 0 (or ground), the flip-flop will ignore the input pulse applied to the T input. The flip-flop will, therefore, remain in the state to which it was set prior to the application of the low signal to the J and K inputs. By selectively implementing the J and K inputs it is feasible, therefore, to enable or inhibit the flip-flops' toggling characteristics.

In the synchronous counter illustrated in Fig. 6-8, both the J and K inputs of the first flip-flop (A) are connected directly to a binary 1 logic level. This will permanently enable the "A" flip-flop to toggle. Each time a *count* pulse appears on the input line the flip-flop will change state in a manner similar to that of the ripple counter previously discussed.

The J and K inputs of the "B" flip-flop, however, are controlled

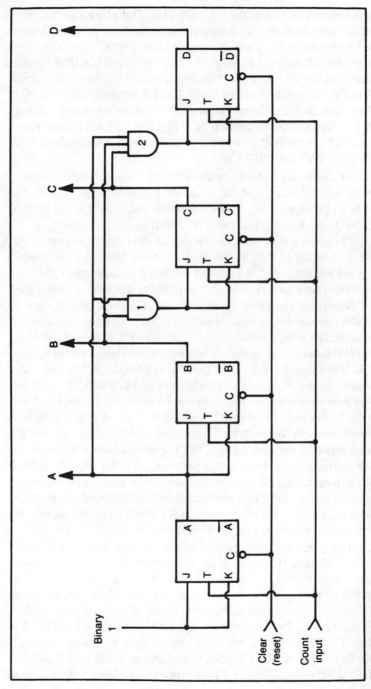

Fig. 6-8. A synchronous binary counter.

183

by the normal output of the "A" flip-flop. Therefore, the "B" flip-flop can change state only during the time flip-flop "A" is *set* (binary 1). Furthermore, the J and K inputs of flip-flop "C" are controlled by the normal outputs of *both* "A" and "B" flip-flops. The normal outputs of the "A" and "B" flip-flops are ANDed together by gate #1 and subsequently applied to the J and K inputs of flip-flop "C." Therefore, both flip-flops "A" and "B" must be set in order to toggle (or change state of) flip-flop "C." Flip-flop "C" will change state, therefore, on the first count *following* the count pulse making both flip-flops "A" and "B" high.

Similarly, the J and K inputs of the "D" flip-flop are controlled by the normal outputs of the A, B, and C flip-flops. In gate #2, the A, B, and C outputs are ANDed together and subsequently applied to the J and K inputs of the "D" flip-flop.

The sequence of the synchronous counter circuit shown in Fig. 6-8 is identical to that of the asynchronous counter illustrated in Fig. 6-1 and described in Figs. 6-2 and 6-3. The only basic difference between these two circuits is the mode and speed of operation.

Analyzing the state changes in the flip-flops of this type of binary counter will reveal its benefits. Assuming that the counter contains the binary number 0111, the J and K inputs of the B, C, and D flip-flops are enabled. Therefore, upon the occurrence of the next input count pulse, all flip-flops will toggle. After this pulse occurs, flip-flops A, B, and C will reset and flip-flop "D" will set. The new number stored within the counter will be binary 1000. It is important to note that at this time all the flip-flops *simultaneously* change state. The maximum delay time between the occurrence of the count pulse and the actual state change of the flip-flops is only as long as the propagation delay time of a *single* flip-flop assuming all the flip-flops are of the same type. Since *different* types of flip-flops have intrinsically different propagation delay characteristics, the maximum delay will be as long as the flip-flop with the *longest* propagation delay time.

The effect of cumulative propagation delay can be illustrated by considering the same state change within the binary ripple counter as shown in Fig. 6-1. When the binary number 0111 is stored in the ripple counter, the output states will change in the following sequence upon the occurrence of an input count pulse. First, the "A" flip-flop will change state and toggle the "B" flip-flop. The "B" flip-flop will then change state and toggle the "C" flip-flop. The "C" flip-flop will then change state and finally set the "D" flip-flop. Since a finite propagation delay time exists in each of these flip-flops, the effect of an input count pulse actually *ripples* through the counter in a manner similar to an ocean wave rushing to the shore, or a stretched-out Slinky toy when suddenly jerked by a short-duration snap. The result is a specific time delay for the actual number to appear in the counter.

To summarize the advantages of the synchronous counter over the asynchronous (or ripple) counter, the following can be said:

1. Given identical types of flip-flops, the counting speed of the synchronous counter is significantly higher. Therefore, the synchronous counter is much faster.

2. Since all flip-flops in a synchronous counter change state at the same time, there can be no ambiguous states which can occur due to cumulative propagation delays inherent in asynchronous counters.

The synchronous counter, like the ripple counter, can be expanded to as many bits as required by the application. Each flip-flop in the counter, however, must be controlled by all previous flip-flops via an AND gate as indicated. The higher order flip-flops, therefore, will require AND gates with as many inputs as there are previous flip-flops. It should be pointed out that although propagation delays of gate circuits are very small compared to that of flip-flops, they must be considered when cascading flip-flops in a synchronous counter and will have a minor effect on the speed of the counter.

CONTROLLING COUNTER FUNCTIONS

The two common control functions often associated with the application of binary counters are *reset* and *preset*. As you may have guessed, resetting a counter is the act of placing all the flip-flops within it to the binary 0 state. This is sometimes referred to as the *clear* function, as well. In many applications it is necessary to reset a counter prior to the application of a new counting operation. Resetting a counter will ensure an accurate count of the input by clearing all flip-flops before commencing a count sequence.

When J-K flip-flops are used, resetting a counter is easily accomplished. The asynchronous *clear* inputs on the flip-flops are normally used to bring the state of the flip-flops to binary 0. The flip-flops are reset by bringing the *clear* inputs low. Figure 6-9 shows a binary counter with a reset feature comprising a common *clear* input line to the flip-flops. As long as the reset line is open or held high, the counter will operate normally. As soon as the reset line is brought low, however, the entire counter will reset to binary 0000 since all the flip-flops will have been cleared. For typical TTL J-K flip-flops, a pulse of at least 100 nanoseconds is required to reset the counter.

A counter is said to have been "preset" when a specific number is loaded into it prior to the start of a count sequence. It is sometimes desirable to program a counter with a special number in order for it to start counting from a particular point. This starting point is first specified and then loaded (or preset) into the counter before it actually begins counting.

When J-K flip-flops are used, the asynchronous *set* inputs are normally used to preset a counter. A J-K flip-flop can be set by bringing the S input low (binary 0). Therefore, by first clearing the flip-flop and then setting the desired flip-flops, any binary number can be preset within the counter. The circuit shown in Fig. 6-9 illustrates the preset feature using the S inputs along with NAND gates. To preset the counter with a given number, the counter must first be reset by applying a binary 0 to the reset input. Then, the binary number to be preset should be applied to the *preset inputs*. A parallel binary number from any source may be used. When the preset line is made HIGH, the outputs of the gates to which the parallel input number are applied will cause the asynchronous "SET" lines on the J-K flip-flops to assume the appropriate states which will preset the desired number into the counter.

For example, if the decimal number 5 were desired to preset the counter shown in Fig. 6-9, then binary 0101 would be applied to the preset inputs. The counter should then receive a *REset* pulse to clear itself and then a momentary *PREset* pulse to transfer the data from the preset input lines into the counter itself. The binary 0 inputs will hold the outputs of gates 2 and 4 high regardless of the state of the preset input. This will keep the S inputs of both the "B" and "D" flip-flops high and will not affect their state. The binary 1 inputs to gates 1 and 3 will force their outputs to go LOW and will cause the "A" and "C" flip-flops to become set as soon as the *PREset* line goes high. The binary number 0101 will then be stored in the counter.

Since two operations are required to preset the counter in Fig. 6-9, it is rather awkward. It is desirable to be able to preset a counter in a single operation instead of having to reset it first and then preset it. The circuits shown in Fig. 6-10 can be implemented to accomplish this function. Keep in mind that since only one J-K flip-flop is shown, it is necessary to have the same circuit applied to

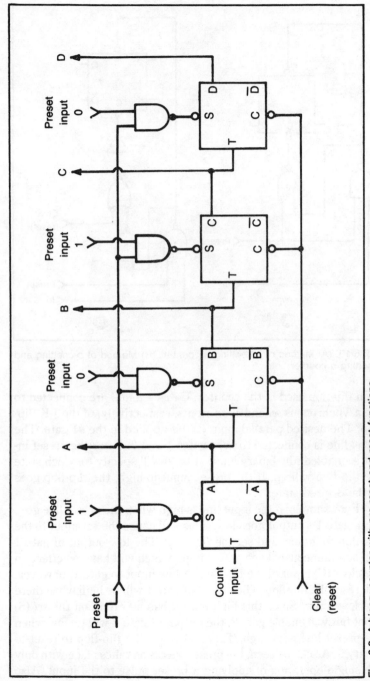

Fig. 6-9. A binary counter with pre-reset and reset functions.

187

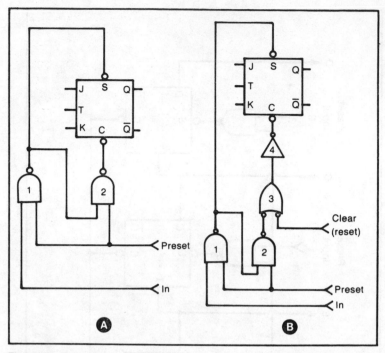

Fig. 6-10. (A) Method of presetting a counter. (B) Method of *presetting* and *resetting* a counter.

each flip-flop used in the counter. Gates 1 and 2 are connected to the asynchronous *set* and *clear* inputs, respectively, of the J-K flip-flop. The desired parallel input (IN) is applied to the #1 gate. The *preset* line is connected to both gates 1 and 2. After the preset input is enabled, the binary input (1 or 0) will specify to which state the flip-flop will go. If the preset input is high, the flip-flop goes to the desired state.

For example, if the input line is high when the preset line goes high, gate 1's output goes low. This will cause the set input to the flip-flop to go low and set the flip-flop. The low output of gate 1 will simultaneously keep gate 2 high, which will have no effect on the clear (C) input of the flip-flop. A low input to gate 1, however, will reset the flip-flop. The output of gate 1 will be high when there is a low input. Since this high output has no effect on the *set* (S) input but will enable gate 2, the output of gate 2 will go low when the preset line goes high. This will cause the flip-flop to reset to binary 0. As can be seen, the preset operation takes place with only the single operation of applying a preset pulse to the input. Also note that since the asynchronous inputs are used for this function, all other flip-flop operations are overridden.

It is sometimes desirable to combine the preset function with the reset function of a counter, as well. Figure 6-10B illustrates how to accomplish this. In addition to the preset function circuit, comprised of gates 1 and 2, gate 4 and inverter 4 provide an ORing function permitting the reset function to be accessed. For example, if the reset line is brought low, gate 3's output will go high and inverter 4's output will go low, thereby resetting the flip-flop regardless of its prior state. It is important to remember that the preset and reset operations are completely independent of each other, and that these same methods of resetting and presetting can be incorporated in any type of binary counter whether synchronous, asynchronous, up, down, or BCD.

INTEGRATED CIRCUIT COUNTERS

Most counter operations can be accomplished by using a single MSI integrated circuit specifically designed for a given function, rather than individual J-K flip-flops. It becomes necessary to design special counters only on rare occasions when an unusual or peculiar type of counter for unique operations is required.

Figure 6-11 shows the logic diagram of the 74193 TTL MSI integrated circuit counter. It is a four bit synchronous up or down counter having a separate clear (C) input. It has the ability to be preset from an external four bit parallel source via its LOAD input.

The counter is comprised of four J-K flip-flops. The reset and preset functions are accomplished via the logic circuitry of gates 1 through 12. This counter is reset by application of a binary high to the *clear* input, which will force all flip-flops to reset in the asynchronous (or immediate) mode.

To preset this counter, a four bit binary word must be applied to the respective DATA INPUT lines and then a binary *low* applied to the LOAD input. Upon application of the low LOAD input, the desired four-bit binary word will immediately be loaded into the counter in the asynchronous mode.

Instead of having a single count input and a separate up or down count enable line, this counter possesses separate up and down count inputs. To increment the counter (up count), count pulses are applied to the up count input. To decrement the counter (down count), count pulses are applied to the down count input.

NOTE: this counter changes state on the *leading* edge of the

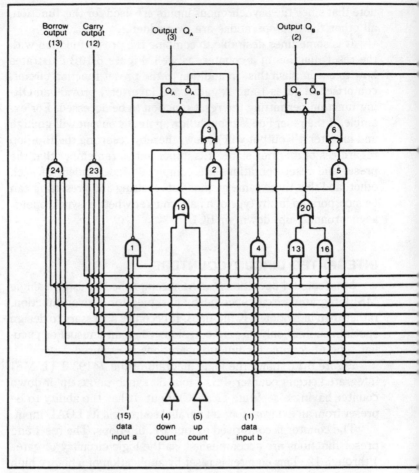

Fig. 6-11. Logic diagram for the 74193 TTL medium-scale-integration (MSI) binary counter.

applied input pulse! In other words, the counter will change state when the input pulses go from binary 0 (low) to binary 1 (high). Therefore, the unused count input line *must* be held high (binary 1) while count pulses are being applied to the opposite input. The sequence of the counter, however, is exactly the same as previously discussed.

Synchronous operation is used in this counter by making the input count pulses simultaneously clock all the flip-flops. This provides coincidental output changes of the counter. In this circuit, gates are used ahead of the T inputs of the flip-flops instead of con-

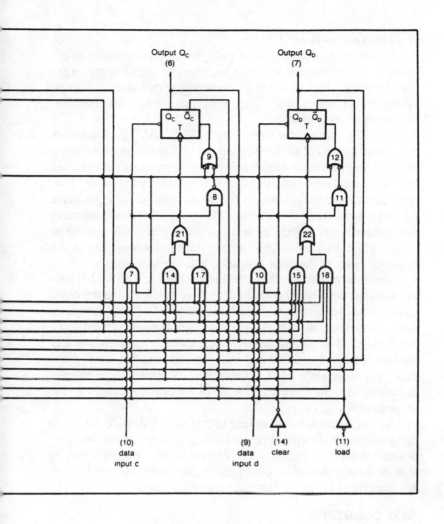

trolling each one via their respective J and K inputs. The flip-flops' outputs control the states of the gates ahead of the T inputs, thereby permitting the count pulses to be applied at the appropriate time. The application of the *up* count pulses to the T inputs are controlled simultaneously by gates 16, 17, and 18. Notice how the outputs of the previous flip-flops are connected to the inputs of these gates in order to control the precise timing of count pulses to toggle a flip-flop. The down count operation is similarly controlled by gates 13, 14, and 15, simultaneously. Finally, gates 20, 21, and 22 are merely OR gates, permitting either the up or down count pulses

191

to toggle the flip-flops' T inputs.

These counters can easily be cascaded to accommodate larger binary numbers. When it becomes necessary to use a counter larger than 16 states, two or more of these integrated circuits can be cascaded to provide multiple lengths of capacities by use of the *borrow* and/or *carry* outputs.

Gate #23 develops the carry output. This NAND gate monitors the normal outputs of all the flip-flops as well as the up count pulse. When it detects that all outputs are high, the carry output line goes low on the application of the following up count input pulse. This carry pulse will remain low only for the duration of the input pulse applied which caused it to go low. This pulse, therefore, indicates the counter is full and the next input count pulse will cause it to recycle to its 0000 state. This carry output pulse is applied to the count up input of the next cascaded counter in sequence.

Similarly, gate 24 produces the borrow output. This NAND gate monitors the *complement* output of the flip-flops as well as the down count pulse. Its output will go low when the counter has been decremented to 0000 and for the duration of the *next* applied down count pulse. This will indicate that the counter is completely empty (has decremented to 0000) and that the next applied down count pulse will recycle it to 1111. The BORROW output of the counter is connected to the down count input of the next cascaded counter in sequence.

As can be seen, this counting unit is a very flexible device. It can perform almost any required basic counting function most often encountered in digital work. The operation of this counter as well as the waveforms for clear, preset, up count, and down count are illustrated in the timing diagram of Fig. 6-12.

BCD COUNTERS

A BCD counter is a sequential circuit that counts by tens. It has 10 discrete states representing the decimal numbers 0 through 9. It is sometimes referred to as a *decade counter* because of its *ten state* nature.

The BCD counter is most commonly used to count in the standard 8421 binary code. This count sequence is illustrated in Fig. 6-13. Notice that the representation of the ten states requires a four bit number. These ten four-bit codes are identical to the first ten codes in the pure binary code. Upon application of the tenth input pulse, however, the BCD counter will recycle from 1001 (decimal 9) to 0000 (decimal 0).

Figure 6-14 shows how to construct an asynchronous 8421 BCD counter with J-K flip-flops. This counter will produce the count sequence defined in Fig. 6-13. It is basically similar to the four bit pure binary counter discussed earlier. The circuit has several modifications, however, which permit it to count in the defined 8421 BCD sequence.

These modifications consist of a feedback circuit from the complement output of the "D" J-K flip-flop back to the J input of the "B" J-K flip-flop and a two input AND gate, monitoring the states of the "B" and "C" J-K flip-flops, which generates a control signal used to operate the J input of the "D" J-K flip-flop. The modifications are employed to manipulate the circuit to recycle itself on every tenth input pulse.

The operation of the 8421 BCD counter is illustrated in the timing diagram of Fig. 6-15. The count sequence for the first eight input pulses is identical to that of the standard four-bit binary counter previously discussed. During the ninth and tenth input

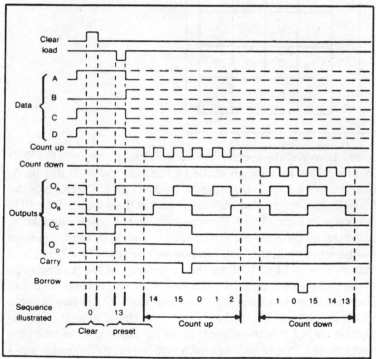

Fig. 6-12. Timing diagram of the 74193 counter showing clear, load, and count sequences.

193

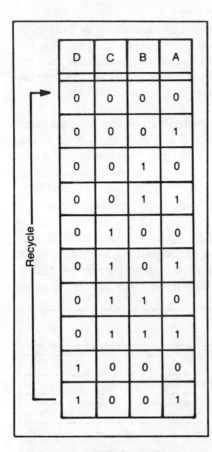

D	C	B	A
0	0	0	0
0	0	0	1
0	0	1	0
0	0	1	1
0	1	0	0
0	1	0	1
0	1	1	0
0	1	1	1
1	0	0	0
1	0	0	1

Recycle

Fig. 6-13. Count sequence of 8-4-2-1 BCD counter.

pulses, however, the operations which occur are unique to the BCD counter. Upon application of the eighth input pulse, flip-flops A, B, and C are set while D is reset. The AND gate is high since the B and C outputs are also high. This causes the J input of the "D" flip-flop to be high, as well. Upon application of the next input pulse, therefore, all flip-flops will change state: The A, B, and C flip-flops will be reset while the "D" flip-flop will be set. The counter will change from 0111 to 1000 on the occurrence of the trailing edge of the eighth input pulse. In this new state the outputs of B and C are low, thereby causing the J input of the "D" flip-flop to again be binary 0 (low). When the J input is 0, the K input 1, and the flip-flop set, all conditions are met for the flip-flop to be reset the next time the T input switches from high to low. Additionally, since the complement output of the "D" flip-flop is low at this time keeping the J input of the "B" flip-flop also low, the occurrence of the

194

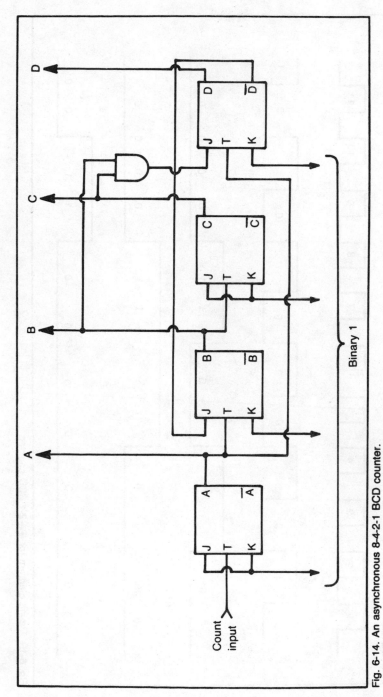

Fig. 6-14. An asynchronous 8-4-2-1 BCD counter.

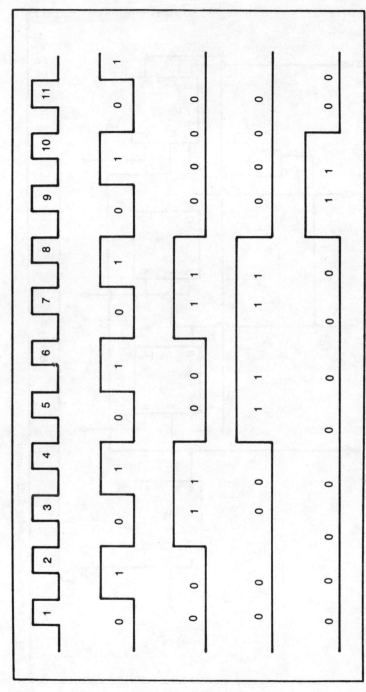

Fig. 6-15. Timing diagram for 8-4-2-1 BCD counter.

next clock pulse will not change the state of the "B" flip-flop which was already reset.

On the occurrence of the ninth input pulse, the "A" flip-flop sets. Nothing else changes at this time. The number stored in the binary counter is now 1001. The transition of the "A" flip-flop is ignored by the T input of the "D" flip-flop. However, on the occurrence of the *tenth* input pulse, the "A" flip-flop will toggle and reset. Since the J input of the "B" flip-flop is low, it will not change from its already reset state as will the "C" flip-flop. The "A" flip-flop state change, however, does cause the "D" flip-flop to reset since its J input is binary 0 (low) and its K input is binary 1 (high). All flip-flops are reset, therefore, on the occurrence of the tenth input pulse.

It is possible to produce numerous variations of the basic BCD counter illustrated in Fig. 6-14. For example, a synchronous BCD counter can be constructed by using the same basic count-modifying techniques. Since all of the flip-flops would be toggled simultaneously by a common input clock, the counting speed of the BCD counter can be significantly increased. Furthermore, it is possible to construct a BCD down counter which will decrement the contents of the counter each time an input pulse is applied thereby making the sequence cycle from 9 to 0.

CASCADING BCD COUNTERS

Since a single BCD counter has a maximum of ten discrete states, it can only represent the numbers 0 through 9. When a counter must be able to count higher than ten pulses, it becomes necessary to cascade two or more BCD counters. Each BCD counter in the chain will represent one decimal digit equivalent. The total number of BCD counters will determine the maximum count capabilities of the system.

A counter chain consisting of four BCD counters is shown in Fig. 6-16. Each BCD counter is represented by a single block. Each counter is comprised of a single input line and 4 flip-flop output lines. In each counter, the A output line is defined to be the LSB while the D line is the MSB. Moreover, the input line to the counter is the least significant digit while the most significant digit is shown on the far right. The maximum count capacity of this counter is 9999 since it contains four BCD counters.

As count input pulses are applied to the input of BCD counter 1, the counter will be incremented as previously discussed. The

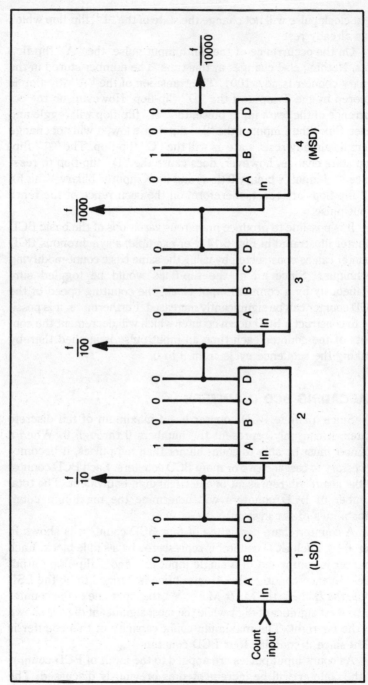

Fig. 6-16. Increasing the count capacity of BCD counters through cascading.

198

output states will change in the standard 8421 BCD code sequence. Notice how the MSB output of each counter is connected to the input of the following counter. This arrangement permits triggering of the next higher order of bit counter to increment each time the lower order bit counter recycles to 0. This can be seen by referring back to the timing diagram of Fig. 6-15. Since the trailing edge of the D output occurs on the trailing edge of the tenth pulse, the lower order counter recycles and simultaneously increments the next counter by 1. The decimal contents of the counter can be determined by examination of the flip-flop outputs. Assuming the counter was initially reset, the counter shown in Fig. 6-16 has counted 2615 pulses.

The BCD Counter As A Frequency Divider

The BCD counter can also be used as a frequency divider much like any counter. It divides the input frequency by a factor of ten since it has ten discrete states. In other words, the output of the MSB flip-flop will be exactly one-tenth that of the input frequency. By examination of the timing diagram of Fig. 6-20 it can be seen that only one pulse occurs for every ten input pulses. Even though this pulse has a duration of *two* pulse widths, it nevertheless has a *frequency* of only one-tenth that of the input.

The input frequency can be divided by any factor of ten by cascading BCD counters. For example, the output of the fourth BCD counter in Fig. 6-16 will be exactly 1/10,000 of the input frequency. The output of the third BCD counter will be exactly 1/1,000 of the input frequency. The output of the second BCD counter will be 1/100 of the input frequency. In other words, if an input signal of 4 MHz were applied to the counter, the D output of the MSD would be 400 Hz. The BCD counter is often referred to as a *decade scaler* when used as a frequency divider.

An Integrated Circuit BCD Counter

The type 7490A is the most widely-used BCD counter integrated circuit. This TTL MSI device is an asynchronous (or ripple) counter which counts in the standard 8421 BCD code. Figure 6-17 shows its logic diagram. It is "logically" identical to the previously discussed BCD counter. The counter is comprised of four J-K flip-flops and appropriate gating necessary to implement the 8421 BCD sequence.

Examination of the logic diagram in Fig. 6-17 reveals the fact

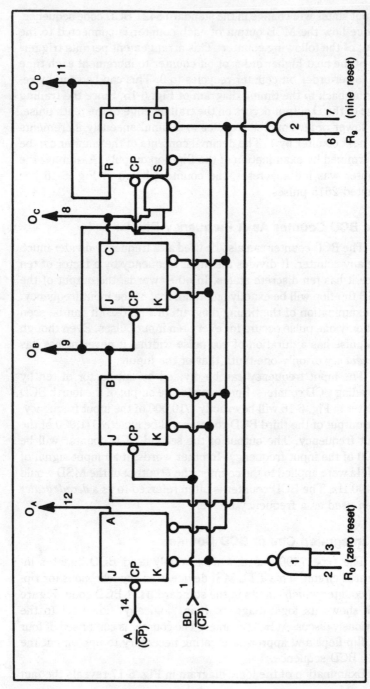

Fig. 6-17. Logic diagram of an 8-4-2-1 BCD counter.

that flip-flop "A" is not internally connected to the other three flip-flops. Therefore, in order to perform the 8421 BCD count an external connection must be made between the "A" and "B" flip-flops. The count input pulses are then applied to the "A" flip-flop input.

The flip-flop can be reset via gate 1, as shown in Fig. 6-17. When both inputs to gate 1 are high, all flip-flops in the counter will be reset to binary 0. This provides the flexibility of having two separate inputs control resetting the flip-flops. Normally, however, only a single input is necessary for this function, and the two inputs can be tied together.

The counter can also be preset to 1001 (or decimal 9) via gate 2 in a manner similar to resetting via gate 1. This particular function is useful in the arithmetic operations which may be performed with BCD counters.

Even though the 7490A BCD counter is an asynchronous counter, it has a maximum count frequency of approximately 32 MHz. It is available in a 14-pin DIP and is widely used in scaling and counting applications.

SPECIAL COUNTERS

The most commonly-used counters in digital systems are binary and BCD counters. Most counting applications can be implemented with MSI binary and BCD counters. Special counters may be required, however, in certain applications. It may be necessary, for example, to count in some peculiar sequence or to have a counter sequence in some special code. Moreover, it may be necessary to scale (or divide) a frequency by some sub-factor other than even powers of two or ten. Some typical examples of these applications are counters to count in the Gray code, or a frequency divider that divides an input frequency by a factor of nine.

Special counters like the ones just described are easily implemented thanks to the flexibility of the J-K flip-flop. Basically, the approach is to construct a standard counter and then introduce feedback and gating control circuits on the J and K inputs to develop the exact count sequence required for any given number of states or operations as desired.

The number of discrete states which a counter can assume is referred to as the *modulus* of the counter. A *modulo-N* counter, therefore, is one having N states. Since a BCD or decade counter can assume ten discrete binary states, it is a *modulo-10* counter.

A counter comprised of *four* flip-flops is a *modulo-16* counter, since it can assume 2^4 (or 16) binary states. Decade counters with a modulo of ten are easily constructed. However, there are other applications which require modulos of other integer values, as well.

Figure 6-18 illustrates a modulo-three counter. The circuit is synchronous since the T inputs of both J-K flip-flops are connected to the count input. The circuit counts by three due to the feedback line from the complement B output to the J input of the "A" flip-flop.

The operation of the counter can be analyzed by first assuming that both flip-flops are initially reset. The A and B output states are, therefore, binary 0. The low output of the "A" flip-flop holds the J input of the "B" flip-flop low. On the trailing edge of the first input pulse, the "A" flip-flop will set since the complement B output going to the J input of the "A" flip-flop is high. Now, since the "A" flip-flop is set and its output is high, the J input to the "B"

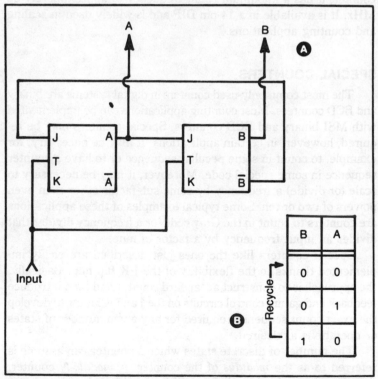

B	A
0	0
0	1
1	0

Fig. 6-18. (A) A modulo-three counter. (B) Count sequence of modulo-three counter.

202

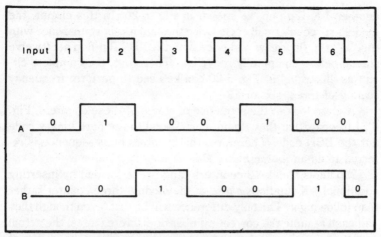

Fig. 6-19. Timing diagram for modulo-three counter.

flip-flop is also high enabling the "B" flip-flop to become set on the trailing edge of the next count input pulse. On the occurrence of the second input pulse, the "A" flip-flop will again toggle, since the complement B output is still high and the "B" flip-flop will also toggle since its J input is also still high. When both flip-flops toggle, flip-flop "A" becomes reset and flip-flop "B" becomes set. On the third count pulse, the "B" flip-flop will reset since its K input is high and its J input is now low. The "A" flip-flop remains reset since its J input is also low as a result of the complement B output being low. Therefore, on the application of the third input pulse, both flip-flops reset and begin the above cycle all over again. The count sequence of the modulo-three counter is also shown in Fig. 6-18 and its timing diagram is shown in Fig. 6-19.

This counter can be used for counting applications requiring a tri-state counter as well as a divide-by-three scaler, since the output of either the "A" or "B" flip-flop is exactly one-third the frequency of the applied input. As illustrated in Fig. 6-19, a single output pulse occurs on each flip-flop for every three input pulses.

Modulo-six and modulo-12 counters are easily formed by merely cascading additional J-K flip-flops as shown in Fig. 6-20. A modulo-six counter is formed by connecting a single J-K flip-flop to the output of a modulo three-counter. The modulo-three counter will cycle once through its three states with the "C" flip-flop reset, and then cycle again through its three states with the "C" flip-flop set before it completely recycles.

A modulo-12 counter is similarly formed by the addition of yet another J-K flip-flop, as shown in Fig. 6-20. In this circuit, the modulo-six counter will cycle twice through its six states; once with the "D" flip-flop reset and once with the "D" flip-flop set (twelve states) before completely recycling. Therefore, the complete circuit as illustrated in Fig. 6-20 can be used to perform frequency scaling of three, six, or 12.

A close look at the sequence of states of these counters, Fig. 6-21, reveals that they do not correspond to the pure binary code *nor* the BCD code. Therefore, this type of count sequence is referred to as an *unweighted* code.

Modulo-six and -12 counters can also be formed by inserting additional J-K flip-flops *ahead* of the modulo-three counter rather than following it. The only difference will be that, even though they will each assume the correct number of discrete states, the actual count sequence will be altered thereby producing a different unweighted code sequence.

Generally, it doesn't matter what code sequence is used when these circuits are used solely for frequency division since the output frequency will still be either 1/6 or 1/12 that of the input. However, in applications where the count sequence is of importance, careful consideration of each arrangement must be given. It should be noted that in the case of the circuit shown in Fig. 6-20, a duty

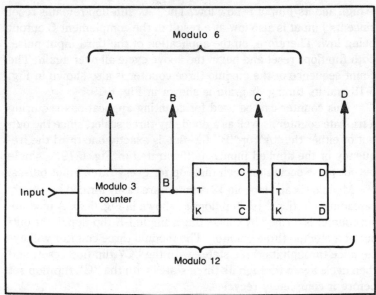

Fig. 6-20. Expanding the modulo-three counter to modulo six and modulo 12.

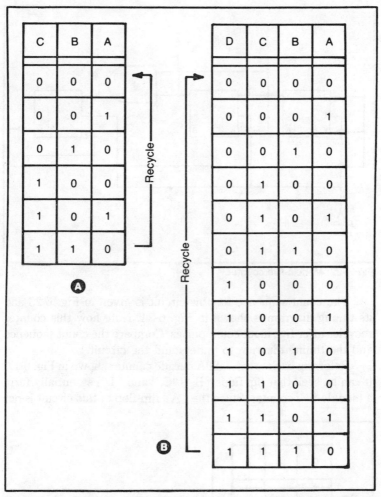

C	B	A
0	0	0
0	0	1
0	1	0
1	0	0
1	0	1
1	1	0

Ⓐ

Recycle

D	C	B	A
0	0	0	0
0	0	0	1
0	0	1	0
0	1	0	0
0	1	0	1
0	1	1	0
1	0	0	0
1	0	0	1
1	0	1	0
1	1	0	0
1	1	0	1
1	1	1	0

Ⓑ

Recycle

Fig. 6-21. (A) Count sequence of modulo-six counter. (B) Count sequence of a modulo-12 counter.

cycle of 50% is produced when the C or D outputs are used. By inserting the modulo-three counter *after* the additional J-K flip-flops, however, a duty cycle other than 50% is produced.

Figure 6-22 shows how to construct a modulo-five counter. This counter produces five discrete three-bit states. Since the count input is applied to the T inputs of all the flip-flops simultaneously, it is considered to be synchronous. A combination of an external logic gate and a feedback circuit is used to cause the counter to count by five.

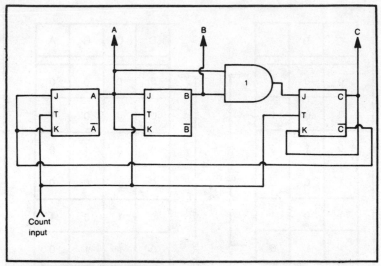

Fig. 6-22. Modulo-five counter.

The count sequence for this circuit is given in Fig. 6-23 and its timing diagram is shown in Fig. 6-24. Note how this counter recycles after five input count pulses. Compare the count sequence and the timing diagram to understand the circuit.

Referring back to the 7490A decade counter shown in Fig. 6-17, it can be seen that flip-flops "B," "C," and "D" essentially form a modulo-five counter. Since the "A" flip-flop of this circuit is not

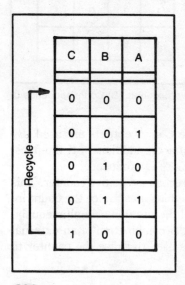

C	B	A
0	0	0
0	0	1
0	1	0
0	1	1
1	0	0

Recycle

Fig. 6-23. Count sequence of modulo-five counter.

206

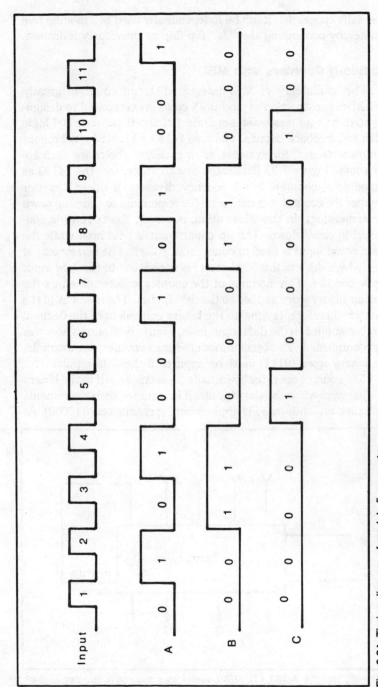

Fig. 6-24. Timing diagram of modulo-five counter.

207

internally connected, it can be independently used as a modulo-five counter by connecting the "A" flip-flop as previously indicated.

Modulo-N Counters with MSI

The availability of MSI integrated circuit counters greatly simplifies construction of modulo-N counters compared to designing specific counters using separate J-K flip-flops, external logic gates and feedback circuits. The type 74193 TTL MSI synchronous up/down counter, for example, is an excellent choice for such applications. Figure 7-25 illustrates how to implement the 74193 as a modulo-N counter. For frequency division, it doesn't matter whether the counter is counting up (incrementing) or counting down (decrementing). In this illustration, however, the counter is connected to count down. The up count input is held high while the down count input is used to count input pulses. The *borrow* output line (which detects the 0000 state) is connected to the *load* input of the counter. The modulus of the counter is determined by the four-bit binary word applied to the data inputs. The modulus of the counter, therefore, is equal to the binary equivalent of the decimal number applied to the data input lines. Figure 6-26 shows how this is accomplished. To obtain a modulo-seven counter, for example, the binary word (0111) must be applied to the data inputs.

The counter operates by initially presetting itself to the binary number applied to the data inputs. The counter then decrements each time an input pulse is applied until it reaches zero (0000). At

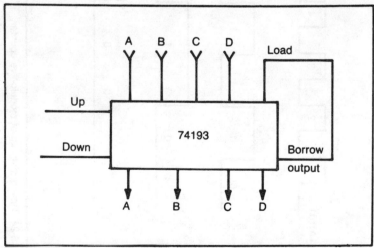

Fig. 6-25. Using a 74193 TTL MSI counter as a modulo-N counter.

208

Modulo	Data inputs			
	D	C	B	A
1	0	0	0	1
2	0	0	1	0
3	0	0	1	1
4	0	1	0	0
5	0	1	0	1
6	0	1	1	0
7	0	1	1	1
8	1	0	0	0
9	1	0	0	1
10	1	0	1	0
11	1	0	1	1
12	1	1	0	0
13	1	1	0	1
14	1	1	1	0
15	1	1	1	1

Fig. 6-26. Parallel data input code and related decimal modulos.

that point, the *borrow* output line goes low, and again presets the counter to the number applied to its data inputs. This sequence is repeated until no further count input pulses are applied.

It is important to note that as soon as the borrow output line goes low, the binary number applied to the data inputs is immediately loaded (asynchronously) into the counter, and the borrow output line will no longer be low since the state of the counter is no longer 0000. Therefore, the duration of the borrow output pulse *must* be long enough to ensure complete data transfer from the input lines to load the counter before it returns to its high state.

This can be accomplished by ensuring the input clock pulse width is greater than the total propagation delay of the gates in the counter associated with presetting the number on the data bus lines. Even though the borrow output line goes high as soon as the counter is preset to the data input number, the internal propagation delays of the circuit are such that all the flip-flops may not become preset *before* the borrow output goes high. The load input signal must propagate through all the flip-flops and gates within the circuit. It is possible, therefore, that erratic operation may be encountered if the propagation delays aren't sufficiently accounted for since these delays vary between specific devices. It is recommended that some propagation delay be added between the borrow output and the load input pins of the counter to improve total reliability of the entire circuit. This can be easily accomplished by cascading an *even* number of inverters between these two pins in the circuit. This will maintain proper polarity of the binary number applied as well as sufficient propagation delay.

SHIFT REGISTERS

The shift register is another widely-used type of sequential logic circuit. A shift register is comprised of binary storage elements similar to those used in counters. While the most commonly-used storage elements in shift registers are flip-flops, other types of circuits are also used. The storage elements are cascaded in a shift register in such a manner to permit the bits of data stored within to be moved or "shifted" from one element to another adjacent element. A single input clock or shift pulse is used to simultaneously actuate or toggle all of the storage registers. The data stored within a shift register is moved one position in either of two directions upon application of a shift pulse. Even though the shift register is basically a storage device for binary data, its ability to be able to *move* data from one element to another, one bit at a time, makes it a valuable device in performing a wide variety of logical operations.

Shift Register Operation

Figure 6-27 illustrates how a shift register operates. In this example, the shift register consists of four binary storage elements, and the initial number stored is binary 1011. Another number, binary 0110, is externally generated, and is serially available to the shift register. Upon application of shift pulses, the number stored within the shift register will be shifted out (one bit at a time) and lost while the externally-generated number will be simultaneously shifted into the shift register (one bit at a time) and retained.

Referring to Fig. 6-27, it can be seen that after one clock pulse, the number originally stored in the shift register is shifted one bit position to the right, and the right-most bit is shifted out and lost. Simultaneously, the first bit of the external number is serially

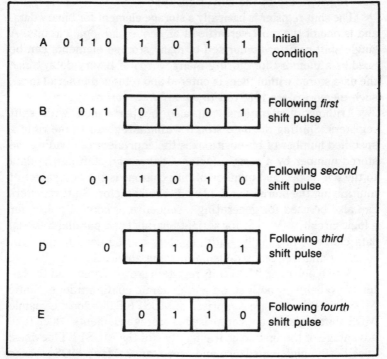

Fig. 6-27. Shift-register operation.

shifted into the *left*-most bit position of the shift register as shown in Fig. 6-27B. The remaining three illustrations, Figs. 6-27C, D, and E, depict the results following the occurrence of three more clock pulses. After four shift pulses, the original number stored within the shift register is completely lost, while the externally-generated number is completely shifted into the register, thereby occupying the same space.

Several important aspects of a shift register are illustrated in this example. First, the basic shift register is serial in nature, although some variations offer both serial and parallel inputs and outputs. The ability to combine both serial and parallel operations makes the shift register an ideal candidate for performing serial-to-parallel and parallel-to-serial data conversions. Second, since data is shifted one bit position for each clock pulse applied, clock pulses have complete control over the operation of the shift register. In this example, the data was shifted to the right. However, in some shift registers it is also possible to shift data to the left as well. The direction of the shift register is determined by the application. Most shift registers are of the shift-right type.

The shift register is basically a storage element for binary data, and is one of the most versatile of all sequential logic circuits. A single shift register comprised of many storage elements can be used as a memory for storing many words of binary data. Since the data stored within them is entered and removed in serial form, such memories are referred to as *serial memories*.

Arithmetic operations can also be performed with shift registers. Shifting the data stored within a register to the right a specified number of bit positions is the equivalent of dividing the stored number by a certain factor. Conversely, shifting the data to the *left* a specified number of bit positions is the equivalent of multiplying the stored number by a certain factor. Shift registers can also be used for generating a sequence of control pulses for a logic circuit, as well as for serial-to-parallel and parallel-to-serial data conversion. Finally, shift registers can be used to perform counting and frequency division in some applications.

Both bipolar and MOS shift registers are available, and the latter is available in both static and dynamic configurations. Static MOS shift registers are comprised of MOSFET flip-flops. Dynamic MOS shift registers are comprised of storage elements which take advantage of the unique characteristics of the MOSFET devices: specifically, high impedance and capacitance. Many MOS storage elements can be manufactured on a single chip of silicon due to the very small size of the MOSFET structure. Even though both types of shift registers are widely used in digital systems, very long shift registers which are capable of storing many words of binary data can be made extremely small and very economical by using MOS shift registers.

BIPOLAR LOGIC SHIFT REGISTERS

J-K flip-flops are usually used to construct TTL and ECL bipolar shift registers. It is also possible to use type-D flip-flops, although J-K flip-flops are much more versatile. Figure 6-28 shows a typical four-bit shift register constructed with J-K flip-flops. Note how the serial input and its complement are applied to the J and K inputs of the "A" flip-flop. The remaining flip-flops are cascaded in a series fashion and all the T input lines are tied together, making this arrangement synchronous. The asynchronous *clear* inputs of all the flip-flops are also tied together to form a master *clear* input to the entire shift register, which is activated by the application of a binary 0 or low level to this line. This shift register arrangement can also be preset to any desired number by using any of the previously-described techniques. Data applied to the input of this circuit will be shifted one bit position to the right upon application of each clock pulse.

The timing diagram of Fig. 6-29 shows how to load a serial data word into the shift register. The binary number 0101 in serial form occurs in synchronism with the input clock (or shift) pulses. When analyzing this diagram remember that time moves from left to right. Therefore, the clock pulses on the right occur *after* those on the left. Similarly, the state of the serial input illustrated on the left occurs *prior* to the states of those shown on the right.

The shift register is initially reset (0000). Prior to the application of the first clock pulse, the serial input is fed with a binary 1. This represents the first bit of the binary word being loaded into the register. On the trailing edge of the first clock pulse, this binary 1 will be loaded into the "A" flip-flop. Since the J and K inputs of the four flip-flops are arranged to transfer the stored data from one flip-flop to a succeeding flip-flop, the state previously stored in the "A" flip-flop will be transferred to the "B" flip-flop. Likewise, the states previously stored within the "B" and "C" flip-flops will be transferred to the "C" and "D" flip-flops, respectively. Since, however, these flip-flops were storing binary 0s, no state change will take place to them upon application of the first clock pulse.

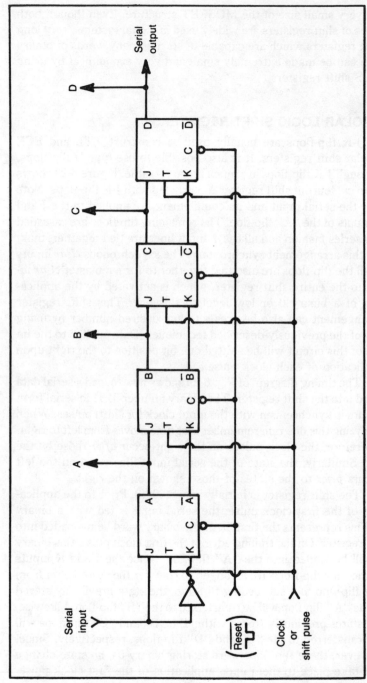

Fig. 6-28. J-K flip-flops used as a four-bit shift register.

Following the first clock pulse, the "A" flip-flop becomes set while the "B," "C," and "D" flip-flops remain reset. The first clock pulse also causes the serial input data to change to the second bit of the word to be loaded, since the clock pulses are common to all circuits in the system in order to keep all functions in complete synchronism. Therefore, the input to the "A" flip-flop now becomes binary 0.

Upon the occurrence of the second clock pulse, this binary 0 will be loaded into the "A" flip-flop and the previously stored binary 1 will be transferred to the "B" flip-flop since the J input of the "B" flip-flop was high. No other state changes will occur since the remaining flip-flops were storing binary 0s. At this time, the first two bits of the serial input binary word have been loaded into the register.

The serial input now becomes binary 1, representing the third bit of the input word. The "A" flip-flop will set upon application of the third clock pulse. The previously stored zero within the "A" flip-flop will be transferred to the "B" flip-flop. The binary 1 previously stored in the "B" flip-flop will be transferred to the "C" flip-flop. The "D" flip-flop remains reset.

The serial input to the shift register now becomes binary 0 and the "A" flip-flop will reset upon application of the fourth clock pulse. The binary 1 previously stored in the "A" flip-flop will be transferred to the "B" flip-flop. The binary 0 previously stored in the "B" flip-flop will be transferred to the "C" flip-flop, and the binary 1 previously stored in the "C" flip-flop will be transferred to the "D" flip-flop. As can be seen, after the application of four clock pulses the complete binary word, 0101, is loaded into the shift register as indicated by the states of the waveforms in the timing diagram of Fig. 6-29.

Even though the above example illustrates the operation of only a four-bit shift register, it can be seen that as many shift registers as needed may be cascaded. Most commonly-available shift registers are made to store only a single binary word. In most of today's digital systems, therefore, shift registers have a storage capacity which is some multiple of four bits.

In most applications, MSI shift registers are used rather than in individual J-K or D-type flip-flops. MSI shift registers are available in both four-bit and eight-bit capacities. The operation of a typical four-bit MSI TTL shift register will now be discussed.

Figure 6-30 shows the logic diagram of the 7495 TTL shift register. It is internally comprised of four J-K flip-flops with appropriate

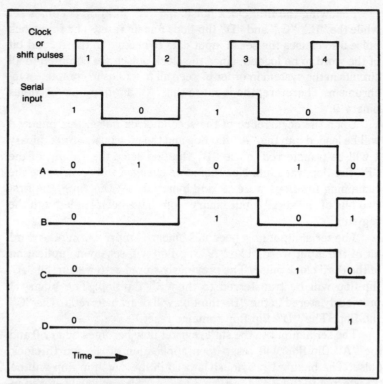

Fig. 6-29. Timing diagram for serially loading binary number 0101 into a shift register.

gating on each one. The input gating, as well as the input clock selection, is controlled by the mode control input line. This permits the use of two independent clock signals.

Gates 1, 4, 7, and 10 are enabled when a binary 1 is placed on the mode control input. This sets the 7495 to perform the shift right operation. Gate 1 is used to receive the serial input and feed gate 3 to J-K inputs of the "A" flip-flop. The output of the "A" flip-flop feeds the input of the "B" flip-flop via gates 4 and 6. Similarly, the output of the "B" flip-flop is fed to the "C" flip-flop via gates 7 and 9. Finally, the output of the "C" flip-flop is fed to the input of the "D" flip-flop via gates 10 and 12. Note also that gate 13 is enabled upon application of a binary 0 on the mode control input. This permits clock pulse #1 to control the flip-flops.

Alternately, gates 2, 5, 8, and 11 are enabled when a binary 0 is placed on the mode control input. This also inhibits gates 1, 4, 7, and 10 and the parallel data inputs are recognized. Note also

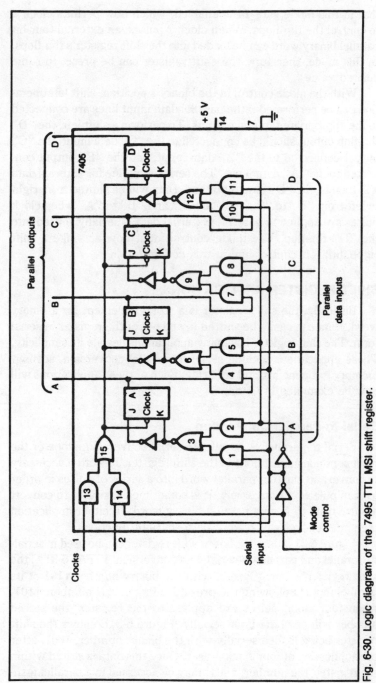

Fig. 6-30. Logic diagram of the 7495 TTL MSI shift register.

that in this mode gate 14 is enabled, which now permits clock 2 to control the flip-flops. When clock 2 pulses, an external four-bit parallel binary word can be loaded into the shift register's flip-flops. In this mode, therefore, the shift register can be preset to some desired value.

With the mode control in the binary 1 position, shift left operation can be performed if the parallel data input lines are connected to the appropriate flip-flop outputs. To perform a shift left, the "D" flip-flop output should be connected to the "C" data input, the "C" output connected to the "B" data input, and the "B" output connected to the "A" data input. The serial input line for external data will then be the "D" data input line. Data will be shifted from right to left from "D" to "C," "C" to "B," and "B" to "A" when clock pulses are applied to gate 14. External data is serially shifted into the "D" flip-flop. The mode control input now acts like a shift right/shift left control line in this configuration.

SHIFT REGISTER APPLICATIONS

Basically, the shift register is a storage element for a binary word. Data can easily be shifted in and out of the register in serial form. The shift register has many applications despite its simplicity. These applications include serial to parallel conversion, scaling, memory, sequencing, and counting. Each of these applications will now be examined in detail.

Serial-to-Parallel Conversion

Serial-to-parallel or parallel-to-serial conversion is one of the most common applications of the shift register. It is often necessary to convert an existing parallel word into a series of pulses in order to manipulate it. Conversely, it is sometimes desirable to convert a pulse train to form a parallel binary word. In either application the shift register can readily perform both functions.

Figure 6-31 illustrates how a shift register can be used in serial-to-parallel and parallel-to-serial data conversion. In Fig. 6-31A, the shift register is being loaded with the binary number 1101 at its parallel input. Following the preset loading of this number, 1101, when four clock pulses are applied to the register, the stored number will be shifted out serially. Figure 6-31B shows the shift register being loaded serially with the binary number, 1001, after the application of four clock pulses. Once this data is stored within the register, the number, 1001, may be accessed in a parallel fashion by simultaneously monitoring the outputs of the individual flip-flops of the shift register.

Scaling

Arithmetic operations such as multiplication and division can also be performed with a shift register. The effect of multiplying a binary number by a power of 2 can be accomplished by shifting the binary number stored in the shift register to the left. Conversely, the effect of dividing a number by some power of 2 may be accomplished by shifting the stored number within the shift register to the right. Shifting operations are an inexpensive and easy way of performing binary multiplication and division.

Figure 6-32 shows a shift register containing the binary number 00011 (decimal 3). Upon shifting of the number one position to the left, it can be seen the new binary number stored will become 00110 (decimal 6). Similarly, each time the stored number in the shift register is shifted one bit position to the left, it is, in effect, the equivalent of multiplying the stored number by a factor of 2. It can be concluded, therefore, the factor by which the number is

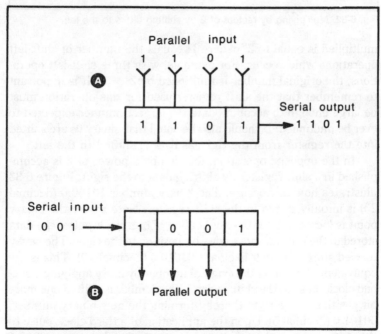

Fig. 6-31. (A) Parallel-to-serial data conversion using a shift register. (B) Serial-to-parallel data conversion using a shift register.

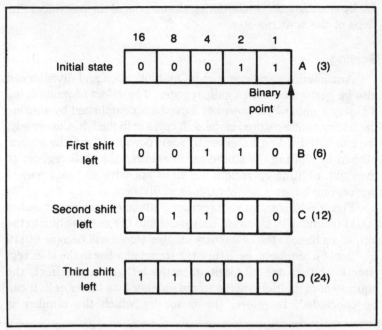

Fig. 6-32. Multiplying by factors of 2 by shifting digits to the left.

multiplied is equal to 2^N where N equals the number of shift-left operations which occur. For example, with three shift-left operations, the original number is multiplied by 2^3 = 8. It is important to remember that the shift register used for this operation must be large enough to accommodate the largest number expected to ever be multiplied. It should also be noted that binary 0s are shifted into the register from the right as data is shifted to the left.

In the opposite operation, division by a power of 2 is accomplished in a shift register by shifting data to the right. Figure 6-33 illustrates how this occurs. The binary number 10100.0 (decimal 20) is initially stored in the shift register. Note where the binary point is located. After the application of one clock pulse, the data stored in the register moves one bit position to the right. The newly formed stored number is binary 01010.0 (decimal 10). This is the equivalent of dividing the original number by 2. By applying a second clock pulse to the shift register, the number is shifted one more bit position to the right thereby forming the new binary number, 00101.0 (decimal 5). Upon the application of a third clock pulse to the shift register, the resulting binary number becomes 00010.1 (decimal 2.5).

It can be concluded, therefore, the value by which the number stored in the register is divided can be expressed as 2^N where N is equal to the number of shift-right operations. In the entire example above the original number, 10100.0 (decimal 20) was divided by 2^3 = 8 or 20/8 = 2.5. Again, it is important to use a shift register large enough to be able to accommodate the smallest number (to the right of the decimal point) expected to be divided by scaling in the shift register operation. If the capacity of the shift register is not great enough to store a sufficient number of bits, data will be lost when shifted out to the right thereby resulting in incorrect arithmetic operations.

Shift Register Memory

Because they store binary data, shift registers are frequently used as temporary memories in digital equipment. Shift registers used for this purpose are usually capable of storing at least one complete binary word, and many binary words can be stored by adding shift registers to any desired length. There are two operations that the memory must perform when used in this application. First, it must be able to accept data. Second, it must be able to

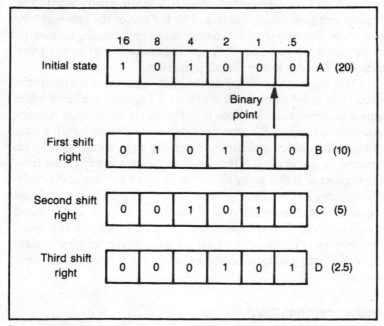

Fig. 6-33. Dividing by factors of 2 by shifting digits to the right.

221

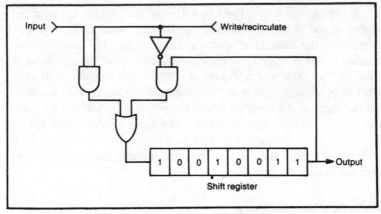

Fig. 6-34. Shift-register memory.

store the data. In other words, new data must be able to be written (input) into the shift register, and this data must be able to be retrieved (or read from the register) upon command. When this stored data is read from the register, however, it must not be lost. A shift register can meet these requirements by the application of external logic circuitry as shown in Fig. 6-34. In this example, an eight-bit shift register is used to store a single binary word. The read or write operation is selected by the use of the external control gates. To write (or store) data into the register, the *write/recirculate* line is set to binary 1. This enables gate 1 to accept input data and transfer it into the shift register.

Once this data is stored in the shift register, the write/recirculate line is set to binary 0 and gate 1 becomes inhibited while gate 2 becomes enabled. Note how the output of the shift register is connected to gate 2. Upon application of clock pulses, the data in the shift register is shifted-out serially and may be used by an external device or circuit. However, as the data is shifted out from the register, it is also being shifted back into the input of the register via gates 2 and 3. In other words, the data is being recirculated within the register and the read-out operation is being accomplished simultaneously. When it becomes desirable to write a new word into the memory, a binary 1 signal is applied to the write/recirculate input line and eight clock pulses are then applied to the shift register.

Sequencer/Ring Counter

The ring counter or sequencer is another popular application

222

of the shift register. Many digital circuits require a sequence of equally spaced timing pulses for synchronizing a series of operations. Figure 6-35 shows how to configure a shift register as a ring counter. The only difference between this circuit and the standard shift register circuit previously discussed is the addition of **the** feedback connection from the "D" flip-flop output to the "A" flip-flop J input and its complement to the K input of the "A" flip-flop. This additional circuitry causes the shift register to continuously rotate or sequence the data within the register. A single bit of data may be preset into the sequencer via the *asynchronous set* and *clear preset* lines. Application of a binary 0 to the preset line causes the "A" flip-flop to become set while simultaneously resetting the remaining three flip-flops. Upon the application of shift pulses, the preset binary 1 in the "A" flip-flop is shifted to the "B" flip-flop, then to the "C" flip-flop, etc. until it recirculates from the "D" flip-flop back into the "A" flip-flop. This sequence is repeated as long as shift pulses are applied to the circuit. The name "ring counter" certainly applies since the original bit initially applied to the "A" flip-flop is continually recirculated. Figure 6-36 shows the timing diagram of the ring counter while Fig. 6-37 illustrates the operation of its bit recirculation.

By examining the waveforms of a four-bit ring counter shown in the timing diagram of Fig. 6-36, it can be seen that the output of any one of the flip-flops has a frequency equal to one-fourth that of the shift pulse clock. In other words, it can be said that a shift register connected as a ring counter produces frequency division

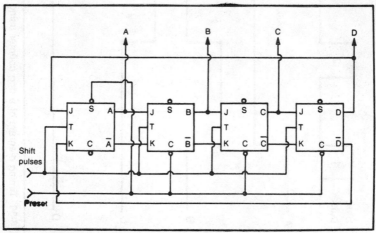

Fig. 6-35. Shift register used as a *ring counter* or *sequencer*.

223

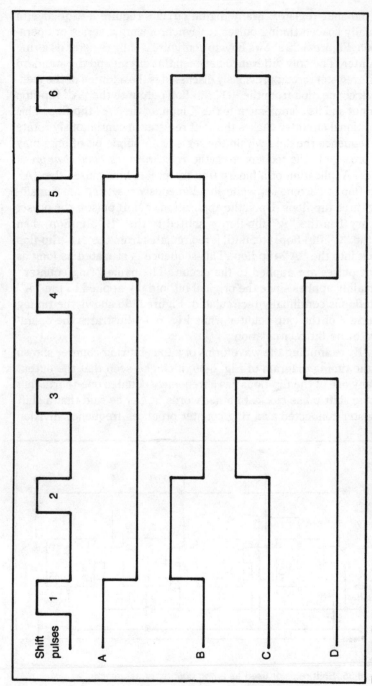

Fig. 6-36. Timing diagram of a ring counter using four-bit shift register.

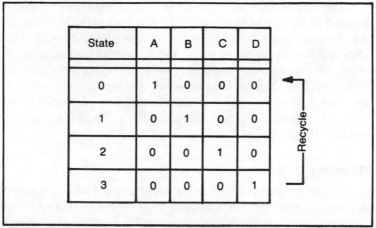

State	A	B	C	D
0	1	0	0	0
1	0	1	0	0
2	0	0	1	0
3	0	0	0	1

Recycle

Fig. 6-37. Count sequence of a ring counter.

equal to the number of flip-flops (or bits) of which it is comprised. The shift register, when connected as a ring counter, therefore, can be used as a frequency divider. Frequency division by any integer can be easily accomplished by simply using as many flip-flops as needed. For example, to divide by nine, a ring counter comprised of nine flip-flops would be required.

Because the ring counter described in Fig. 6-35 must initially be preset in order to function properly, it has an inherent disadvantage. When this circuit is initially "powered-up," the flip-flops in the register can come up in any state. Moreover, the previously-described operation will not occur if any random state is allowed. This means that the preset operation must initially take place to load one of the flip-flops with a binary 1 and the remaining flip-flops with a binary 0. Figure 6-38, however, shows how to overcome this by incorporating a self-correcting circuit. In this circuit, the NAND gate monitors the outputs of the "A," "B," and "C" flip-flops. The output of this NAND gate and its complement are connected to the K and J inputs, respectively, of the "A" flip-flop. With this arrangement, the shift register will automatically correct itself—only one of the flip-flops can be set while the remaining three are reset regardless of which one of the sixteen possible states the counter can initially assume. After a maximum of two shift pulses, the contents of the shift register will automatically be corrected so that only a single flip-flop is set regardless of the initial states of the flip-flops. The shift register will subsequently recirculate the single bit stored within.

The ring counter can also be used as a sequencer by simply connecting the output pulses from the flip-flops to the logic circuits which the sequence is to be controlled. The timing interval of the shift registers is precisely controlled by a fixed-frequency clock, which permits very tight control of the external logic circuits. Additionally, it is not necessary to use all of the pulses derived from the shift register. As more circuits need to be controlled or sequenced, additional flip-flops can be added to the shift registers to produce them.

Counters

A shift register can also be used as a counter when connected as a ring counter. For certain operations, they may replace binary counters. As clock pulses are applied to the four-bit ring counter, the four distinct states it can assume repeat or recycle.

The Johnson counter shown in Fig. 6-39 is a very popular type of shift register counter. A five-bit circuit is often used although any number of flip-flops may be cascaded to form the Johnson counter. Note how the output of the last flip-flop is connected back to the input of the first flip-flop in order to recirculate the data. As can be seen, the main difference between the Johnson counter and the ring counter is that the normal output of the last flip-flop is connected to the K input of the first flip-flop while the complement output of the last flip-flop is connected to the J input of the first flip-flop. Because of this, the Johnson counter is sometimes

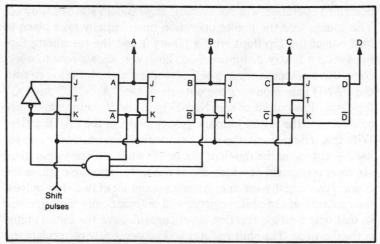

Fig. 6-38. Self-correcting ring counter using shift registers.

226

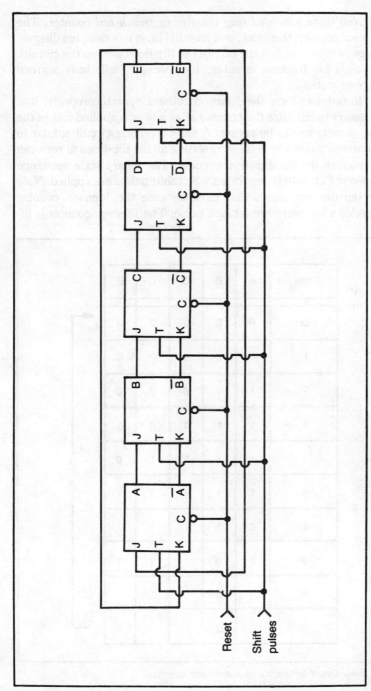

Fig. 6-39. A shift register used as a Johnson counter.

referred to as a *twisted ring* counter or *switch tail* counter. The Johnson counter, therefore, will have 2N or, in this case, ten discrete states (where N equals the number of flip-flops used in the circuit). An eight-bit Johnson counter, for example, will have sixteen discrete states.

In order to have the Johnson counter operate properly, it is necessary to initialize the counter after power is applied just as the ring counter has to be preset. A self-correcting circuit similar to that described in Fig. 6-38 or resetting all the flip-flops to zero can accomplish the initialization process. The binary state sequence shown in Fig. 6-40 is generated when shift pulses are applied. Note the ten discrete states that exist because the Johnson counter recycles after every tenth clock pulse. The Johnson counter is of-

State	A	B	C	D	E
0	0	0	0	0	0
1	1	0	0	0	0
2	1	1	0	0	0
3	1	1	1	0	0
4	1	1	1	1	0
5	1	1	1	1	1
6	0	1	1	1	1
7	0	0	1	1	1
8	0	0	0	1	1
9	0	0	0	0	1

Recycle

Fig. 6-40. Count sequence of a Johnson counter.

228

ten used as a divide-by-ten frequency scaler since it has ten individual states. Although other counting operations can often be done with the Johnson counter, many of them are difficult and inconvenient to implement because of the nonweighted codes generated by the counter.

MOS SHIFT REGISTERS

Bipolar integrated circuits, such as TTL or ECL, are used in applications requiring shift registers with limited bit capacity. These registers are generally used to store only a single binary word. Depending upon the application, these words can be as short as four bits or as long as thirty-two bits. Additional flip-flops, or MSI shift registers, can be cascaded to form memories to store multiple binary words. Such shift register memories, however, become very large and expensive when implemented with standard bipolar or CMOS integrated circuits. MOS shift registers, therefore, can be of greater value in these applications.

For memory applications, MOS shift registers with literally thousands of storage elements are commonly available. To store 128 eight-bit binary words, for example, a shift register with a capacity of $8 \times 128 = 1024$ bits would be required. MOS shift registers this large are very practical and commonly used in any application requiring the temporary storage of a large volume of binary data. Since parallel loading and reading out of data are not generally performed with MOS shift registers, most MOS LSI shift registers are of the serial in/serial out variety.

The two basic types of MOS shift registers are static and dynamic. A static shift register is one in which no loss of data will occur when the clock signal is stopped. This is the type of shift register discussed previously in this chapter. In other words, the clock signals are applied to the circuit only to shift data in or out of the register. When the clock pulses are stopped, however, the data is retained intact within the storage elements of the shift register.

In the dynamic type of MOS shift register, the data stored within the elements will be lost if the clock is halted for any reason. The clock pulses must run continuously if data is to be retained, due to the intrinsic characteristics of this device. In order to prevent a loss, therefore, data must be continuously recirculated or *refreshed*. From a standpoint of convenience and operation, the static shift register is generally more desirable. Since, however, static

MOS shift registers are more complex and consume more power, dynamic shift registers offer the advantage of being smaller in size, operate much faster, and consume significantly less power. Most MOS shift registers are completely compatible with TTL and CMOS circuits and, therefore, require no special interfacing.

DYNAMIC MOS SHIFT REGISTERS

Whether a MOS shift register is static or dynamic, the basic storage element used is the inherent capacitance which exists between the gate and the source of the MOSFET transistor. Even though this capacitance is very small (on the order of only a few tenths of a picofarad), the high impedance of the MOSFET allows a charge voltage to be placed on this capacitance and retained for a period of time. The impedance between the gate and the source of an enhancement mode MOSFET is at least 10^{15} ohms—essentially an open circuit. If a voltage is applied between the gate and the source of a MOSFET, the gate capacitance will charge and retain a voltage until the charge eventually leaks off through the very high impedance between the source and the gate. This discharge time can be as long as one millisecond in high quality MOSFETs.

A MOSFET inverter is a storage element used in a MOS shift register, with the data stored in the input capacitance of the inverter. Figure 6-41 illustrates how two MOSFET inverters, I1 and I2, are combined with MOSFET transmission gates, Q1 and Q2, to form a single-bit storage element. The input data is applied to inverter I1 via transmission gate Q1, which is used only as an on/off

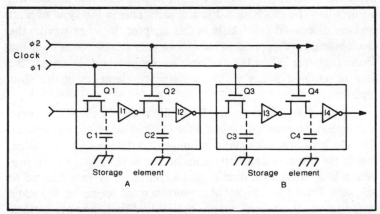

Fig. 6-41. MOS dynamic shift register.

230

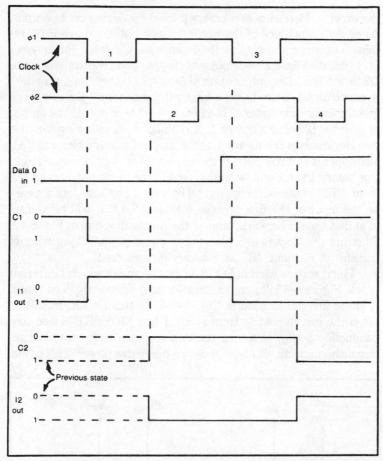

Fig. 6-42. Timing diagram of clock and *data* of a MOS dynamic shift register.

switch to connect and disconnect the input to capacitor, C1. The output of inverter I1 is fed to the input of inverter I2 via transmission gate, Q2, which is also used as an on/off switch. The transmission gate switching is controlled by two clock oscillators, *phase 1* and *phase 2*. As can be seen from Fig. 6-42, when phase 1 clock is on, phase 2 clock is off and vice-versa.

Assume the use of p-channel MOS circuits where 0 volts equals binary 0, and binary 1 is some negative voltage level. The data to be stored into storage element "A," is applied to the data input line. If a binary 1 input is applied, when clock pulse 1 occurs, transmission gate Q1 will conduct. This causes capacitor C1 to charge to the input voltage. Applying a binary 1 input voltage to the inverter I1 results in a binary 0 level appearing on its output. After the occurrence of the phase 1 clock pulse, capacitor C1 retains its charge and acts as the input source voltage for inverter I1. Next, the phase 2 clock pulse occurs, causing transmission gate Q2 to conduct. The output state of inverter I1, therefore, transfers to capacitor C2. Since this is a binary 0, capacitor C2 has no charge and the input to inverter I2 is a binary 0. This results in the output of inverter I2 being a binary 1. As can be seen, following the first two clock pulses the binary 1 at the input of storage element "A" also appears at its output. On the next cycle of the two-phase clock, this binary 1 value will be transferred to the following storage element, "B," of the shift register. Of course, if any new data appears on the input of the first storage element, "A," it will be shifted in at that time. The waveforms of the timing diagram of Fig. 6-42, illustrate the storage of a binary 1 in element "A" along with its transfer to element "B" as a binary 0 is entered.

The inverters used in Fig. 6-41 can be any of several different types. Figure 6-43 illustrates the two most commonly used types. A static inverter is used in Fig. 6-43A. In this circuit, transistor Q2 is the inverter while transistor Q1 is a MOSFET biased into conduction acting as a load resistance. Since transistor Q1 continuously conducts, this type of device dissipates power. This power

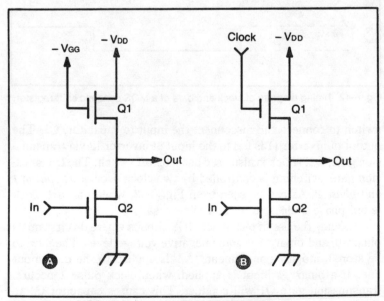

Fig. 6-43. (A) MOS static inverter. (B) MOS clocked inverter.

232

dissipation means that long MOS shift registers can produce a significant amount of heat. Figure 6-43B, on the other hand, shows an inverter circuit using a clocked load device. In this circuit, transistor Q2 is the inverter element while transistor, Q1, is the load element. The only time transistor, Q1, conducts is while a clock pulse is applied. When such an inverter is used in the dynamic shift register circuit shown in Fig. 6-41, the load element is clocked during the phase 1 or phase 2 along with the associated output transmission gate. The load element in inverter I1, for example, would be clocked at phase 2 time while the load element in inverter I2 would be clocked at phase 1 time. This arrangement, therefore, greatly reduces the power dissipation of the device.

The clock must run continuously and the data must be continually recirculated from output to input in order to keep the data from being lost during the shifting process. The mode of operation is selected at the input of the shift register via the write/recirculate logic. If the clock pulses ever cease, the data stored as charges on the capacitances in the circuits will leak off and be lost. Depending upon the circuitry used, this loss of data can occur in as little as a few hundred microseconds. Most typical dynamic MOS shift registers, therefore, use a minimum clock rate of 5 kHz although versions with minimum clock rates of 100 Hz range are also available.

STATIC MOS SHIFT REGISTERS

In some digital systems it is desirable to stop the clock without losing data. For these applications, static MOS shift registers in which data is retained without the clock signal are available. With them, it is not necessary to continuously recirculate the data in order to retain it.

Figure 6-44 shows a typical storage element for a static MOS shift register. For temporary data storage it uses the gate capacity of a MOSFET inverter, with two such inverters used as the storage element. One inverter is transistor Q3, while the associated load element is transistor Q2. The other inverter is transistor Q7, with its load being transistor Q6. These two inverters are cross-coupled through transmission gates, transistors Q4 and Q5. A latch type flip-flop is formed when transistors Q4 and Q5 conduct. Transistor Q1 is used as a transmission gate to load data into the storage element.

Assume that p-channel devices and negative logic are used in

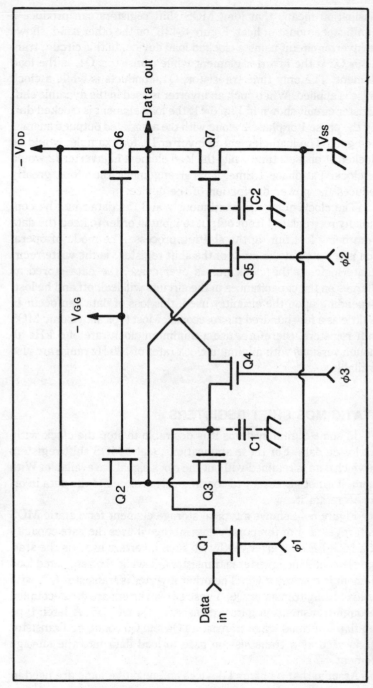

Fig. 6-44. MOS single-bit storage element for a static shift register.

the following explanation of the operation of this circuit. A three-phase clock is required to properly operate this shift register. Figure 6-45 shows these three clock signals. Note that the phase-3 clock is merely a delayed replica of the phase-2 clock. In some static MOS shift registers, the phase-3 and sometimes the phase-2 clock signal, as well, are generated right on the chip itself, requiring only a single- or two-phase external clock for operation.

To load data into the circuit, the desired bit is applied to the data input line. Transmission gate, Q1, conducts when the phase-1 clock pulses. This causes the gate capacitance of transistor Q3 to charge to the proper state. If a binary 1 is applied, for example, the data input, C1, will assume a negative charge. This negative charge is then applied to inverter Q3 which conducts and forces the drain low, which represents a binary 0.

Next, the phase-2 clock generates a pulse and causes transistor Q5 to conduct, thereby transferring the state of transistor Q3 to capacitor C2. The output of inverter, Q7, is then a negative-level binary 1. The phase-3 clock signal pulse then causes transistor Q4 to conduct. This, in turn, applies the negative signal back to the gate of transistor Q3 keeping it turned on. The data is latched at this time. The shift register will remain in this state until the state of the input is changed and the next clocking cycle has been completed.

CLOCKS AND ONE-SHOTS

A clock circuit is used to drive most sequential logic circuits. The clock is a periodic signal which causes logic circuits to be stepped, or incremented, from one state to another. Sequential logic circuits use clock signals to step them through their normal operating states.

A clock oscillator generates the clock signal pulses. This oscillator generates rectangular output pulses of specific frequency, amplitude, and duty cycle. An astable multivibrator is one of the most commonly-used clock oscillators, because it can be easily constructed with discrete components or logic gates.

The *one-shot* is another example of a widely-used sequential triggering device. The one-shot is a monostable multivibrator which produces an output pulse of fixed duration, controlled by external components, each time it receives an input trigger pulse. A wide variety of sequential circuits can be implemented by cascading one-shot circuits.

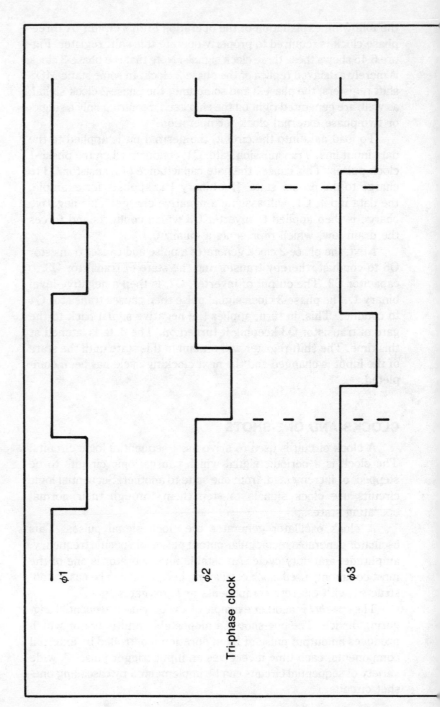

$\phi1$

$\phi2$

Tri-phase clock

$\phi3$

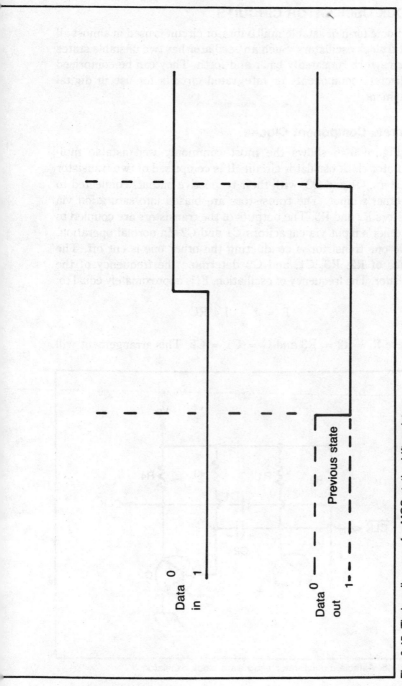

Fig. 6-45. Timing diagram of a MOS static shift register.

CLOCK OSCILLATOR CIRCUITS

Some form of astable multivibrator circuit is used in almost all digital clock oscillators. Such an oscillator has two unstable states which switch repeatedly back and forth. They can be comprised of discrete components or integrated circuits for use in digital equipment.

Discrete Component Clocks

Figure 6-46 shows the most commonly-used astable multivibrator clock oscillator circuit. It is comprised of two transistor inverters, Q1 and Q2, with their respective outputs connected to the other's input. The transistors are biased into saturation via resistors R2 and R3. The outputs of the transistors are coupled to the other's input via capacitors C1 and C2. In normal operation, while one transistor is conducting the other one is cut off. The values of R2, R3, C1, and C2 determine the frequency of the oscillator. The frequency of oscillation, F, is approximately equal to:

$$F = 1 \div 1.4 \ RC$$

Where $R = R2 = R3$ and $C = C1 = C2$. This arrangement will

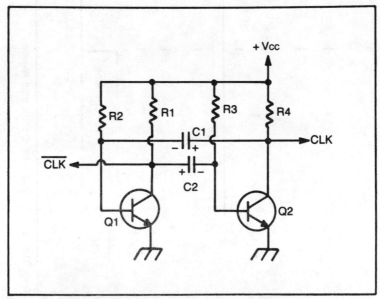

Fig. 6-46. Astable multivibrator used as a clock oscillator.

238

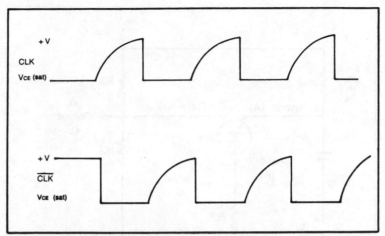

Fig. 6-47. Timing diagram of an astable multivibrator.

produce a 50% duty cycle output square wave. For a duty cycle other than 50%, capacitors of unequal values can be substituted.

The circuit output is illustrated in Fig. 6-47. The complementary outputs are taken directly from the collectors of the transistors. The outputs switch between the supply voltage, VCC, and the VCE (sat) of each transistor. This clock oscillator circuit can directly drive most standard logic families such as TTL and CMOS. Interface circuitry may be required to drive other types of logic, however.

Figure 6-48A shows another form of clock circuit known as the relaxation oscillator. This circuit incorporates a single *programmable unijunction transistor* (PUT). The PUT is a four-layer semiconductor device comprised of a cathode (K), anode (A), and gate (G). It is used as a threshold-sensitive switching device. The PUT will conduct current between its gate and cathode when its anode is properly biased. It will not normally conduct if the anode potential is equal to or less than the gate voltage. The voltage at the gate is fixed by resistors R3 and R4. In most applications, R3 = R4 to make the gate voltage equal to one-half the supply voltage, + V. In operation, capacitor C, charges via resistor R1. As soon as this charge is equal to 0.7 volt more positive than the gate voltage, the PUT will conduct current between the gate and cathode. The PUT becomes a very low resistance during conduction and capacitor C discharges via resistor R2. The capacitor discharges quickly since the value of resistor R2 is low. During the discharge of the capacitor, a voltage is formed across resistor R2 which is used for the output of the oscillator. Figure 6-48B shows the waveforms of this

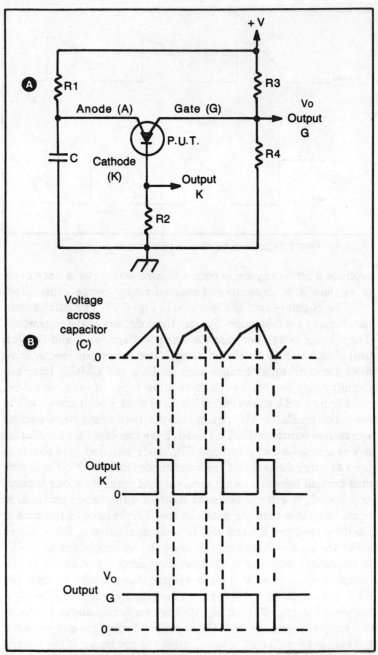

Fig. 6-48. (A) A programmed-unijunction transistor (PUT) clock oscillator. (B) PUT oscillator timing diagram.

circuit. The output pulse duration produced by this circuit is rather narrow by design because of the rapid discharge time of capacitor C when the PUT conducts. The frequency of oscillation of this circuit is a function of the RC time constant (R1 • C) and the voltage at the gate of the PUT.

The operation of the PUT can also be simulated by using complementary bipolar transistors configured as shown in Fig. 6-49. Transistors Q1 and Q2 are connected to form a switch which is controlled by the charging of capacitor C and the voltage divider, R2/R3. This circuit operates identically to the PUT circuit just described.

IC Clock Circuits

Integrated circuit gates or inverters can be used to provide the clock waveforms described in Fig. 6-47. An astable circuit using TTL inverter circuits is shown in Fig. 6-50A. It is practically identical in operation to the circuit described in Fig. 6-46. The frequency of oscillation is a function of the values of resistance and capacitance of the circuit components. In this circuit, the oscillation frequency is approximately equal to:

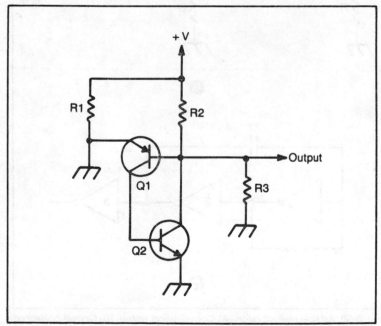

Fig. 6-49. Npn-pnp equivalent of the PUT astable clock oscillator.

241

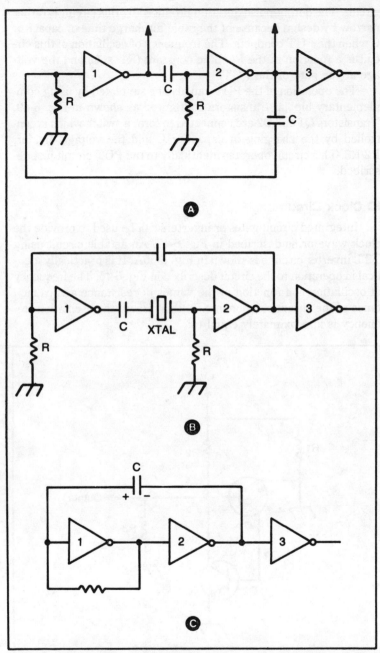

Fig. 6-50. Astable multivibrator: (A) Conventional circuit. (B) Crystal-controlled astable multivibrator. (C) Simplified astable multivibrator.

$$F = 1 \div 2RC$$

where F is expressed in kilohertz, R in ohms, and C in microfarads. The output of this circuit will be a square wave with a 50% duty cycle.

Figure 6-50B is a modification of the astable multivibrator which includes a frequency-determining quartz crystal. The values of R and C are chosen to oscillate close to the desired frequency, but the circuit will actually oscillate at the crystal frequency. This circuit is desirable when a very stable and accurate clock frequency must be used.

Finally, another version of an astable multivibrator circuit is shown in Fig. 6-50C. In this circuit, only a single RC network is employed. Resistor R is used to bias inverter 1 near its linear region. When standard TTL inverters or OR gates are used, the value of resistor R is very critical and should be between 150 and 220 ohms.

Operation of this type of astable multivibrator is somewhat different than the ones previously discussed. When the output of inverter 2 goes low, it is coupled to the input of inverter 1 via capacitor C. This, in turn, forces the output of inverter 1 to go high. This high input to inverter 2 causes its output to remain low. Capacitor C charges through resistor R at this time, providing a signal at the output of inverter 1. When the voltage at the input of inverter 1 reaches approximately 1.5 volts, the output of inverter 1 will go low and thereby force the output of inverter 2 to go high. The high output from inverter 2, summed with the charge on capacitor C ensures a high level to the input of inverter 1 keeping its output low. Now, capacitor C begins to discharge via resistor R until its voltage becomes low enough to switch the output of inverter 1 high causing the output of inverter 2 to go low. This cycle will repeat at a frequency approximately equal to:

$$F = RC \div 3$$

In all the circuits shown in Fig. 6-50, inverter 3 is used to isolate the output load from the frequency determining components and act as a buffer.

Two-Phase Clocks

So far in this section all the circuits discussed have been single-phase clocks. Bipolar logic circuits and CMOS usually operate from a single-phase clock. For most MOS integrated circuits, however, a two-phase clock is required. Although there are many different methods of generating a two-phase clock, the most common is illustrated in Fig. 6-51. A synchronous two-bit binary counter is implemented with two TTL J-K flip-flops. The count sequence, therefore, is: 00, 01, 10, and 11. Gates 1 and 2 are used to detect the AB and $\overline{AB}$ states of the counter which, in turn, drive the transistors, Q1 and Q2. These transistors form the interface circuitry for developing the proper logic levels for operating pMOS integrated circuits. Both phases of the clock switch between + VEE and – VCC, with these levels being typically + 5 and – 5 volts.

When both flip-flops are set, inverter 3's output goes high. Transistor Q1 cuts off and phase 2 output becomes – VCC. When the output of inverter 3 goes low, transistor Q1 conducts and the output becomes + VEE. The operation of transistor Q2 is similar, but occurs at a distinctly different offset time, as defined by the operation of the two J-K flip-flops. The waveforms of the two-phase clock are shown in the timing diagram of Fig. 6-52.

ONE-SHOT MULTIVIBRATORS

The one-shot multivibrator generates a rectangular output pulse of a specific duration each time it receives an input trigger pulse. By varying the value of external circuit components, the output pulse duration can be adjusted. A variety of sequential logic circuits can be implemented by merely cascading these circuits.

Discrete Component One Shot

A one shot multivibrator circuit is shown in Fig. 6-53. This circuit has two states: 1. A stable state in which transistor Q2 conducts and transistor Q1 is cut off; and 2. An unstable state in which transistor Q1 conducts and transistor Q2 is cut off. When it is not being triggered, the circuit normally exists in its stable state. When the circuit receives a trigger pulse, however, the unstable state is initiated and remains there for a period of time determined by the values of C1 and R2.

To trigger the circuit into its unstable state, the application of an input pulse is required. The input pulse is differentiated by the C2 and R5 network. The sharp input pulses are then applied to diode D1 which permits only the negative-going pulses to be coupled to the base of transistor Q2. These negative pulses reverse-bias

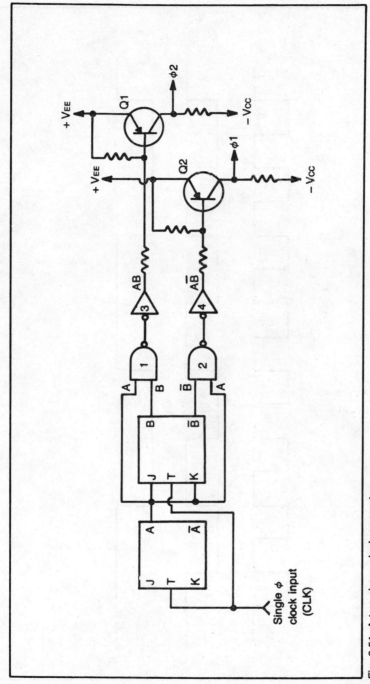

Fig. 6-51. A two-phase clock generator.

245

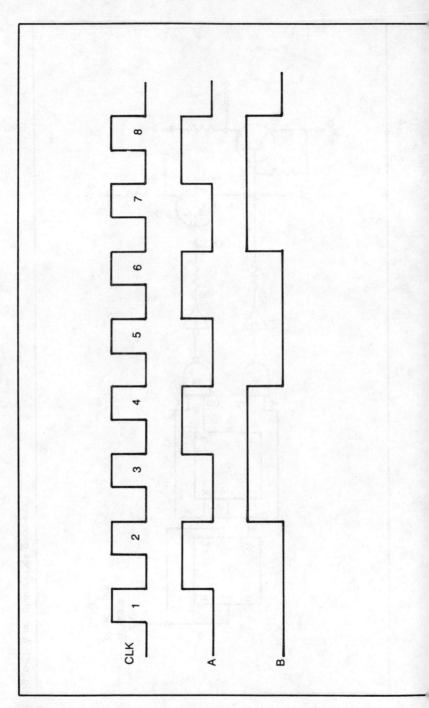

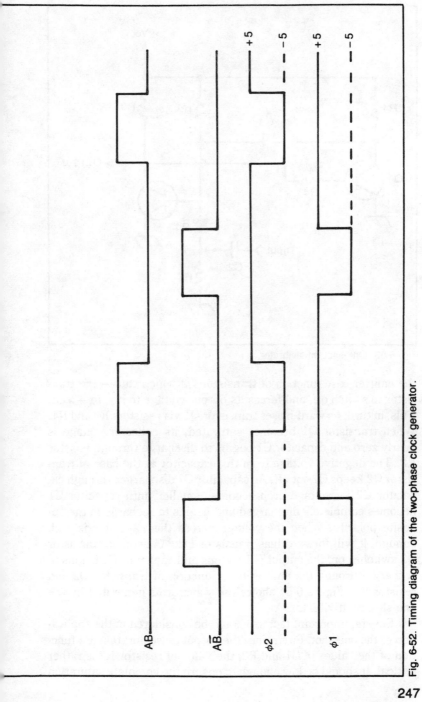

Fig. 6-52. Timing diagram of the two-phase clock generator.

247

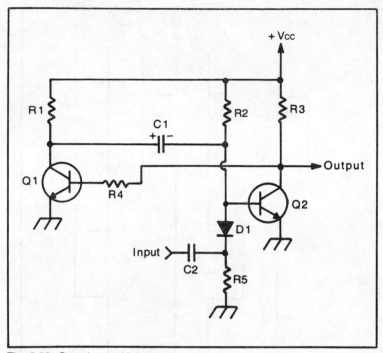

Fig. 6-53. One-shot multivibrator.

the emitter-base junction of transistor Q2 which causes the transistor to switch off, and forces its output voltage to rise to + Vcc. This, in turn, forward-biases transistor Q1 via resistors R3 and R4. When transistor Q1 becomes saturated, its collector voltage is nearly zero and capacitor C1 begins to discharge through resistor R2. The negative voltage from this capacitor at the base of transistor Q2 keeps Q2 cut off. As capacitor C1 discharges through capacitor C2 its voltage drop becomes smaller until capacitor C1 becomes completely discharged and begins to recharge in the opposite polarity. When the voltage across this capacitor is high enough, it will forward bias transistor Q2. As soon as transistor Q2 switches on, the output pulse stops and capacitor C1 begins to recharge through the emitter-base junction of transistor Q2 and resistor R1. Figure 6-54 shows the waveforms generated by the one-shot multivibrator.

Several important factors should be considered in the application of the one-shot. First, since the output pulse duration is a function of the values of C1 and R2, the value of resistor R2 is rather critical. It should be low enough to ensure the complete saturation

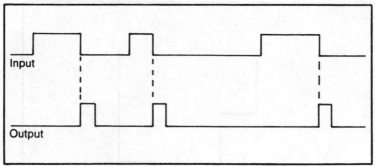

Fig. 6-54. Timing diagram of a one-shot multivibrator.

of transistor Q2 during its normal operation. The value of capacitor C1 however, can be almost anything. The time duration of the output pulse of the one-shot can be approximately expressed as:

$$T = 0.69 \; R2 \bullet C1$$

The output pulse can be adjusted anywhere from nanoseconds to seconds in most practical one-shot multivibrator circuits.

The duty cycle of the monostable multivibrator is generally limited to a maximum of around 90%. Unreliable operation will result if this limit is exceeded, because sufficient time must be provided for the circuit to recover between input pulses. There is no lower limit on the duty cycle, however, and duty cycles of only a few percent can be obtained.

Duty Cycle. Duty cycle is defined as the ratio of the output pulse length to the total length of time of the trigger input pulse expressed in terms of a percent:

$$\text{Duty Cycle} = (T \div P) \bullet 100 \text{ percent}$$

where T is the output pulse duration in seconds and P is the period of the input pulse in seconds. For example, if an output pulse duration is five milliseconds with an input frequency of 50 Hz, the input period is, therefore, 1/50 = .02 seconds = 20 milliseconds. To calculate the duty cycle:

$$\text{Duty Cycle} = 5/20 \times 100 \text{ percent} = 25\%$$

Figure 6-55 illustrates the waveforms generated by the one-shot in the above example.

249

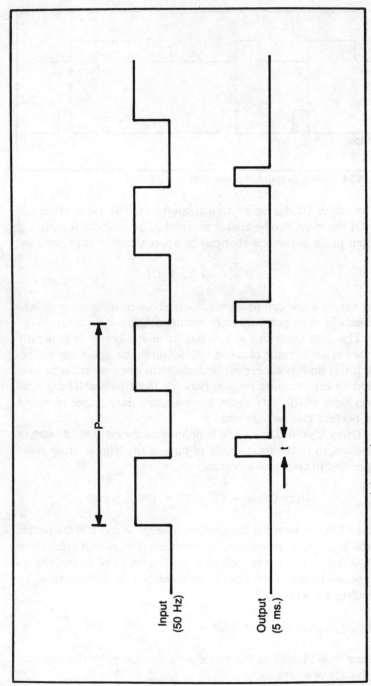

Fig. 6-55. Illustration of the concept of duty cycle.

Integrated Circuit One Shots

Most one-shot circuits used today are in integrated circuit form. Their operation is exactly the same as their discrete component counterparts.

The logic symbol used to represent the IC one-shot is shown in Fig. 6-56. The one-shot may be triggered by any of its three inputs. If the *B* input is held high, the one-shot can be triggered by the trailing edge of either A1 or A2 input pulse. Both the normal and complementary outputs are available.

The one-shot can also be triggered by the *B* input as long as the other inputs, *A1* and *A2*, are held low. When the *B* input is used to trigger the one shot, the *leading* edge of the input pulse triggers the one-shot. The *B* input, however, is generally used to either inhibit or enable the *A1* and *A2* inputs. The one-shot also incorporates an asynchronous reset line. The output pulse can immediately be terminated during a timing pulse by bringing this line low. When the one-shot is not triggered, the normal output, Q, is binary 0 while its complement is binary 1. When a trigger pulse is received, the one-shot enters its unstable state where output, Q,

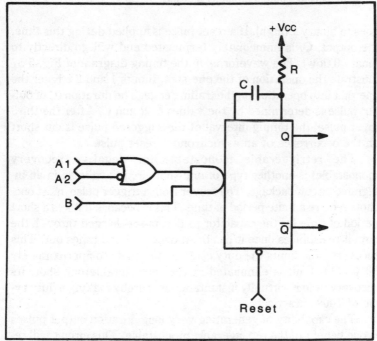

Fig. 6-56. Integrated circuit one-shot multivibrator.

251

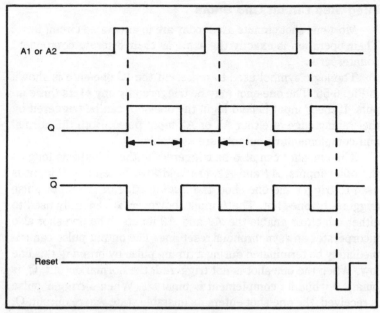

Fig. 6-57. Timing diagram of the IC one-shot.

goes to binary 1 (high). If a reset pulse is applied during this time, the output, Q, is immediately terminated and will go directly to binary 0 (low). The waveforms in the timing diagram of Fig. 6-57 illustrate the operation of the one-shot. Inputs 1 and 2 trigger the one shot into operation on the trailing edge. The duration (t) of output pulse is determined by the values of R and C. After the third input pulse, the timing interval of the triggered pulse is cut short on the occurrence of an asynchronous reset pulse.

The retriggerable monostable (or negative recovery monostable) is another type of one-shot circuit available in an integrated circuit package. To recover from a trigger pulse, most one-shots require a finite period of time. This is because it takes a short period of time for the capacitor to become recharged through the circuit resistances once it has been triggered and times out. This recovery time limits the duty cycle of one-shots to approximately 90%. This limit is eliminated in the retriggerable one shot. Its recovery time is virtually instantaneous thereby making a duty cycle of 100% practical.

The capability of generating very long duration output pulses is one benefit of the retriggerable monostable. This circuit will remain in the triggered state for a very long period by adjusting the

252

external resistor and capacitor values to provide an output pulse of longer duration than the interval between input pulses. The waveforms in the timing diagram of Fig. 6-58 illustrate this effect. Initially, the one-shot is in its normal, stable state. The monostable is triggered, however, on the trailing edge of pulse 1. Input pulse 2 occurs before the retriggerable can complete its output pulse and, therefore, the duration of a new pulse is begun. In this example since no other pulse occurs after pulse 2, the one-shot is finally allowed to complete its output pulse (t) and times itself out.

The retriggerable one-shot can also be used as a missing pulse detector. The one-shot can be made to remain triggered during a sequence of input pulses by making the pulse width of the multivibrator slightly longer than the period of an input pulse. If, therefore, one of the input pulses should be lost or malfunction, the one-shot will time out and indicate the missing pulse.

APPLICATIONS OF ONE-SHOTS

Many sequential operations can be quickly and easily implemented thanks to the flexibility of the integrated circuit one-shot. The ability of varying the output pulse width by changing the values of only a few external components, coupled with its retrigger and reset features make the one-shot a versatile component. The nature of the one-shot makes it a desirable selection for pulse generation, timing, and sequencing. To generate a specific pulse width, for example, all that is needed is to connect an appropriate resistor and capacitor to a one-shot integrated circuit.

Figure 6-59 shows how to connect a one-shot to generate a se-

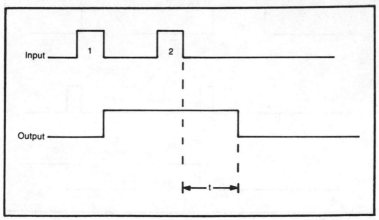

Fig. 6-58. Timing diagram of a retriggerable monostable multivibrator.

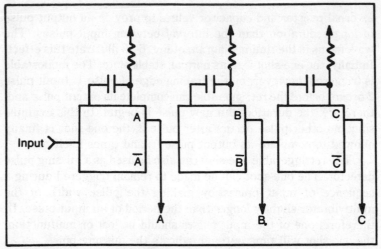

Fig. 6-59. One-shot pulse sequence generator.

quence of timing pulses. In this illustration, the one-shots, labeled "A," "B" and "C," trigger one another in sequence. The waveforms for this circuit are shown in the timing diagram of Fig. 6-60. One-shot "A" is triggered upon application of an input pulse

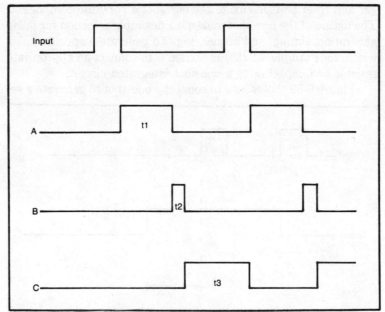

Fig. 6-60. Timing diagram of a one-shot pulse generator.

254

input rise to initiate the trigger operation. The waveforms of timing diagram 6-?? b-?? exhibits the delay inherent if used the pulse without one-shot C can be initiated trailing age of the input pulse.

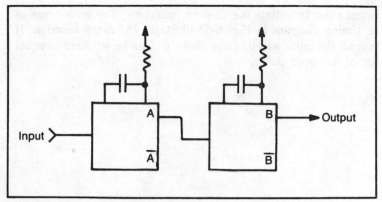

Fig. 6-61. Pulse delay using one-shots.

which generates pulse width, t1. One-shot "B" is triggered following the trailing edge of pulse, t1, which generates pulse, t2. Finally, one shot "C" is triggered by the trailing edge of pulse, t2, and generates pulse, t3. This type of "chain" of one-shots provides a simple method of sequencing digital circuits.

Implementing a fixed delay is another useful application of the one shot. In some applications, it is necessary to purposely delay the operation of a particular portion of a circuit. This is essentially a timing operation and a one-shot can provide this timing delay. Figure 6-61 shows how the input signal to be delayed is applied to the one-shot "A." One-shot "A" provides the necessary time delay which, subsequently, triggers one-shot "B" and produces the

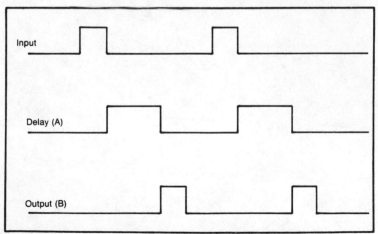

Fig. 6-62. Timing diagram of a one-shot pulse delay circuit.

255

output pulse to initiate the desired operation. The waveforms of the timing diagram in Fig. 6-62 illustrate the delay function. If desired, the pulse width of one-shot "B" can be adjusted to equal that of the input pulse.

Chapter 7

Combinational Logic Circuits

C OMBINATIONAL LOGIC CIRCUITS ARE DIGITAL CIRCUITS COM-
prised of combinations of gates and inverters. The states of
the inputs, the types of gates used, and how they are configured
determine the output. There are many different ways to configure
(or interconnect) logic gates to implement any unique binary function with combinational circuits.

Certain combinational circuits regularly reoccur in digital electronics. Most digital equipment, therefore, can be implemented with
only a few basic types. These circuits, called *functional logic circuits*, include decoders, encoders, multiplexers, demultiplexers,
comparators, and code converters.

DECODERS

The decoder is one of the most frequently used combinational
logic circuit. It is a circuit designed to detect the existence of a
specific binary number or word. The decoder's input is a parallel
binary word, and its output signal indicates either the presence or
absence of a specific number or word.

The basic decoder circuit is the AND gate. The output of the
AND gate is binary 1 only when *all* of its inputs are also binary
1. The presence of any binary number, however, can be detected
with the AND gate by properly interfacing its inputs to the source
data to be detected.

Figure 7-1A shows how to configure a two-input AND gate to detect the presence of the binary number 01. The 2-bit number to be detected is *A* and *B*, with *B* being the LSB. When *A* is 0 and *B* is 1, both inputs to the AND gate will be high and the output, C, will also be high (binary 1) which indicates the presence of the desired number. The decoder will ignore any other combination of inputs by producing a binary 0 output upon their presence on its inputs.

The performance of this circuit can be analyzed by examining

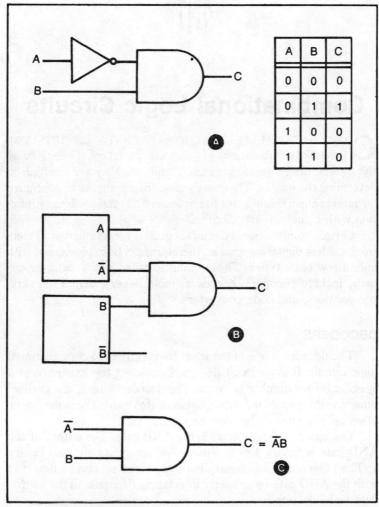

Fig. 7-1. Detecting binary 01 with two-input AND gate decoders.

258

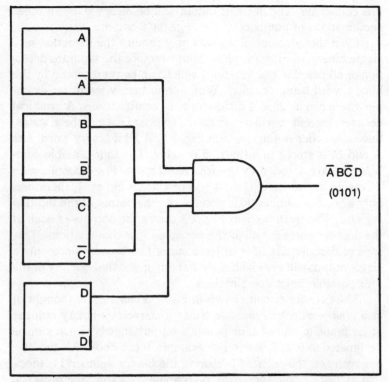

Fig. 7-2. Decoding binary 0101 with a four-input AND gate.

the truth table in Fig. 7-1A. The output, C, is binary 1 *only* when the input number is 01. The output is binary 0 for all other input combinations.

Figure 7-1B shows how the AND gate decoder is used when the input source comes from a flip-flop register. The inverter is not needed here, since both the normal and complementary outputs are available from the flip-flops. The AND gate input source is often omitted to simplify drawings of decoder circuits as illustrated in Fig. 7-1C. The gate input sources are designated only with the proper states which will provide the desired output.

The presence of any binary number, regardless of size, can be detected by using an AND gate. The number of bits in the binary word to be detected will determine the number of inputs required for the AND gate, however. Figure 7-2 illustrates how a four-input AND gate can detect the binary number $\overline{A}B\overline{C}D = 0101$. In this example, the output of the decoder gate will be binary 1 only when the number 0101 is present at the output of the register to which it is connected. The decoder output will be binary 0 for all other combinations of numbers at the register's output.

Even though some situations may require the detection of a single binary word, most applications require the separate detection of all possible combinations which can be represented by the binary word being decoded. With a 2-bit binary word, for example, there can be 2^2 = 4 different input combinations. A practical decoder, therefore, will detect the existence of each of these states. Such a decoder is illustrated in Fig. 7-3. A 2-bit binary word, bits A and B, is stored in a flip-flop register. The four possible combinations are decoded by the four AND gates. For example, gate 4 detects the 00 state. Gate 4 will produce a binary 1, therefore, only when the number 00 is detected on the output of the flip-flop register. The truth table in Fig. 7-3 shows the outputs of each of the decoder gates for all of the possible input combinations. This type of decoder circuit is called a *one-of-four decoder* since only a single output will ever be binary 1 at any given time for any of the four possible input combinations.

The decoder circuit shown in Fig. 7-3 can also be thought of as a *binary-to-decimal converter* since it converts a binary number at its input to one of four possible output signals which can be designated as 0, 1, 2, and 3. For example, if flip-flops "A" and "B" are both set, the register is storing the binary number 11_2 (decimal 3). Gate 1 will, therefore, be enabled indicating the presence of that particular number in the register. The output of gate 1 could then be used to control a device labeled with decimal 3.

BCD-to-Decimal Decoder

Binary-to-decimal conversion is one of the most common applications of decoder circuits. The BCD-to-decimal decoder is a widely-used type. The decoder's input is a parallel 4-bit number which represents the BCD digits 0000 through 1001. Ten AND gates are used to monitor the inputs and decode the ten possible output states, 0 through 9. Upon application of a BCD number to the input one of the ten output lines will go high, indicating the presence of that particular number.

Figure 7-4 shows a typical BCD-to-decimal decoder circuit. The 4-bit BCD number (ABCD) is applied to the inverters, which generate the normal and complement representations of the inputs to be applied to the decoder gates. For the decoding process, note how NAND gates are used as opposed to the AND gates previously discussed. The output from a NAND gate will be binary 0 when

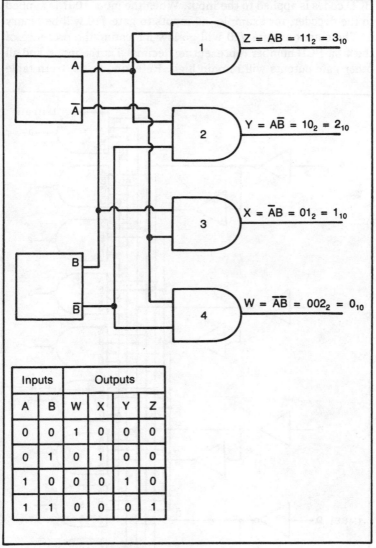

Inputs		Outputs			
A	B	W	X	Y	Z
0	0	1	0	0	0
0	1	0	1	0	0
1	0	0	0	1	0
1	1	0	0	0	1

Fig. 7-3. One-of-four decoder.

all of the inputs to it are binary 1. The output will be binary 1 for all other input combinations. This is why all of the outputs from the gates of this decoder are high (binary 1) except for the single one that represents a specific input number.

The truth table for the BCD-to-decimal decoder is shown in Table 7-1. The appropriate output will go low when one of the ten

BCD codes is applied to the input. When the input 1001 is applied to the decoder, for example, all inputs to gate #10 will be binary 1. The output of gate #10 will go low indicating the presence of the 4-bit BCD number representing decimal 9 at the input, and all other gate outputs will remain high. Referring to the truth table

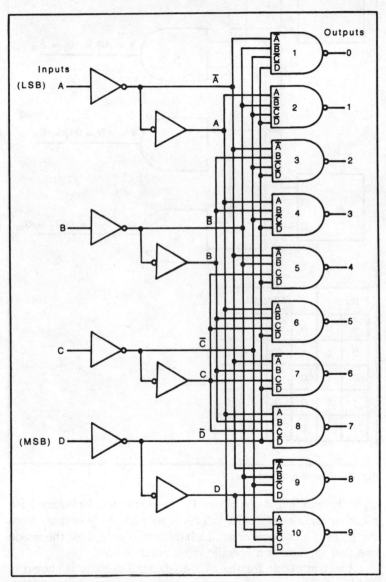

Fig. 7-4. BCD-to-decimal decoder.

262

in Table 7-1, note that if any one of the six invalid 4-bit code numbers is applied to the input of the decoder, all outputs remain high. Therefore, this BCD decoder does not recognize the 4-bit words which are not included in the standard 8421 BCD code.

Individual logic gates can readily be used to construct the decoder circuit shown in Fig. 7-4. A typical SSI logic gate provides two 4-input NAND gates in a single dual inline package. Five of these integrated circuits, therefore, would be required to decode the ten output states. Six of the necessary eight inverters could be obtained in a single package with a hex inverter such as a 7404 TTL IC. Since eight inverters are required, two hex inverters will be needed, and therefore, a total of seven integrated circuit packages will be required to implement the BCD-to-decimal decoder. Fortunately, however, modern technology has eliminated the necessity for constructing the decoder with SSI circuits. The entire BCD-to-decimal decoder is available on a single 16-pin DIP as shown in Fig. 7-4. It is considered to be an MSI circuit because of its complexity.

Octal and Hexadecimal Decoders

The one-of-eight (octal) and the one-of-sixteen (hexadecimal) decoders are two other widely-used circuits. The octal decoder accepts a parallel 3-bit word and decodes all eight output states, which represent the decimal numbers 0 through 7. By using only the A, B, and C inputs, the BCD decoder circuit shown in Fig. 7-4 can be used as an octal decoder. The D input would simply be wired to a binary 0 state and the outputs 8 and 9 from gates 9 and 10 would be ignored. A hex decoder is a one-of-sixteen decoder and all sixteen states represented by four input bits are recognized by this decoder.

A simplified block diagram is shown in Fig. 7-5. The decimal weights of the inputs and the decoded output equivalents are indicated within the block to identify its function.

BCD to Seven-Segment Decoder

The BCD-to-seven-segment decoder/driver is a special form of decoder circuit. It is a combinational logic circuit which accepts the standard 8421 BCD input code and generates a unique 7-bit output code, which may be used to drive the widely-used seven-segment decimal readout display. Although normally used to only display the decimal numbers 0 through 9, a seven-segment display

Table 7-1. Truth Table for BCD-to-Decimal Decoder.

No.	BCD input A	B	C	D	Decimal output 0	1	2	3	4	5	6	7	8	9
0	L	L	L	L	L	H	H	H	H	H	H	H	H	H
1	H	L	L	L	H	L	H	H	H	H	H	H	H	H
2	L	H	L	L	H	H	L	H	H	H	H	H	H	H
3	H	H	L	L	H	H	H	L	H	H	H	H	H	H
4	L	L	H	L	H	H	H	H	L	H	H	H	H	H
5	H	L	H	L	H	H	H	H	H	L	H	H	H	H
6	L	H	H	L	H	H	H	H	H	H	L	H	H	H
7	H	H	H	L	H	H	H	H	H	H	H	L	H	H
8	L	L	L	H	H	H	H	H	H	H	H	H	L	H
9	H	L	L	H	H	H	H	H	H	H	H	H	H	L
invalid	L	H	L	H	H	H	H	H	H	H	H	H	H	H
invalid	H	H	L	H	H	H	H	H	H	H	H	H	H	H
invalid	L	L	H	H	H	H	H	H	H	H	H	H	H	H
invalid	H	L	H	H	H	H	H	H	H	H	H	H	H	H
invalid	L	H	H	H	H	H	H	H	H	H	H	H	H	H
invalid	H	H	H	H	H	H	H	H	H	H	H	H	H	H

H = Binary 1
L = Binary 0

264

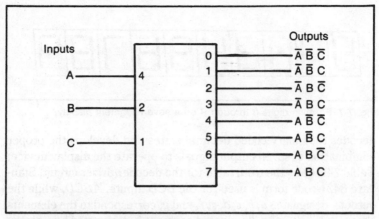

Fig. 7-5. Octal (one-of-eight) decoder.

may also be used to display a few special alpha (letter) characters, as well. Figure 7-6 shows the standard seven-segment display configuration. Figure 7-7 illustrates the standard representation of the ten digits indicated by the seven-segment display.

The segments of the display can be implemented with a number of different light-producing devices such as an incandescent filament, a light-emitting diode, a gas-discharge glow element; or with a transmissive or reflective liquid crystal, as illustrated in Fig. 7-8. By activating the proper segments, the numbers from 0 to 9, as well as some letters, can be displayed.

A BCD-to-seven-segment decoder/driver circuit is used to operate these display devices. It is an MSI logic circuit which

Fig. 7-6. Format of a seven-segment display.

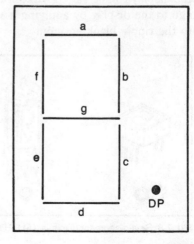

Fig. 7-7. Forming digits 0 through 9 on a seven-segment display.

decodes the binary-coded decimal states and develops the proper combination of seven output signals to operate the display device. Table 7-2 shows the truth table for the decoder/driver circuit. Standard 8421 code form is used for the BCD inputs, *ABCD*, while the outputs, designated *a*, *b*, *c*, *d*, *e*, *f*, and *g*, correspond to the elements shown in Fig. 7-7. An illuminated segment is designated by a binary 0 in the output columns of the truth table.

Figure 7-9 shows the logic diagram of one type of BCD-to-seven-segment decoder/driver. This circuit has a lamp test input, a blanking input, and a ripple blanking input as well as the four BCD inputs. All seven segments of the display are turned on to be sure that none has failed when the lamp test input is brought to binary 0. Conversely, when the blanking input is brought low, all segments are turned off. This feature can be used to automatically blank out leading zeros when a number of displays are grouped to read out a multi-digit number. For example, in an 8-digit display without leading zero suppression, the number 1694 would be displayed as 00001694. With leading zero suppression, however, only the digits 1694 will be illuminated. The intensity of the display can be varied without changing the power supply voltage to the display by applying a variable duty cycle pulse signal to the ripple blanking input.

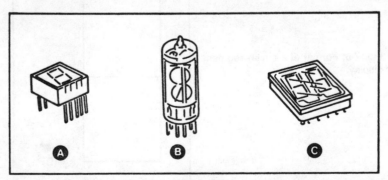

Fig. 7-8. Seven-segment displays: (A) LED. (B) Incandescent. (C) Gas-discharge.

266

Table 7-2. Truth Table for BCD-to-Seven-Segment Decoder.

Inputs					Segment outputs						
Decimal	A	B	C	D	a	b	c	d	e	f	g
0	0	0	0	0	0	0	0	0	0	0	1
1	0	0	0	1	1	0	0	1	1	1	1
2	0	0	1	0	0	0	1	0	0	1	0
3	0	0	1	1	0	0	0	0	1	1	0
4	0	1	0	0	1	0	0	1	1	0	0
5	0	1	0	1	0	1	0	0	1	0	0
6	0	1	1	0	1	1	0	0	0	0	0
7	0	1	1	1	0	0	0	1	1	1	1
8	1	0	0	0	0	0	0	0	0	0	0
9	1	0	0	1	0	0	0	1	1	0	0

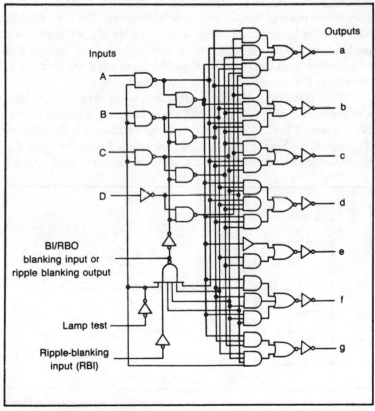

Fig. 7-9. BCD-to-seven-segment decoder/driver circuit.

267

Figure 7-10 shows a typical circuit configuration for a single segment of the decoder/driver. As its name implies, the circuit operates (or drives) the light-producing segment as well as decoding the BCD input states. The output is usually an open-collector saturating transistor. When the transistor in Fig. 7-10 conducts, the collector output goes low and current flows through the LED, thereby turning it on. A series dropping resistor is required to limit the current through the LED to a safe value and sets the intensity of light it produces.

ENCODERS

An encoder is a combinational logic circuit that accepts at least one input and generates a multi-bit binary output code. It can be thought of as being exactly opposite of a decoder.

A simple encoder circuit is illustrated in Fig. 7-11. The inputs are comprised of three pushbuttons, 1, 2, and 3. The circuit consists of two positive NAND/negative NOR gates. The outputs, AB, form a 2-bit binary code. The output of gate 2 goes high when pushbutton 1 is depressed. Both inputs to gate 1 are high at this time, which makes it output low. By depressing pushbutton 1, therefore, the output code 01 is generated.

When pushbutton 2 is depressed, the output of gate 1 goes high and the output of gate 2 is low. The output code is 10, therefore. Both gates, 1 and 2, go high when pushbutton 3 is depressed. Therefore, the binary code, 11, is generated. As can be seen, the binary code corresponding to the decimal digit assigned to each

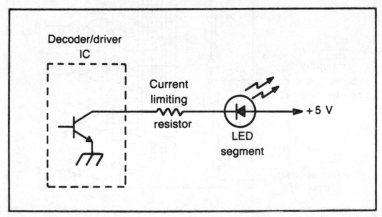

Fig. 7-10. Typical output circuit and external connections of seven-segment decoder/driver.

268

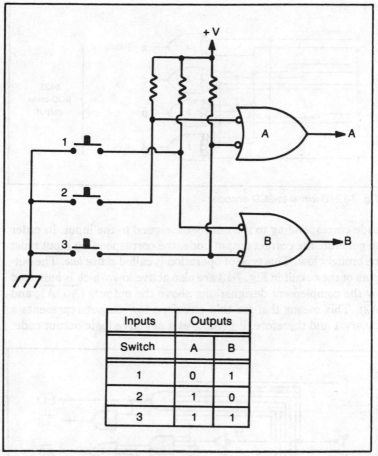

Inputs	Outputs	
Switch	A	B
1	0	1
2	1	0
3	1	1

Fig. 7-11. Simple encoder circuit.

input pushbutton is generated when the respective switch is depressed. The output code is 00 when all of the switches are open. The truth table in Fig. 7-11 summarizes the operation of this circuit.

Translating a decimal keyboard input signal into a binary or BCD code is a typical application for an encoder circuit. Figure 7-12 illustrates a decimal-to-BCD encoder circuit. When any of the input lines is brought low, the corresponding 4-bit BCD output code is generated. This circuit, like all encoders, generates a unique output code for each individual input.

Figure 7-13 shows a typical example of a contemporary binary encoder circuit. This is an 8-input TTL MSI priority encoder. The encoder accepts data from eight input lines and generates a binary

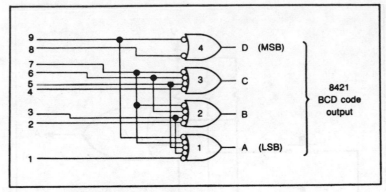

Fig. 7-12. Decimal-to-BCD encoder.

code corresponding to the number assigned to the input. In order to generate the correct output code, the corresponding input must be brought low. This type of operation is called *active low*. The outputs of the circuit in Fig. 7-13 are also active low which is indicated by the complement designations above the outputs ($\overline{A0}$, $\overline{A1}$, and $\overline{A2}$). This means that for this circuit, a low output represents a binary 1 and therefore, it generates a negative logic output code.

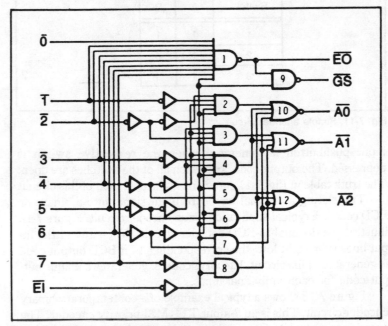

Fig. 7-13. Eight-input priority encoder circuit.

Table 7-3. Truth Table for 8-Input Priority Encoder.

Inputs									Outputs				
$\overline{EI}$	$\overline{0}$	$\overline{1}$	$\overline{2}$	$\overline{3}$	$\overline{4}$	$\overline{5}$	$\overline{6}$	$\overline{7}$	$\overline{GS}$	$\overline{A0}$	$\overline{A1}$	$\overline{A2}$	$\overline{EO}$
H	X	X	X	X	X	X	X	X	H	H	H	H	H
L	H	H	H	H	H	H	H	H	H	H	H	H	L
L	X	X	X	X	X	X	X	L	L	L	L	L	H
L	X	X	X	X	X	X	L	H	L	H	L	L	H
L	X	X	X	X	X	L	H	H	L	L	H	L	H
L	X	X	X	X	L	H	H	H	L	H	H	L	H
L	X	X	X	L	H	H	H	H	L	L	L	H	H
L	X	X	L	H	H	H	H	H	L	H	L	H	H
L	X	L	H	H	H	H	H	H	L	L	H	H	H
L	L	H	H	H	H	H	H	H	L	H	H	H	H

The unique feature of this particular circuit is that a priority is assigned to each input. Therefore, when two or more inputs are simultaneously low, only the input with the highest priority will be represented at the output. The inputs with the higher numerical value will have the highest priority in this case. For example, if the 3 and 6 inputs are both low, only the binary code representing input 6 will be generated at the output.

The enabling input is designated by $\overline{EI}$. When this input is high, the output of its associated inverter is low. This inhibits gates 1 through 8 and forces the there binary output lines high. Conversely, when the $\overline{EI}$ input is brought low, the output of its associated inverter goes high thereby enabling all of the gates.

All eight input lines are monitored by the 8-input NAND gate, 1. If any one line should go low, the output, $\overline{EO}$, goes high, which indicates that one or more of the inputs has been activated. The $\overline{GS}$ output also goes low. If all inputs are high (or open), the output line, $\overline{EO}$, is low. By implementing the $\overline{EI}$ input with the $\overline{EO}$ and $\overline{GS}$ outputs, several of these devices may be combined to encode any number of different input states. Table 7-3 is the truth table for the operation of this encoder circuit.

MULTIPLEXERS

A multiplexer is a circuit which selects and routes one of many input signals to a single output. In its simplest form, a single-pole, multi-position rotary switch can be thought of as a multiplexer. Figure 7-14 illustrates a 6-input multiplexer using a single pole 6-position rotary switch. In this example, any one of six inputs can be selected to the output line simply by rotating the switch to the desired position. Even though mechanical selector switches are widely used for a variety of multiplexing applications in electronic circuits, many operations require a multiplexer to operate at high speeds and be automatically selectable. Such multiplexers must be constructed with electronic components.

The two basic types of multiplexers are analog and digital. The simple selector switch used in the example of Fig. 7-14 will work with both types of signals. When electronic multiplexers are constructed, however, they are designed primarily for only one or the other type of signal. Electromechanical and bipolar or MOSFET switches are commonly used for analog applications. For digital applications involving binary signals multiplexers made up of logic gates are used.

The simplest form of digital multiplexer is illustrated in Fig. 7-15A. It has two inputs and a single output. Either one of the two inputs may be selected and routed to the output. The AND gates, 1 and 2, control the selection of inputs while the flip-flop controls the two AND gates to determine which input is permitted to pass through the OR gate, 3, to the output. When the flip-flop is set, the Q output will be high thereby enabling gate 1. Gate 2 will be inhibited by the complement output from the flip-flop. Data source 1, therefore, will be permitted to pass through gate 1 and through gate 3 to the output. Resetting the flip-flop will have the opposite effect and will enable gate 2 thereby passing data source #2 through gate 2 and to the output. This circuit is equivalent in operation to a mechanical single-pole double-throw switch, as shown in Fig. 7-15B.

Figure 7-16 shows an MSI functional circuit implementing the basic 2-input multiplexer. A multiplexer for two 4-bit words is comprised of four 2-input multiplexers. Word #1 has bits $A1$, $B1$, $C1$,

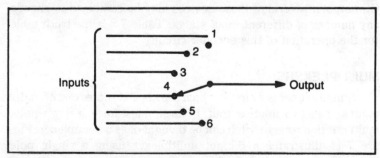

Fig. 7-14. Simple multiplexer using a rotary switch.

272

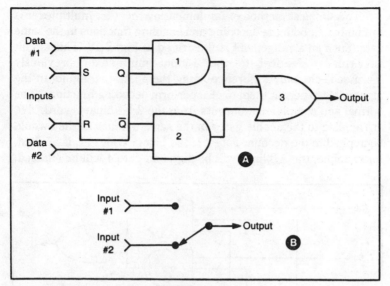

Fig. 7-15. Two-input digital multiplexer circuit.

and $D1$, while word #2 has bits $A2$, $B2$, $C2$, and $D2$. The circuit is controlled by the active low enable input, $\overline{E}$. When input, $\overline{E}$, is low, the circuit is enabled.

Which one of the two 4-bit words will appear at the output is specified by the select input, S, of the multiplexer. When the select input, S, is high, gates 2, 5, 8, and 11 will be enabled, permitting input word #1 to appear at the output. When the S input goes low, however, gates 1, 4, 7, and 10 will be enabled thereby permitting word #2 to be fed to the output.

Figure 7-17 shows a 4-input multiplexer circuit. Each input is applied to a NAND gate which is controlled by a 1-of-4 decoder. Gate 5 is used to OR the outputs of the NAND gates. With this arrangement, as with all multiplexers, only a single input can be enabled to pass through to the output at any given time. The 1-of-4 decoder circuit is used to select which one of the inputs will be fed to the output by the application of the 2-bit binary input word, AB, to the decoder's input. The decoder will recognize which one of the four possible input codes is being applied and subsequently enable the appropriate gate. For example, when the 2-bit input word is 11, the AB output line is high which will enable gate 4 thereby permitting input #4 to pass through to the output. Similarly, input code 01 will enable gate 2, input code 10 will enable gate 3 and input code 00 will enable gate 1.

The simplest method of implementing the 4-bit multiplexer is by combining both the decoding and enabling functions in the same gate. Such an arrangement is illustrated in Fig. 7-18. This circuit is virtually identical to the 4-input multiplexer previously discussed—the only difference being the additional inputs to the input gates to permit them to also perform decoding functions. The normal and complement outputs from the 2-bit binary word, *AB*, are applied to the enable gates in the same manner as they would be applied to the decoder gates. If the binary code, 11, is applied, for example, the AB lines will be high and gate 4 will be enabled.

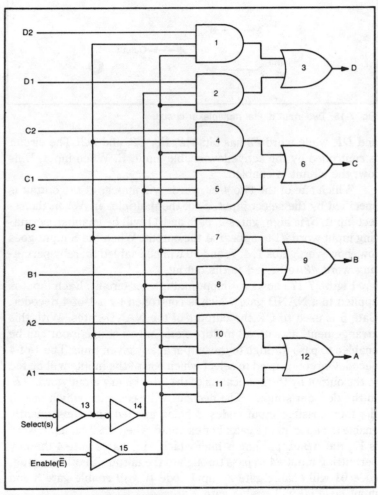

Fig. 7-16. Quad two-input multiplexer.

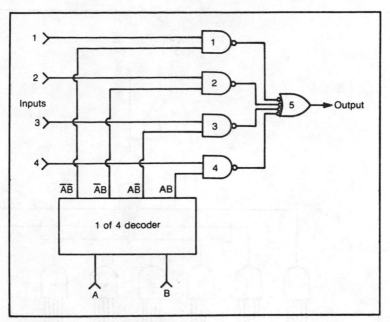

Fig. 7-17. Four-input multiplexer circuit.

This will permit input #4 to pass through gate 4 and gate 5. Gates 1, 2, and 3 will be inhibited at this time.

This same technique is used in the 8-input TTL binary multiplexer shown in Fig. 7-19. Gates 1 through 8 are used to control the eight data input lines, D0 through D7. Depending upon the

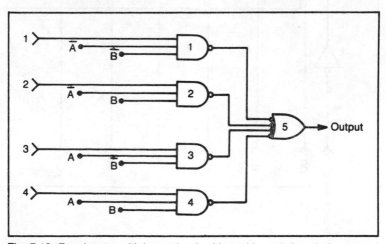

Fig. 7-18. Four-input multiplexer circuit with enable and *decode* functions.

275

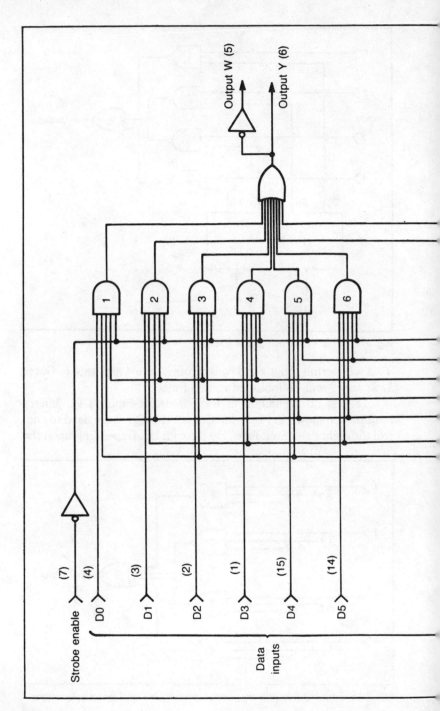

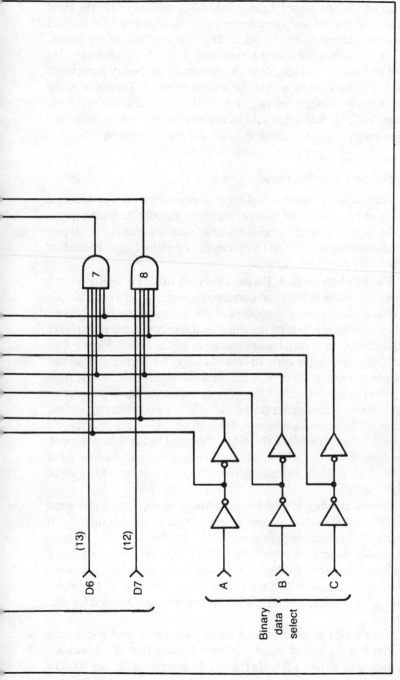

Fig. 7-19. 74151 TTL eight-input multiplexer IC.

D6 (13)

D7 (12)

7

8

A

B

C

Binary
data
select

input code, a 3-bit binary input word, ABC, enables one of the eight gates. The normal and complement signals required by the select gates are generated by the six inverters at the data select inputs. This 3-bit input word is an address code which designates the data input line selected to appear at the output. If the binary input word is 101, for example, data input *D5* will be selected. The *strobe enable* line controls all eight select gates. Both the normal (Y) and complement (W) outputs are available. Because of its function, *data selector* is another commonly-used name for the multiplexer circuit.

Multiplexer Applications

A multiplexer has several applications other than providing a means of routing one of several inputs to its output. Multiplexers can be used to provide parallel-to-serial data conversion, serial pattern generation and provide a means for simplified implementation of Boolean functions, as well.

Parallel-to-Serial Data Conversion. Parallel-to-serial-conversion is one of the most common applications of a multiplexer. A parallel binary word is applied to the inputs of the multiplexer, and by sequencing through the input enabling codes, the multiplexer output becomes a serial representation of the word. Figure 7-20 illustrates how this occurs. In this example, a 4-bit register is used to store the input word, *WXYZ*. A 2-bit binary word, *AB*, from a counter is used to select the desired input. As the 2-bit counter is incremented, the input select code, *AB*, is stepped through it four states, 00 to 11. Subsequently, the output, M, of the multiplexer is equal to the state of the flip-flop connected to the selected input, as shown in the truth table. By sequencing through all four input states at a fixed rate, the parallel input word is converted to a serial output word.

Serial Binary Word Generator. The generation of a serial binary word is another common application of the multiplexer. It is virtually identical in operation to the parallel to serial converter previously described with only one exception: the word being generated is fixed. In digital circuits, there are some occasions where the generation of a fixed word is necessary and, therefore, there is no requirement for the additional circuitry needed for conversion.

Figure 7-21 shows how an 8-bit multiplexer is used to generate the fixed serial binary word, 10011010. Note that the inputs are connected to either +5 volts (binary 1) or ground (binary 0). The

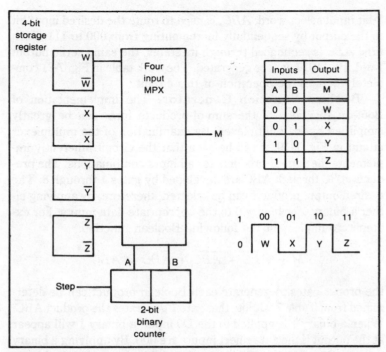

Inputs		Output
A	B	M
0	0	W
0	1	X
1	0	Y
1	1	Z

Fig. 7-20. Parallel-to-serial converter using a four-input multiplexer: circuit, truth table, and sequence diagram.

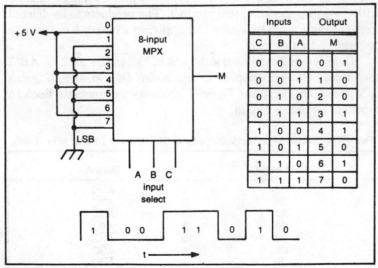

Inputs			Output
C	B	A	M
0	0	0	0 1
0	0	1	1 0
0	1	0	2 0
0	1	1	3 1
1	0	0	4 1
1	0	1	5 0
1	1	0	6 1
1	1	1	7 0

Fig. 7-21. Generation of the serial binary word 10011010 using an eight-input multiplexer.

3-bit input select word, *ABC*, is used to route the desired input bit to the output by sequentially incrementing from 000 to 111. Each time *ABC* is sequenced through its states, the same serial output word, 10011010, will be generated. The truth table in Fig. 7-21 completely defines the operation of this circuit.

Boolean Function Generator. The implementation of Boolean functions of the sum-of-products form can be greatly simplified by the multiplexer. By examination of the multiplexer circuit in Fig. 7-19, it can be seen that the circuit inherently implements the sum-of-products for all input combinations. The products *ABC* through ABC are developed by gates 1 through 8. The desired output products can be selected, therefore, by applying either a binary 1 or binary 0 to the appropriate data inputs. For example, to implement the following Boolean function:

$$M = A\overline{B}\,\overline{C} + \overline{A}\,\overline{B}C + \overline{A}BC + ABC$$

the proper gates to generate each Boolean product can be determined from Table 7-4. Note that gate 1 generates the product $\overline{A}\,\overline{B}\,\overline{C}$. When a binary 1 is applied to the *D0* input, a binary 1 will appear at the output if the data select inputs are 000. By applying a binary 0 to the *D0* input, the 000 input state will be ignored and a binary 0 will appear at output W. The desired Boolean products can be selected by applying a binary 1 to the appropriate input associated with the gate generating that product. The products to be deleted from the output can be ignored by applying a binary 0 to the gate generating that product.

To generate the expression $M = A\overline{B}\,\overline{C} + \overline{A}\,\overline{B}C + \overline{A}BC + ABC$, therefore, 1 states are applied to inputs, *D1*, *D4*, *D6*, and *D7* (gates 2, 5, 7, and 8 in Fig. 7-19). Figure 7-22 shows the complete Boolean function generator circuit.

Table 7-4. Sum-of-Products Outputs of Multiplexer Circuit (Fig. 7-19).

Data Input	Gate #	Output
D0	1	$\overline{A}\,\overline{B}\,\overline{C}$
D1	2	$A\overline{B}\,\overline{C}$
D2	3	$\overline{A}B\overline{C}$
D3	4	$AB\overline{C}$
D4	5	$\overline{A}\,\overline{B}C$
D5	6	$A\overline{B}C$
D6	7	$\overline{A}BC$
D7	8	ABC

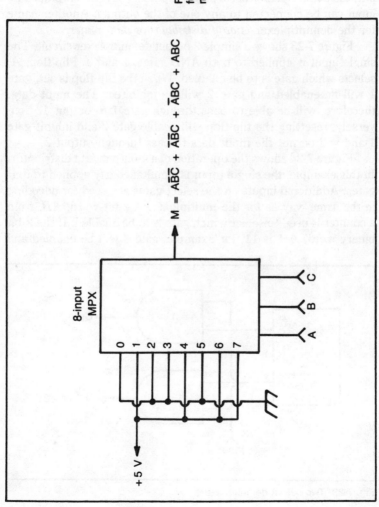

Fig. 7-22. Boolean sum-of-products function generator using eight-input multiplexer.

$M = A\overline{B}\,\overline{C} + \overline{A}B\overline{C} + \overline{A}BC + ABC$

More-complex Boolean functions can also be implemented with multiplexers by connecting other variables to their inputs, instead of fixed binary 1s and 0s. For example, four variable sum-of-products from inputs A, B, C, and D can be implemented with an 8-input multiplexer by connecting the D and $\overline{D}$ input states to selected multiplexer inputs to implement the desired function.

DEMULTIPLEXERS

As its name implies, a demultiplexer is basically the reverse of a multiplexer. Instead of having multiple inputs and a single output, the demultiplexer has a single input and several outputs. The input can be connected to any one of the outputs. Another name for the demultiplexer is *data distributor* or *data router*.

Figure 7-23 shows a simple 2-output demultiplexer circuit. The single input is applied to both AND gates, 1 and 2. Flip-flop, A, selects which gate is to be enabled. When the flip-flop is set, gate 1 will be enabled and gate 2 will be inhibited. The input data, therefore, will be able to pass through gate 1 to output 1. Conversely, resetting the flip-flop will enable gate 2 and inhibit gate 1 and will permit the input data to pass through output 2.

Figure 7-24 shows the operation of a 4-output data distributor. In this example, the single input is simultaneously applied to four gates. Additional inputs on the select gates are used for decoding in the same way as for the multiplexer. A 2-bit word, AB, from a counter is used to select which gate is to be enabled. If the 2-bit binary word, AB, is 11, for example, gate 4 will be enabled and

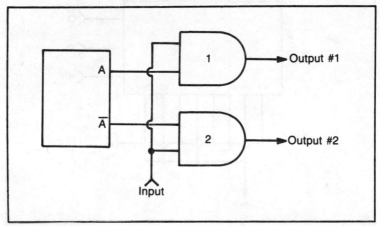

Fig. 7-23. Two-output demultiplexer.

282

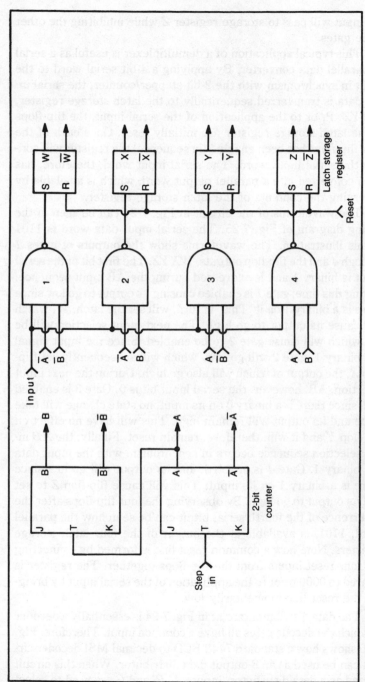

Fig. 7-24. Serial-to-parallel converter using a four-input demultiplexer.

283

the input will pass to storage register Z while inhibiting the other three gates.

This typical application of a demultiplexer is useful as a serial to parallel data converter. By applying a 4-bit serial word to the input in synchronism with the 2-bit stepper/counter, the serial input data is transferred sequentially to the latch storage register, $WXYZ$. Prior to the application of the serial input, the flip-flops in the latch storage register are initially reset. Once each of the four flip-flops has been enabled (in sequence) the register will contain the serial input word. The serial input word, therefore, has been converted into a parallel output word, which is available by observing the contents of the latch storage register.

The waveforms of the circuit in Fig. 7-24 can be seen in the timing diagram of Fig. 7-25. The serial input data word is 1101 in this illustration. The waveforms show the outputs of gates 1 through 4 and the flip-flop outputs, $WXYZ$. The first bit of the serial input is binary 1 and is addressed during the $\overline{A}\overline{B}$ input sequence. During this time, gate 1 is enabled causing its output to go low since there is a binary 1 on it. This, in turn, will set the latch, W, which will cause its output to go high. The next input selection will be $\overline{A}B$ which will cause gate 2 to be enabled. Since the input signal is a binary 1, gate 2 will go low, which will subsequently set flip-flop X, the output of which will also go high. During the next input selection, $A\overline{B}$, however, the serial input bit is 0. Gate 3 is enabled and, since there is a binary 0 on its input, no state change will take place and its output will remain high. This will have no effect on flip-flop Y and it will, therefore, remain reset. Finally, the AB input selection sequence occurs in synchronism with the input data bit, binary 1. Gate 4 is enabled, and its output will go low since there is a binary 1 on its input. This will cause flip-flop Z to set and its output to go high. By observing the four flip-flops after the occurrence of the fourth serial bit, it can be seen how the parallel word, 1101, is available at the output of the four latch storage registers. Note how a common reset line is formed by connecting the four reset inputs from the flip-flops together. The register is cleared to 0000 prior to the application of the serial input by bringing the reset line momentarily low.

The data distributor circuit in Fig. 7-24 is essentially a decoder in which the decode gates all have a common input. Therefore, Fig. 7-26 shows how a standard 7442 BCD-to-decimal MSI decoder circuit can be used as an 8-output data distributor. When this circuit is used as a data distributor, inputs A, B, and C are used to select

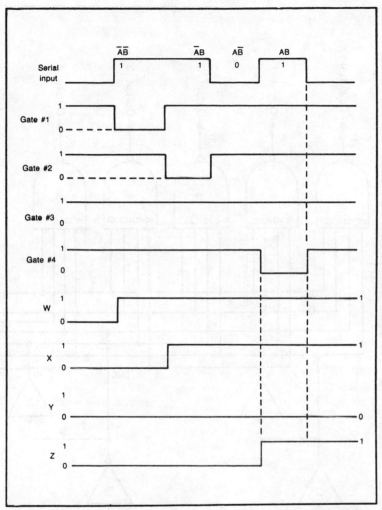

Fig. 7-25. Timing diagram of a serial-to-parallel converter using a demultiplexer.

the desired output. These three inputs will enable one of the gates, 1 through 8. Input data will be applied to the input, D, of the integrated circuit. Note how the data is inverted by inverter 17 and then applied to gates 1 through 8. The data input will, therefore, appear at the output of the gate selected by the 3-bit input word, ABC. For example, if the input state, ABC, is 000, gate 1 will be enabled, and the data applied to the input, D, will appear at the output of gate 1. Gates 9 and 10 of the decoder circuit are not used in this application.

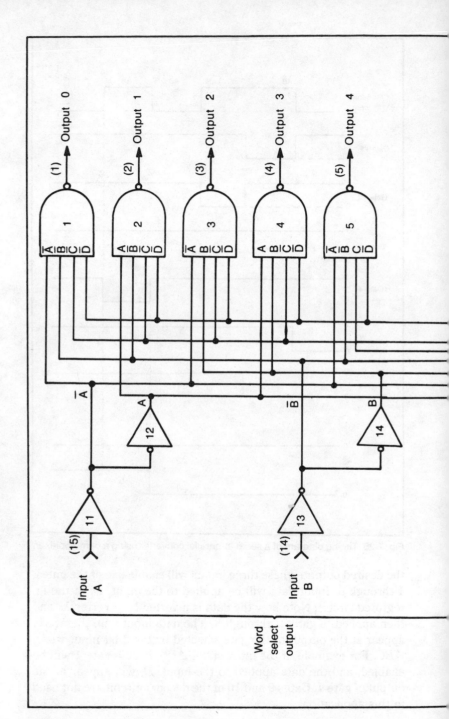

286

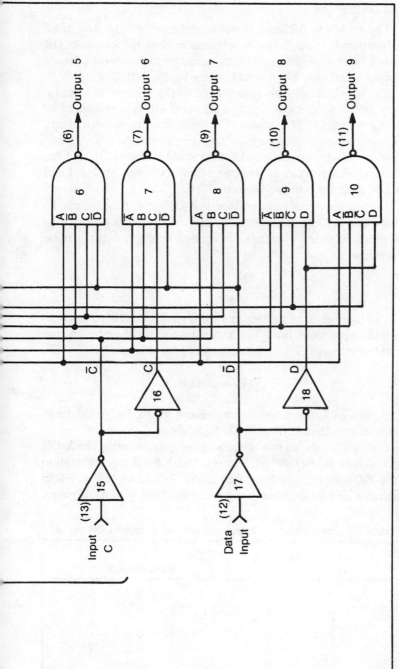

Fig. 7-26. Eight-output data distributor using a 7442 decoder IC.

287

EXCLUSIVE OR

The exclusive OR gate is one of the most widely used of all combinational logic circuits. As its name implies, the exclusive OR gate is a 2-input combinational logic circuit which produces a binary 1 output when one, *but not both*, of its inputs is binary 1.

The standard OR logic circuit is generally referred to as an *inclusive OR*. It produces a binary 1 output if any one *or more* of its inputs is a binary 1. The *exclusive* OR logic circuit produces a binary 1 at its output only when its inputs are complementary. Table 7-5, below, compares the output of the standard inclusive OR and the exclusive OR logic circuits. Inputs to these gates are labeled A and B while their outputs are labeled C.

The exclusive OR (also written as X-OR) logic function can be written as a Boolean expression. By observing the input conditions that produce binary 1 outputs, the sum-of-products output can be written as:

$$C = \overline{A} B + A \overline{B}$$

The symbol used to designate the exclusive OR function in Boolean expressions is a $\oplus$. The exclusive OR of inputs, A and B, whose output is C can be expressed, therefore:

$$C = A \oplus B = \overline{A} B + A \overline{B}$$

Figure 7-27 shows how to implement the exclusive OR function with standard AND and OR logic gates.

Figure 7-28 shows two other ways of implementing the X-OR function with NAND and NOR gates. The NAND implementation of the X-OR function is illustrated in Fig. 7-28A, while Fig. 7-28B illustrates how to implement the same function with NOR gates.

Table 7-5. Comparison of Outputs of OR and Exclusive OR Gates.

Inclusive OR			Exclusive OR		
A	B	C	A	B	C
0	0	0	0	0	0
0	1	1	0	1	1
1	0	1	1	0	1
1	1	1	1	1	0

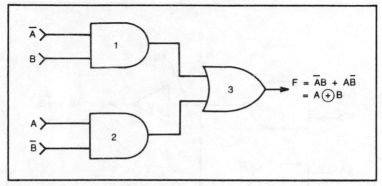

Fig. 7-27. Exclusive-OR (X-OR) logic circuit.

Figure 7-29 shows how to implement the X-OR function using the wired OR connection. In this illustration, the open collector outputs of either TTL or DTL gates can be connected together to produce the X-OR function.

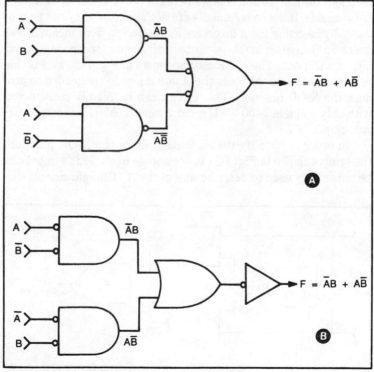

Fig. 7-28. X-OR implementation with NAND gates.

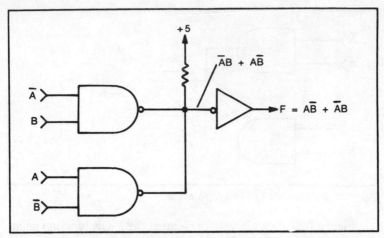

Fig. 7-29. X-OR implementation with NOR gates.

The X-OR circuits shown in Figs. 7-27, 7-28 and 7-29 all assume that both the normal and complements of the A and B input signals are available. If the complements are not available, they can be produced by inserting input inverters in the circuit. This means, however, an increase in the number of circuit components and interconnections. The X-OR circuit shown in Fig. 7-30 avoids this problem. In this circuit, only the A and B inputs are needed to produce the X-OR function. This circuit can be readily constructed with only a single 7400 TTL quad 2-input NAND integrated circuit chip.

In order to simplify the logic diagram of the X-OR function, the symbol shown in Fig. 7-31 is commonly used. This symbol can be universally used to describe any of the X-OR logic circuits dis-

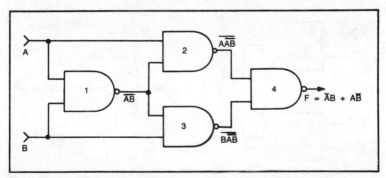

Fig. 7-30. X-OR function that does not require complement inputs.

290

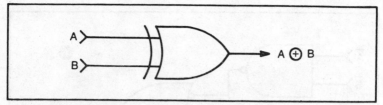

Fig. 7-31. Exclusive-OR logic symbol.

cussed so far in this section. Furthermore, it is not generally necessary to actually construct X-OR logic circuits from individual gates. Exclusive OR logic gates are available in MSI form in such packages as the 7486 TTL quad X-OR integrated circuit. The 7486 IC contains four independent exclusive OR logic gates in a single DIP.

EXCLUSIVE NOR

A commonly used variation of the X-OR gate is the exclusive NOR (X-NOR) circuit. The truth table for this circuit is shown in Table 7-6 below. It can be seen from the truth table that the output of this circuit is binary 1 only when the inputs are equal to each other. Therefore, the X-NOR circuit is sometimes referred to as an *equivalence circuit* or *comparator*. It can also be concluded that the output of the X-NOR circuit is equal to the complement of the X-OR circuit. The Boolean equation of the X-NOR circuit can be written from the truth table as:

$$C = A B + \overline{A}\,\overline{B}$$

Since the above equation is similar to that of the X-OR in the respect that it, too, is a sum-of-products; the equivalent function can be implemented by using any of the previously discussed X-OR circuits and simply rearranging the inputs, or merely complementing the outputs. Figure 7-32 illustrates two methods of im-

Table 7-6. Truth Table of Exclusive-NOR (XNOR) Circuit.

A	B	C
0	0	1
0	1	0
1	0	0
1	1	1

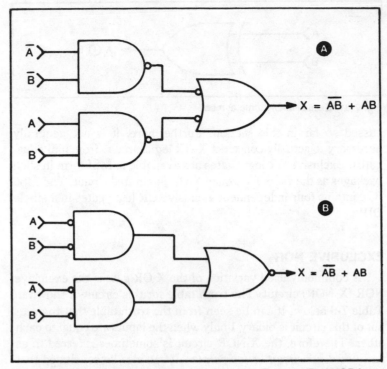

Fig. 7-32. Implementing: (A) X-OR function with NAND gates. (B) X-NOR function with NOR gates.

plementing the X-NOR function. The simplified logic symbol shown in Fig. 7-33 is commonly used to denote the X-NOR operation.

APPLICATIONS OF THE X-OR

There are numerous special combinational logic circuits that take advantage of the characteristics of the exclusive OR. These include binary adders, parity generators/checkers, and binary com-

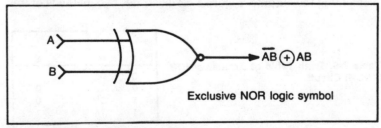

Fig. 7-33. Exclusive-NOR logic symbol.

parators. Each of these applications will be examined.

Binary Adder

Simply stated, a binary adder is a logic circuit designed to add two binary numbers. The output of the binary adder, therefore, is the sum of the two input numbers. It is the basic computational circuit used in digital computers, calculators, and other systems employing mathematical operations.

Below are the very simple rules for binary addition:

$$
\begin{array}{cccc}
0 & 0 & 1 & 1 \\
+0 & +1 & +0 & +1 \\
\hline
0 & 1 & 1 & 10 \\
\end{array}
$$

The above rules show how single-bit numbers are added. However, these rules can be extrapolated to multibit numbers in the same way. For example:

$$
\begin{array}{cc}
7 & 0111 \\
+11 & +1011 \\
\hline
18 & 10010 \\
\end{array}
$$

By closely examining the rules for binary addition, it can be seen that the truth table for this operation would be *identical* to that of the exclusive-OR circuit! In other words, the X-OR inputs, A and B, are the two single bits to be added together while the output, C, is the single-bit sum of the inputs. The only function the X-OR circuit cannot handle by itself is the carry operation.

When two binary 1 bits are being added, a binary 1 carry bit will be generated. This carry operation can be implemented with the addition of an AND gate that will produce a binary 1 output only when both inputs to the X-OR gate are binary 1. A basic single-bit binary adder circuit can be developed by combining the AND gate with the X-OR gate as shown in Fig. 7-34. This configuration is generally referred to as a *half adder*.

When multibit numbers are to be added together, a circuit for each of the two corresponding bits must be provided. Therefore, an adder circuit must be designed to add the two input bits together, and then add to that sum the carry bit from the previous least-significant-bit position. Such a circuit can be designed from two

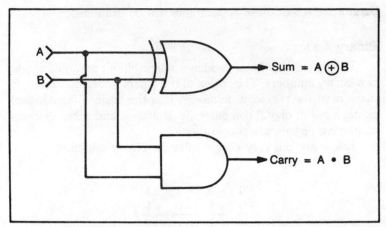

Fig. 7-34. Half-adder circuit.

half-adders to form a full adder like the one shown in Fig. 7-35.

The half adder comprised of the X-OR gate 4 and the AND gate 1, performs the addition of the two input bits, *A* and *B*. The output of the X-OR gate, 4, is the sum of these two bits. To this sum, the carry input, CI, is added from the adjacent lower order bit position. The sum of bits A and B is added to the carry input of the half-adder circuit, comprised of X-OR gate 5 and AND gate

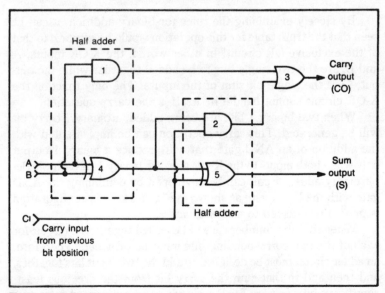

Fig. 7-35. Full-adder circuit.

294

2. The output of the X-OR gate, 5, is the correct sum. Note there will be two carry outputs since two half-adders are being used. A carry bit can be generated from either the addition of the two inputs, A and B, or the addition of their sum and carry. The two carry outputs, therefore, are ORed together in gate 3 to produce the correct carry output (CO) to the next most significant bit adder.

A block diagram of an adder circuit used to produce the sum of two 4-bit binary numbers is illustrated in Fig. 7-36. The inputs are two 4-bit binary numbers, A and B. Input A is comprised of bits $A1$, $A2$, $A3$, and $A4$. Likewise, input B is comprised of bits $B1$, $B2$, $B3$, and $B4$. Each of the corresponding bits of these two numbers is added in an adder circuit. Note the least-significant bits, $A1$ and $B1$, are added in a half-adder, since there is no lesser significant bit, and no carry output will be generated. All other bit positions require a full-adder, however, to accommodate the carry input from the preceding lower-order bit position. The output of the adder, $S1$, $S2$, $S3$, and $S4$, is a 4-bit parallel sum of the two input numbers, A and B. The carry output of the most-significant-bit full-adder is used to represent the *fifth* output bit in situations where the 4-bit input numbers produce a 5-bit sum.

Although the adder circuit described above can be constructed from individual X-OR and AND gates, it is generally not necessary to do so, since 4-bit adders are available in complete MSI packages such as the 7483 TTL 4-bit full adder.

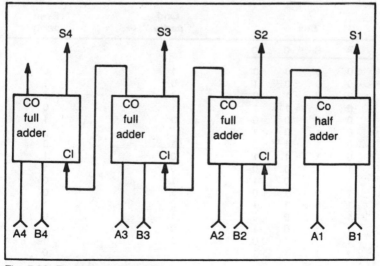

Fig. 7-36. Four-bit parallel adder.

295

Parity Generator/Checker

A parity generator is a combinational logic circuit that indicates the presence or absence of a bit error in a binary word. In some high-speed digital applications there is a likelihood of an error being made during the transmission of binary data from one location to another. Because of electrical noise or circuit malfunction, a binary 1 bit may be transmitted, received, or stored in a memory location as a binary 0, or vice-versa. It is desirable, therefore, to incorporate a means to detect when such errors occur. A parity generator circuit is used to perform this function.

In operation, the parity generator examines the binary word being transmitted or stored and generates a single output called a parity bit. This parity bit is subsequently added to the other bits of the word and either transmitted or stored with it. A *parity check* is then performed on the word, when it is either written into or retrieved from memory. The parity checker generates a parity bit from the binary word and compares this bit with the parity bit stored or transmitted along with the original information. If these two parity bits are identical, no error exists. However, if a discrepancy results, an error has been detected.

Generating a parity bit can be accomplished by observing the binary word and determining the quantity of binary 1s contained

Table 7-7. 4-Bit Binary Words, with Associated Even and Odd parity Bits.

Bits				Odd parity	Even parity
A	B	C	D		
0	0	0	0	1	0
0	0	0	1	0	1
0	0	1	0	0	1
0	0	1	1	1	0
0	1	0	0	0	1
0	1	0	1	1	0
0	1	1	0	1	0
0	1	1	1	0	1
1	0	0	0	0	1
1	0	0	1	1	0
1	0	1	0	1	0
1	0	1	1	0	1
1	1	0	0	1	0
1	1	0	1	0	1
1	1	1	0	0	1
1	1	1	1	1	0

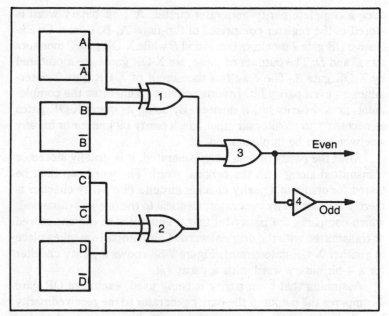

Fig. 7-37. Four-bit parity generator circuit.

in that word. Whether the number of 1s, including the parity bit, is odd or even will dictate if a parity bit will be generated or not. Table 7-7 shows all sixteen possible combinations of 4-bit binary words. Adjacent to the columns of the words are the odd and even parity bits associated with each word. Note that for odd parity a binary 1 or binary 0 is added to make the total number of bits in the word, including the parity bit, odd. Conversely, for even parity, the reverse is true.

The exclusive OR circuit is the basic element used to generate the parity bit. By examination of the truth table of the X-OR gate (Table 7-5), it can be determined that it can be considered an odd or even detector circuit. In other words, if the two inputs are equal (or even) the output of the X-OR is binary 0. Conversely, if the two inputs are unequal (or odd) the output is a binary 1. The X-OR gate, therefore, can be used to compare two binary bits and indicate whether or not they are odd or even. An exclusive OR gate is used to monitor each 2-bit group of a binary word in a parity generator. These X-OR outputs are then further compared to the other X-OR outputs until a single output bit is generated indicating the parity of the word being examined.

Figure 7-37 illustrates how X-OR gates are cascaded to produce a complete parity generator circuit. A 4-bit binary word is stored in the register comprised of flip-flops A, B, C, and D. Exclusive OR gate *1* monitors bits *A* and *B* while X-OR gate 2 monitors bits *C* and *D*. The outputs of these two X-OR gates are monitored by X-OR gate 3. The result of the output of X-OR gate 3 determines an even-parity bit. Inverter circuit 4 generates the complement, or odd-parity bit, if desired. By using as many X-OR gates as necessary to monitor all input bits, a parity bit generator for any size word can be implemented.

After the parity bit has been generated, it is usually stored or transmitted along with the original word. The word can then be tested for errors in a parity checker circuit. The parity checker is merely another parity generator, identical to the one just discussed, which compares the parity bit that it generates to the one stored or transmitted with the original word. This comparison takes place in another X-OR gate circuit. Figure 7-38 shows a parity checker for a 4-bit binary word with a parity bit.

Assuming that even parity is being used, exclusive OR gate *4* compares the output of the parity generator to the received parity bit, *P*. If the internally-generated parity bit is identical to the received parity bit, the output of the X-OR gate will be binary 0, which indicates no parity error. On the other hand, if the two bits are different, the output of the X-OR gate will be binary 1 which will indicate a parity error.

The signal indicating the detection of a parity error can be used in a variety of ways. Some of these include turning on an indicator lamp, initiating a series of logical operations which will either accept or reject the data depending upon the error status, or simply counting and recording the number of error bits occurring.

As can be visualized, a parity error checker scheme does not

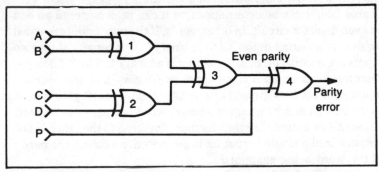

Fig. 7-38. Four-bit parity checker.

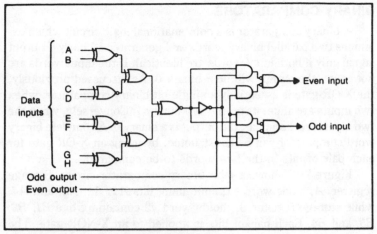

Fig. 7-39. Parity-generator parity-checker IC.

completely ensure total error detection. It assumes that an error will occur in only a single bit of any given word. It is possible, though, for a word to be transmitted or stored with *two* bit errors—which will result in *no* parity error. Even though this situation rarely occurs since the reliability of contemporary transmission and storage systems are relatively high, the possibility of multibit errors still exists. However, single-bit errors are more common and the use of parity bit error detection is a very useful and reliable indicator of errors.

In systems requiring even higher reliability and performance, more sophisticated circuits have been developed which not only detect bit errors, but also *correct* bit errors at the same time! In some of today's high-speed and ultra-sophisticated computer systems these errors are automatically detected and corrected even before the information is processed.

Complete parity generators and checkers are commercially available in MSI form. Figure 7-39 shows the logic diagram of the 74180 9-bit parity generator/checker integrated circuit. This circuit is capable of either generating a parity bit or checking for parity errors. As a generator, it can monitor up to nine input bits. The ninth input bit is applied to either the odd or even input as required by the application. As a parity checker, it will monitor an 8-bit word, and generate the appropriate parity bit, which is then compared to a received parity bit applied to either the odd or even input. The error indication will appear at the appropriate output depending upon whether odd or even parity is being detected.

BINARY COMPARATORS

A binary comparator is a combinational logic circuit which examines two parallel binary words and generates a binary 1 output signal only if both input words are identical. If the input words are not equal, the output will be a binary 0. As discussed previously, the X-OR gate is essentially a single-bit binary comparator: when two inputs are alike, its output is a binary 1. Conversely, when the two inputs are dissimilar, the output is a binary 0. A complete binary word comparator can be constructed, by using an X-OR gate for each pair of bits in the two words to be compared.

Figure 7-40 shows a 4-bit binary comparator circuit. Storage register, *A*, holds word #1, containing bits *A1, A2, A3,* and *A4*, while storage register, B, holds word #2 containing bits *B1, B2, B3,* and *B4*. Each pair of bits is applied to an X-NOR gate. The outputs of the X-NOR gates are fed to a 4-input AND gate. When the two input words are identical, the outputs of the X-NORs will both be binary 1s. With all binary 1s to the inputs of the AND gate, the output will also be binary 1 indicating equality between the two input words. If, however, one or more bits of the input words are different, the output of the associated X-NOR gate will be binary 0 and so will the output of the AND gate, indicating inequality. Any size word can be compared in this manner by simply providing ad-

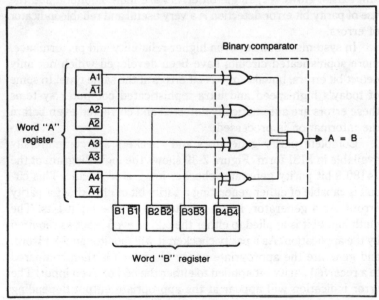

Fig. 7-40. Four-bit binary comparator.

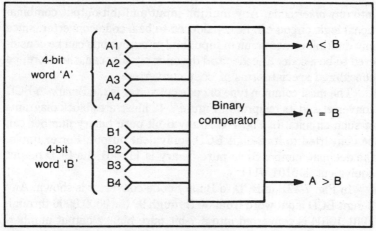

Fig. 7-41. Pinout diagram of a four-bit MSI comparator IC.

ditional X-NOR gates, and incorporating the appropriate-size AND gate at the output.

Commercially-available MSI binary comparators are common, which usually eliminates the need to construct comparators from individual gates. These comparators are designed for comparing two 4-bit binary words and generating three outputs. One output indicates the equality of the two input words, the second indicates when one word is larger than the other word, while the third indicates when one word is smaller than the other word. Figure 7-41 shows a block diagram of such a comparator, similar to the 7485 integrated circuit. If the input word, A, is a larger binary number than input word, B, then the $A > B$ output will be binary 1. Conversely, if input word, B, is larger than is input word, A, then the $A < B$ output will be binary 1. Of course, if input word, A, is equal to input word, B, then the $A = B$ output will be binary 1.

CODE CONVERTERS

A code converter is a combinational logic circuit which converts one type of binary code into another. Two or more different binary codes are used in many applications of digital systems. By using code converters various circuits can be made compatible with each other. Some of the most common types of code converters are: binary-to-BCD, BCD-to-binary, ASCII-to-EBCDIC, EBCDIC-to-ASCII, Gray-to-binary, 8421 BCD-to-XS3 and XS3-to-8421 BCD.

Code converters can be constructed that will convert *any* code into *any other* code. Any multibit-input/multibit-output combinational logic circuit can be considered to be a code converter, since any multibit combination of input bits or output bits can be considered to be a code. Encoder and decoder circuits can, therefore, be considered special forms of code converters.

The most common type of code converter is the Binary-to-BCD converter and its reciprocal. Figure 7-42 illustrates block diagrams of such circuits. In Fig. 7-42A any 6-bit pure binary number can be converted to its 2-digit BCD equivalent output. For example, the decimal number 57 in pure binary is 111001. Its BCD output equivalent is 0101 0111.

In Fig. 7-42B, a BCD to Binary code converter is shown. Any 2-digit BCD input word from 00 through 99 (or 0000 0000 through 1001 1001) is converted into a 7-bit pure binary output number.

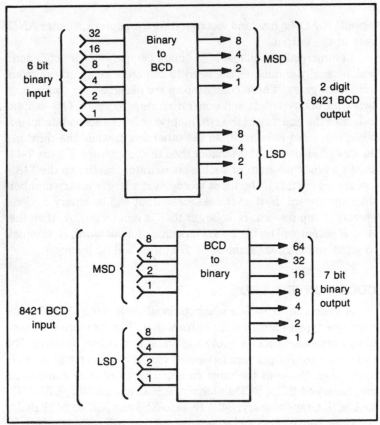

Fig. 7-42. BCD-to-binary code converter.

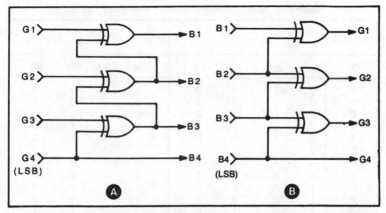

Fig. 7-43. (A) Gray-code to binary-code converter. (B) Binary-code to Gray-code converter.

Both of these code converters are available as MSI combinational integrated circuits.

Binary-to-Gray and Gray to binary code converters are also common. Many applications exist where the Gray cyclical code must be used in order to minimize errors when changing from one state to another. The Gray code, however, cannot be used in arithmetic operations. Therefore, the Gray-to-Binary code converter becomes a necessity.

Figure 7-43A shows the Gray-to-Binary code converter, and the Binary to Gray converter is illustrated in Fig. 7-43B. Since the most-significant bit of the words in both Gray and Binary will be the same, no code conversion is necessary. Note the use of X-OR gates to perform the code conversion. The Gray and Binary code equivalents are shown in Table 7-8.

Many types of code converters use sequential circuits, even though code conversion is most often accomplished with combinational logic circuits. Numerous combinations of flip-flops, counters, and shift registers can be implemented to perform code conversion. One such simple example is the serial Gray-to-Binary converter shown in Fig. 7-44. In this example, a serial Gray code is applied to the J-K inputs of a flip-flop, MSB first. The normal output of the flip-flop is the serial binary code equivalent.

READ-ONLY MEMORIES

Binary information is permanently stored in a device known as a *read-only memory* or *ROM*. Practical ROMs are available for

Table 7-8. Comparison of Binary and Gray Codes.

Decimal	Binary				Gray			
D	B4	B3	B2	B1	G4	G3	G2	G1
0	0	0	0	0	0	0	0	0
1	0	0	0	1	0	0	0	1
2	0	0	1	0	0	0	1	1
3	0	0	1	1	0	0	1	0
4	0	1	0	0	0	1	1	0
5	0	1	0	1	0	1	1	1
6	0	1	1	0	0	1	0	1
7	0	1	1	1	0	1	0	0
8	1	0	0	0	1	1	0	0
9	1	0	0	1	1	1	0	1
10	1	0	1	0	1	1	1	1
11	1	0	1	1	1	1	1	0
12	1	1	0	0	1	0	1	0
13	1	1	0	1	1	0	1	1
14	1	1	1	0	1	0	0	1
15	1	1	1	1	1	0	0	0

storing as many as 131,072 bits (128 k) of data. The data can be written into the memory when it is manufactured and usually cannot be changed thereafter. This is in contrast to electronic read/write memory circuits that can both store and read data: *random-access memory* or *RAM*.

The configurations of both read/write memories (RAM) and read-only memories (ROM) is basically the same. Both can store a number of pieces of data in various memory locations. The main

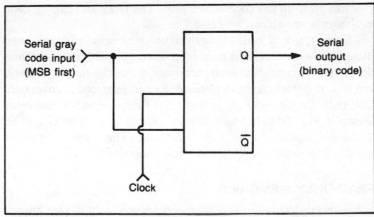

Fig. 7-44. Serial-Gray-code to binary-sequential-code converter.

difference, however, is that in the ROM, the data is permanently stored, although it can be read out in any order (random access). The RAM is more expensive but more flexible, and is normally used as the main storage section of a digital computer. In this section, however, the ROM will be discussed as the primary subject.

ROM Operation

Figure 7-45 illustrates the general block diagram of a read-only memory. It is comprised of three major sections: the address decoder, the memory storage elements, and the output circuits.

The address decoder accepts a multibit binary input word and decodes all possible input states. As with any binary decoder, only one of the outputs will be activated. Figure 7-45 shows an address decoder with five input bits or a total of $2^5 = 32$ different states which can be decoded. This 5-bit input word, called the address, designates one of the 32 individual memory locations at a time.

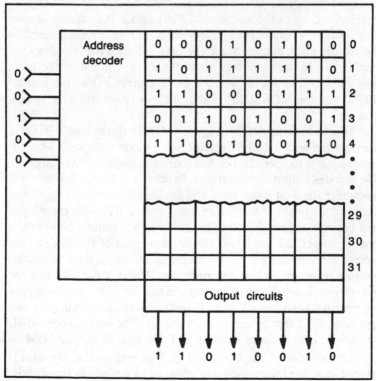

Fig. 7-45. Read-only memory (ROM) block diagram.

The memory itself is comprised of electronic circuits used to store binary data. These storage elements are arranged to store a specific number of binary words. For example, the organization of the ROM in Fig. 7-45 permits the storage of 32 8-bit words. The memory addresses are designated 0 to 31. By application of a 5-bit address code to the input of the ROM, the contents of the memory location being addressed will appear at the output. At this time, all other memory locations will be ignored. A buffer circuit is also used at the ROM's output to permit this data to be used in other logic circuits.

ROM Construction

Read-only memories can be implemented in many different ways. Any circuit or component capable of storing a bit of binary data can be used. Capacitors and magnetic cores are only two examples of elements used to store binary data in a ROM. Most contemporary ROMs, however, use either bipolar or MOS semiconductor circuits and are generally large-scale ICs capable of storing significant amounts of binary data. ROMs are considered to be custom-made circuits since the user specifies the memory contents prior to the manufacture of the device. Some of the most popular types of ROMs are the diode matrix ROM, the bipolar ROM, and the MOS ROM. Each of these types will now be discussed.

Diode Matrix ROM. Figure 7-47 illustrates how a ROM is constructed with a 1-of-8 decoder and a diode matrix. A 3-bit address input is accepted by the 1-of-8 decoder and generates all possible decoded output combinations. In other words, the decoder will recognize the 3-bit input word and enable only one of its eight outputs. For example, if the binary input word is 011, only the #3 output line will go low. All other output lines will remain high. When the #3 output line goes low, the cathode ends of the diodes connected to the #3 line also go low and will conduct via their associated pull-up resistors. In this example, the Z and X output lines are forced low. Lines Y and W are high at this time because their pull-up resistors keep the $+V$ voltage on their lines. Observing the output lines, $ZYXW$, the output code is 0101. The output code, 0101, therefore, is at address location 011 (decimal 3) in this ROM.

Examination of the ROM in Fig. 7-46 reveals that the data is stored as either the presence or absence of a diode in the matrix. A diode connection between the decoder's output and the output

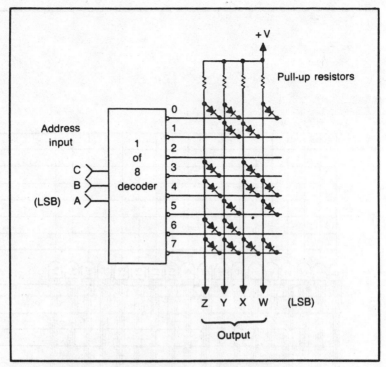

Fig. 7-46. ROM formed from decoder and diode matrix.

line causes a binary 0 to be read when that address is enabled. Conversely, the absence of a diode at an output location causes a binary 1 to be read. Another way to conceptually visualize the ROM is to consider each output line with its associated diodes and pull-up resistors as a diode OR gate. A low on any diode input causes the output to go low and vice versa.

Some commercially available ROMs are designed and constructed exactly like the one shown in Fig. 7-46. Integrated circuit ROMs are initially constructed so that a diode is connected at each possible memory location. Therefore, all memory locations are initially programmed with binary 0s. To store data in the memory, an external pulse must be applied to the output lines in such a manner as to reverse-bias certain diodes to cause them to be destroyed. This method is called *"burning a ROM"* by causing it to open a diode. By "burning" a diode and, thereby causing it to open, a binary 1 state is programmed. Such ROMs can either be programmed by the manufacturer or the user. ROMs that permit the user to "burn" a program or data into its memory are called pro-

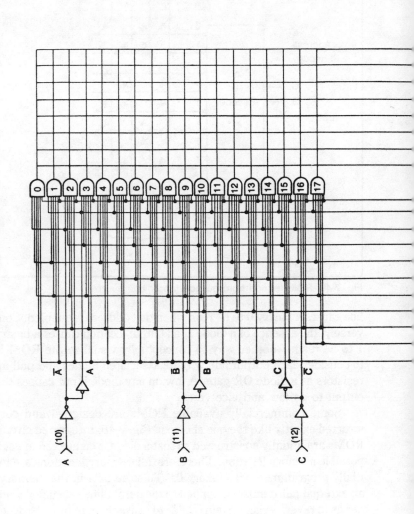

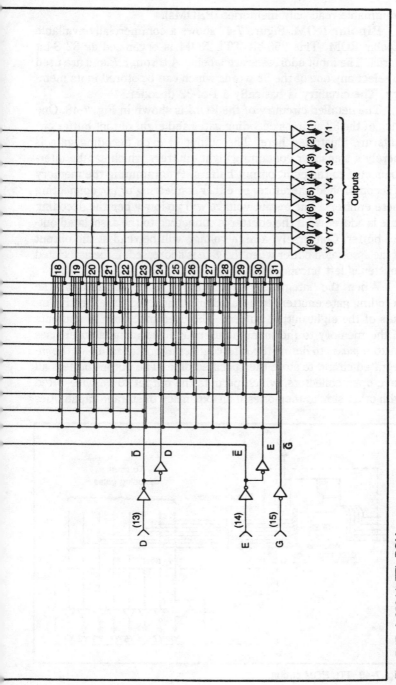

Fig. 7-47. A 256-bit TTL ROM.

grammable read only memories (PROMs).

Bipolar ROM. Figure 7-47 shows a commercially-available bipolar ROM. This 256-bit TTL ROM is organized as 32 8-bit words. The input addresses are labeled *A* through *E* and are used to select any one of the 32 words which can be stored in its memory. The circuitry is basically a 1-of-32 decoder.

The detailed circuitry of the ROM is shown in Fig. 7-48. One each of the 32 address decoding gates and eight output buffer circuits are illustrated here. The output of each decoding gate is merely a transistor containing eight emitters which can be interconnected to the eight output buffers. Programming the memory is accomplished, therefore, by either connecting or not connecting these emitters. The output voltage will go low when the decoding gate is addressed if the emitter is connected to the associated output buffer. Conversely, a high voltage will be read at the output of the associated buffer when the gate is addressed, if the associated emitter is left unconnected.

When the integrated circuit ROM is manufactured, the decoding gate emitters to be used are connected to respective inputs of the eight output buffers. The user specifies the contents of the memory to the manufacturer, and the manufacturer uses custom *masks* to define the interconnecting metalization of the integrated circuit to store the specified data. The output buffers all have open collectors, which permits the output to be wire-ORed with other similar memories if an expansion of storage capabilities

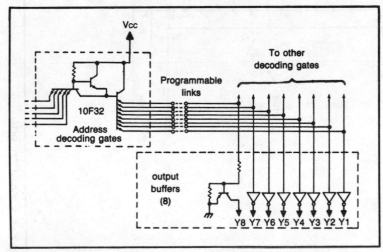

Fig. 7-48. TTL ROM circuit.

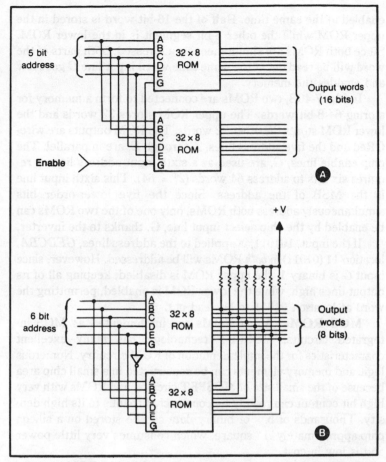

Fig. 7-49. Increasing the: (A) Storage locations, and (B) Available storage locations of a ROM.

is desired. Tri-state output circuitry is used on some TTL ROMs in order to enable or disable the circuitry when it is combined with other similar memories for expansion purposes. In the ROM shown in Fig. 7-47, the G input line performs this function, and is often referred to as the *chip select* line because it is used as an extra address bit input for expanded memories.

Standard-size ROMs can be used in two ways to make larger memories, as shown in Fig. 7-49. In Fig. 7-49A, two ROMs are connected to form a memory for 32 16-bit words. Each ROM can store 32 8-bit words, as indicated by the designation: *32 × 8* or *32 by 8*. Since the five address lines are in parallel, each ROM is enabled at the same time. Half of the 16-bit word is stored in the upper ROM while the other 8-bit segment is in the lower ROM. Since both ROMs are simultaneously addressed, both parts of the word will be read out at the same time when input line G goes low and enables the memory.

In Fig. 7-49B, two ROMs are connected to form a memory for storing 64 8-bit words. The upper ROM stores 32 words and the lower ROM stores the other 32 words. The ROM outputs are wire-ORed and the five address lines, A through E, are in parallel. The chip enable lines, G, are used as a sixth input address line. It requires six bits to address 64 words ($2^6 = 64$). This sixth input line is the MSB of the address. Since the five lower-order bits simultaneously address both ROMs, only one of the two ROMs can be enabled by the chip select input line, G, thanks to the inverter.

If the input, 101011, is applied to the address lines, $GEDCBA$, location 11 (01011) in *both* ROMs will be addressed. However, since input G is binary 1, the upper ROM is disabled, keeping all of its output lines high, while the lower ROM is enabled, permitting the word at location 01011 to be read out.

MOS ROMs. Many ROMs are implemented as MOS integrated circuits. MOSFET technology has many excellent characteristics for the implementation of ROM circuitry. Numerous logic and memory elements can be constructed in a small chip area because of the small size of MOSFET circuits, and ROMs with very high bit content can readily be constructed thanks to its high density. Thousands of bits of binary data can be stored on a silicon chip approximately .1″ square, which consumes very little power and is low in cost.

The basic structure and organization of a MOS ROM is essentially the same as is in any ROM. An address decoder selects the desired output word, and the absence or presence of a semiconductor device in a matrix network specifies either a binary 0 or binary 1, respectively, stored in the addressed location. The basic storage element in MOS ROMs is an enhancement-mode MOSFET.

The internal structure of a typical PMOS ROM is shown in Fig. 7-50. P-type material is diffused into the substrate in long strips called bit lines, as indicated. These p-type diffusions form the source and drain connections of the MOSFETS. The metal word-select lines are perpendicular to the p diffusion areas, and from the gate elements of the MOSFETs. Several examples of how MOSFETs are formed are shown in Fig. 7-50. To program the memory, the MOSFETs are either enabled or disabled by appropriate masking

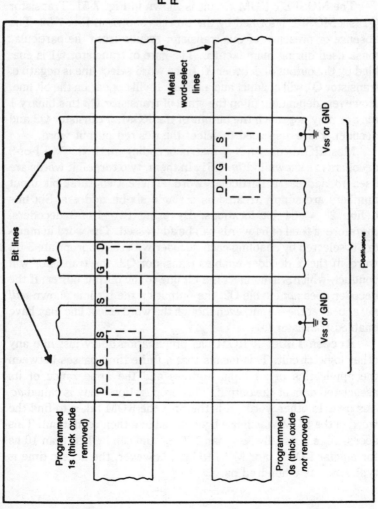

Fig. 7-50. Basic structure of PMOS
ROM.

operations during manufacture. If the MOSFET is enabled, a binary 1 will be stored. Conversely, if a MOSFET is disabled, a binary 0 will be stored.

The word-select lines are connected to the gates of the MOSFETs in locations where binary 1s are stored in the structure. A decoder output drives these word-select lines. The source terminals of the MOSFETs are connected either to ground or to the source supply voltage, Vss. The drain connections of the MOSFETs are designated as the bit lines. If one of the word select lines goes negative, the MOSFETs associated with that word will conduct and either ground or Vss will appear on the bit line.

The MOSFET ROM circuit is shown in Fig. 7-51. Transistor Q1 is a MOSFET formed by the process shown in Fig. 7-50. The absence or presence of this transistor results from the particular mask used during manufacture. The gate of transistor Q1 is enabled by the output of decoder X. If the word-select line is negative, transistor Q1 will conduct and a binary 1 will appear on the bit line. However, depending upon the state of transistor Q2 this binary 1 may or may not reach the output of the ROM. Transistor Q2 and decoder Y are also used to select the desired output word.

Most ROMs use an X-Y matrix decoding method. Two 1-of-8 decoders are shown in Fig. 7-51. In them, two three-bit words are used to address a particular word. These two three-bit input numbers are simply treated as a single six-bit address. Six bits define $2^6 = 64$ bit locations. By using two 1-of-8 decoders, therefore, a total of 64 words can be addressed. The word in memory is selected by enabling each decoder with the appropriate 3-bit word. If the Y decoder enables transistor Q2, the transistor will conduct, which will connect the bit line to the output buffer. If the decoder does *not* enable Q2, the output on the bit line shown *will not* appear at the output, even though the word select line may have enabled transistor Q1.

Access Time. A ROM has propagation delay just like any other logic circuit. This means that a finite time passes between the application of an input address and the appearance of its associated data at the output. This propagation delay is called *access time*. In other words, it is the time the ROM takes to find the word in the ROM which has been called and then read it out. This access time is usually less than 100 ns, and can be less than 10 ns for bipolar ROMs. For MOS ROMs, however, the access time is typically a few hundred ns.

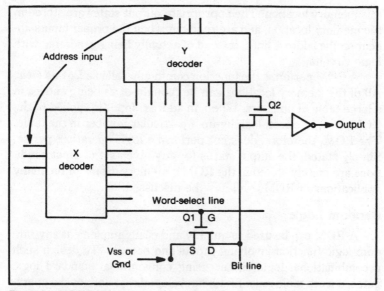

Fig. 7-51. MOS ROM

ROM APPLICATIONS

ROMs are extremely versatile for implementing logic functions. Many different types of combinational circuits may be replaced by a single, appropriately-programmed ROM. In particular, ROMs are most useful in replacing complex logic functions that have a large number of inputs and outputs. ROMs offer the advantages of faster and easier circuit design, lower cost, smaller size and, frequently, lower power consumption.

Combinational logic circuits produce output signals which are a function of the following criteria:

1. Their input states,
2. The types of gates used, and
3. The particular and unique configuration of the gates.

The desired output states for a given set of inputs are produced by properly interconnecting the designated types of logic gates. This same logical function can be simulated by a ROM. With the ROM, for each input applied to the address lines, a unique memory location is specified. A binary bit pattern which duplicates that produced by an equivalent combinational logic circuit is contained in

315

this memory location. The appropriate output states are stored in the memory location, and are read out when the proper inputs appear on the address lines, instead of actually being generated with logic circuits.

A ROM performs the function commonly called a *look-up table*. All of the memory locations can be thought of as being entries in a large table of numbers. When an address input is applied to the ROM, it is, in effect, looking-up a particular number in the table. The ROM, therefore, does not perform a logic operation, per se. Simply stated, the output states for any given set of input conditions are merely stored in the ROM's memory. Some of the many applications of ROMs will now be discussed.

Random Logic

A ROM can be used to quickly and easily implement any random logic function involving inputs and outputs. To design such a combinational logic circuit using conventional standard logic gates, a truth table must first be developed that defines the operations to be performed. The Boolean equations are then written from this truth table, minimized by using Boolean algebra and, finally, the actual circuit is designed and implemented with gates and inverters.

When a ROM is used, however, the *only* design step required is the implementation of the truth table! Since the truth table defines all the inputs and outputs, it is all the information necessary to define the ROM's program to perform the desired logic function or functions. The input logic states are assigned as address inputs while within the memory of the ROM, locations corresponding to the addresses are stored as binary words. It is possible, therefore, to go from truth table directly to a finished logic circuit in a single simple step by using a ROM. A considerable amount of design time can be saved with this technique.

Since a ROM is more expensive than standard SSI logic circuits, it is not practical nor economical to use a ROM where very simple logic functions are required. If only a few inputs and a few outputs are involved in a circuit, it is generally wiser to implement it with conventional logic gates. However, if the number of inputs or outputs is at least four, then the ROM becomes a more practical choice.

Code Conversion

As discussed earlier, code conversion refers to any multi-

316

input/multi-output combinational logic circuit. A code converter is merely a special application of such a logic circuit. Since ROMs can readily replace multi-input/multi-output combinational logic circuits, they provide simple and inexpensive means of code conversion.

To use a ROM as a code converter, the input code is used as the binary address code for the ROM. The desired output code is in the memory location specified by the input or address code. The desired output codes are merely stored in the memory locations and read out when they are called by the equivalent input code or address. Although no complex logic functions can be implemented, all of the most commonly-used code conversions can be implemented with ROMs.

Arithmetic Operations

Some of the most difficult functions to implement with digital logic circuitry are arithmetic operations. Simple combinational logic circuits have been developed to perform addition, subtraction, multiplication, and division. However, more complex functions such as trigonometric and logarithmic functions are more difficult to implement. The ROM provides a rather simple and direct method of implementing such more-complex arithmetic operations.

A significant amount of logic circuitry is necessary to multiply two binary numbers. A ROM, however, can perform this operation without the need for complex circuitry, its related high cost or space requirement. As a plus, the ROM also performs the operation at significantly higher speed.

The concept of multiplying two binary numbers using a ROM is illustrated in Table 7-9. For simplicity, only 2-bit binary numbers will be discussed; however, larger numbers can also be multiplied using the same technique. Multiplication of two binary numbers produces a product with a length equal to the sum of bits comprising both input numbers. The 2-bit binary numbers serving as multiplier and multipicand in this example, therefore, will result in a 4-bit product. The two input numbers or words, are grouped to form a single 4-bit binary input number, which becomes the input address to the ROM. The correct 4-bit product corresponding to the two 2-bit numbers is stored in the memory location at the address called by the 4-bit input. The correct product is read out, therefore, when any combination of the 2-bit input numbers appears on the ROM address lines. For example, when one input is 11

Table 7-9. Truth Table for 2-Bit ROM Multiplier.

Inputs				Outputs			
0	0	0	0	0	0	0	0
0	0	0	1	0	0	0	0
0	0	1	0	0	0	0	0
0	0	1	1	0	0	0	0
0	1	0	0	0	0	0	0
0	1	0	1	0	0	0	1
0	1	1	0	0	0	1	0
0	1	1	1	0	0	1	1
1	0	0	0	0	0	0	0
1	0	0	1	0	0	1	0
1	0	1	0	0	1	0	0
1	0	1	1	0	1	1	0
1	1	0	0	0	0	0	0
1	1	0	1	0	0	1	1
1	1	1	0	0	1	1	0
1	1	1	1	1	0	0	1

(decimal 3) and the other is 10 (decimal 2), the input address is grouped as 1110. The number 0110 (decimal 6), which is the product of 2 and 3, is stored at this location in the memory of the ROM. Numbers requiring more bits can be multiplied by employing a larger ROM.

A ROM is particularly useful in handling complex mathematical operations, such as trigonometry and logarithms. The ROM simply stores the trigonometric functions corresponding to the angles, instead of a digital circuit being used to actually compute the sine, cosine, tangent or other function of a number. Similarly, a ROM can be used to store the logarithms of specified input numbers. The desired input number of angle is applied to the ROM as an input address, and the desired result will be accessed at the output.

MICROPROGRAMMING

Microprogramming is a technique developed to systematically perform automatic control logic in a digital computer. A ROM is the heart of a microprogrammed control unit, and is combined with other logic elements to perform sequential logic operations. The complete circuit is called a *microprogrammed controller*.

Counters and shift registers combined with combinational logic circuits carry out most sequential operations. These circuits are used to produce a sequence of timing pulses which will control operations in other parts of the system. The pulses may increment or decrement counters, cause data transfers to occur between registers, enable or inhibit logic gates, select a multiplexer channel, or permit a decoding process to begin. All of these operations will be timed to occur in the proper sequence to perform the desired operation.

Control logic circuitry can become very large and complex in some digital systems. By using a microprogrammed controller, an entire network of sequential and combinational logic circuits can be replaced by a very simple circuit containing a ROM. Two methods of implementing sequential logic functions with a ROM are shown in Fig. 7-52.

In Fig. 7-52A the ROM is driven by a binary counter. A periodic clock signal increments the 4-bit binary counter, and the ROM address input is fed by the counter output. In this case, the address

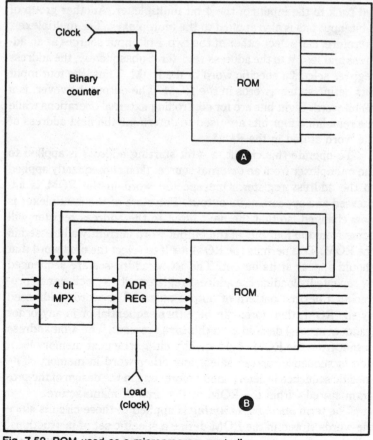

Fig. 7-52. ROM used as a microprogram controller.

decoder is assumed to be part of the ROM itself. The output of the ROM consists of parallel 8-bit words, the ROM containing 16 8-bit words, since there are four input bits. A sequence of 8-bit words appears at the ROM's output as a binary counter is incremented. The words which are stored in the ROM are programmed so that the binary states appearing at its output will cause the desired logic operations to take place in the proper sequence. The output lines in this example can be used for a variety of control purposes. The states of these outputs are strictly a function of the bits which are stored within the ROM, with the rate of change of the ROM's output being function of the frequency of the clock pulses which step the binary counter.

Figure 7-52B shows a more sophisticated version of the same circuit. In this circuit, note how four of the ROM's output bits are fed back to the inputs of the 4-bit multiplexer. Another group of 4-bit input bits is also applied to the multiplexer. The multiplexer, therefore, can select either of the two 4-bit input sources as an address and feed it to the address register. Subsequently, the address register selects a specific word in the ROM. Thus, the four input bits define sixteen words in the ROM. The output, however, is a 12-bit word: Eight bits are for controlling external operations while the remaining four bits are used to determine the next address of the word stored in the ROM.

To operate this circuit, a 4-bit starting address is applied to the multiplexer from an external source, then subsequently applied to the address register. One specific word in the ROM is addressed and appears at its output. The state of the multiplexer is now changed, so that the next input to the address register will come from the four bits of the output word currently addressed in the ROM. This permits the ROM itself to select the next word that should appear at its output. The ROM addresses are sequenced by repeatedly loading the address register with a clock signal, producing a desired pattern of output pulses. The words addressed by the ROM, therefore, can be either sequential or in any order (random access) desired with this arrangement. The 4-bit address output from the ROM could specify either the next memory location in sequence, or can select any other word in memory. The specific sequence is determined beforehand in the design of the program stored within the ROM at the time of manufacture.

The term *microprogramming* is applied to these circuits since the words stored in the ROM define a specific set of instructions, called a *program*, for carrying out a specific function or functions.

Each word stored within the ROM is called a *microinstruction*. Certain operations are caused to occur as a result of the bits of the word appearing at the output of the ROM. In other words, the output word from the ROM instructs the external circuitry of the function to be performed. All the words or microinstructions stored within the ROM comprise the microprogram, and define the complete operation to be executed. The configurations shown in Fig. 7-52 are only two of many different ways that microprogrammed operations can be implemented.

Chapter 8

Digital Design

DEFINING WHAT THE CIRCUIT MUST ACCOMPLISH IS THE first step in designing a digital circuit. By outlining the circuit specifications, the specified purpose and desired performance will accurately be detailed. The remaining design steps consist of converting the set of specifications into a practical working circuit that meets the design objectives. However, some standard for evaluating a design must be employed to determine if all design criteria have been met. The primary design criterion for any type of electronic circuit is to achieve maximum performance at minimum cost. Many combinations of components may perform a function, but the selection can be narrowed by defining what is meant by "maximum performance" and "minimum cost." Both of these considerations will now be discussed.

Maximum Performance. Depending upon the equipment or circuit being designed, the term "maximum performance" can have several meanings. Therefore, the definition of maximum performance is a direct function of the application. Operating speed, size, reliability, power consumption, and other unique features are some of the factors that comprise "maximum" performance.

Minimum Cost. In order to achieve the design objective of maximum performance with minimum cost, both the cost materials and that of time spent must be considered. A low-cost design will contain fewer components and, therefore, require a smaller circuit board on which to mount them. Furthermore, the fewer the number of parts in any circuit, the higher will be its reliability in direct proportion.

The time spent to design and produce any product must be included in its manufacturing cost. The easier and faster a circuit is to design, construct and test, the lower its end cost will be.

DESIGN TRADE-OFFS

An efficient design is one that achieves maximum performance at a minimum cost. In practical situations, trade-offs are generally necessary if the primary design is to achieve the *highest* performance possible at the *absolute minimum* cost. In reality, high performance always costs more money. In other words, if extremely high performance standards must be met, the penalty of higher cost *must* be accepted. In such an application, for example, high-cost digital integrated circuits must be used to achieve the highest possible operating speed. Higher operating speed almost invariably means higher power consumption as well. Therefore, cost and power consumption must be sacrificed for higher operating speed. Additionally, high-performance designs are generally more complex which translates into more design time. In almost any design, an efficient, middle-of-the-road solution should be sought by juggling the performance requirements and cost factors to achieve a practical performance level at a reasonable cost.

COMBINATIONAL LOGIC CIRCUIT DESIGN

Using modern integrated circuits, the steps in the design procedure are as follows:
1. Defining the problem
2. Developing a truth table
3. Writing the logic equations
4. Minimizing the logic equations
5. Implementing the design by selecting the circuitry

Each of the above steps will be discussed in detail. The technique of minimizing logic equations without the use of Boolean algebra, using Karnaugh maps, will also be described.

Defining the Problem

Defining the complete problem is the first step in the design of any logic circuit. This means that *all* functions of the circuit must be thoroughly identified. From the specific application of the circuit, the exact operations must be known and be outlined.

The most thorough method of problem definition is to write down a complete description of the application and the functions to be performed. Doing this forces the designer to completely identify and explain exactly what will be taking place. Included in such a description will be the types and number of input and output signals the circuit will accommodate. The circuit description should be as complete as possible. It is not important how the description is written; it can be narrative in paragraph form, or simply a list of inputs, functions to be performed, and outputs.

After completing a functional description of the circuit make up a table of specifications. Some of the information in the description of the circuit may be duplicated in the specification table. However, the information should be more concisely stated. The specification table should list the number and types of inputs and outputs, desired operating speed and power consumption, cost, size, and weight objective, types of integrated circuits to be employed, interfacing requirements for all inputs and outputs including logic level assignments, and any other pertinent information concerning the operation of the circuit. All of the information necessary to complete the design of any circuit should be included in the problem definition, functional description, and specification table.

Problem definition is a valuable exercise when designing a combinational logic circuit. In preparing this information many things may be discovered about the circuit which may not have been initially thought of, making it a vital step in the design procedure which may determine the success or failure of the final design. A good definition also means that a complete set of documentation for the completed circuit will be available for later use in preparing an instruction or maintenance manual for the finished system.

DESIGNING A BCD INVALID-CODE DETECTOR

As an exercise in logic circuit design, let us develop a combinational logical circuit which will monitor a 4-bit binary word and generate a binary 1 output signal whenever any one of the six invalid 4-bit states in the 8421 BCD code occur.

Specifications

1. 4-bit parallel binary input word
2. Output signal will be binary 1 each time any one of the six invalid BCD Code numbers occurs
3. TTL integrated circuits will be used with standard logic

levels of binary $0 = +0.4$ volts and binary $1 = +3.5$ volts

4. Propagation delay of this design should be less than 100 nanoseconds. (The output will become binary 1 in less than 100 nanoseconds from the time the input detects any one of the six invalid BCD values.)

5. The entire circuit should be contained within a single DIP integrated circuit to minimize cost, size and power consumption.

Developing a Truth Table

Converting the problem into a truth table is the next step in the design procedure. The truth table is merely a chart that completely identifies all possible input combinations and corresponding output states. It completely defines the operation of the circuit, and can be developed directly from the problem description and specification table.

In developing a truth table, the first step is to determine the number of inputs to the logic circuit. This will of course, be a function of the application, and should have been defined in the problem definition. The number of inputs will determine the maximum number of input states which can occur with this number of variables. The maximum number of input states which can occur is equal to 2^n where n is equal to the number of inputs. Depending upon the application, all or only some of the possible states may occur. These should be identified in the problem definition.

Begin the truth table by writing down all possible input states. This can be done by simply listing the binary numbers from zero all the way through the maximum upper limit of the total number of possible input states; e.g., for four inputs (16 possible states), list all 4-bit binary numbers from 0000 through 1111 in sequence. This will completely define all possible input states.

In a column adjacent to the list of input states, identify the output variables specified in the problem. In this column, next to each possible input combination, record the desired output state for each corresponding input combination. In some of the input states aren't used, identify them as being "invalid" or "don't care."

The truth table for the BCD invalid-code detector is shown in Table 8-1. The input is a parallel 4-bit word. Each of the input bits is labeled with a letter for identification. Short mnemonics designating the signal may also be used if it suits the application. The output of the circuit, labeled F, is the logic signal which will be binary 1 if an invalid code is detected.

Inputs				Output
A	B	C	D	F
0	0	0	0	0
0	0	0	1	0
0	0	1	0	0
0	0	1	1	0
0	1	0	0	0
0	1	0	1	0
0	1	1	0	0
0	1	1	1	0
1	0	0	0	0
1	0	0	1	0
1	0	1	0	1
1	0	1	1	1
1	1	0	0	1
1	1	0	1	1
1	1	1	0	1
1	1	1	1	1

Table 8-1. Truth Table for BCD Invalid-Code Detector.

All sixteen possible input combinations of the four bits are listed in the truth table. The first ten states, 0000 through 1001, are the valid 8421 BCD Codes. Since these ten states are valid, the output, F, will be binary 0 upon their occurrence. For the inputs 1010 through 1111, however, the output, F, should be 1. In this example, there are no unused or "don't care" states, and the truth table completely defines the circuit's operation.

Although this example has only a single output, F, other combinational logic circuits may have multiple outputs. In those instances, the other outputs will also have to be defined, as well. Each output will be listed in a separate column of the truth table.

Logic Equation Development

In the design process, the next step is to write the Boolean logic equations from the truth table. This will permit the logic function to be manipulated with Boolean algebra, and allow minimization of logic circuitry required to implement the design. It may not be necessary to minimize the equations with algebra in some applications. Depending upon the types of circuits to be used, the equations can simply be used as a guide in the implementation of the functions.

From the truth table, a logic equation is written by observing the outputs and writing a product term of the inputs for each corresponding output where a binary 1 state occurs. The final result will be a sum-of-products logic equation. This will lead to a separate Boolean equation for each output where multiple output logic circuits are being designed.

Examination of the BCD invalid code detector's truth table in Table 8-1, the output equation can be written:

$$F = A \bar{B} C \bar{D} + A \bar{B} C D + A B \bar{C} \bar{D} + A B \bar{C} D + A B C \bar{D} + A B C D$$

It is possible at this point to implement the Boolean equation directly with logic circuits. This function can be performed with a combination of AND and OR gates. However, it is desirable in most cases to use Boolean algebra (or other techniques) to reduce the equation to a simpler form. This can minimize the number of gates and, therefore the number of integrated circuit packages required to implement the design. Ultimately, minimization will lead to lower cost, smaller size, and reduced power consumption.

Circuit Minimization

Using the Boolean algebra techniques described in *Chapter 4* of this book, the logic equation developed in the previous step can be reduced as shown below:

$$F = A \bar{B} C \bar{D} + A \bar{B} C D + A B \bar{C} \bar{D} + A B \bar{C} D + A B C \bar{D} + A B C D$$

Reduce by factoring:

$$F = A \bar{B} C (D + \bar{D}) + A B \bar{C} (D + \bar{D}) + A B C (D + \bar{D})$$

Reduce by Law of Complements and Law of Intersection:

$$F = A \bar{B} C + A B \bar{C} + A B C$$

Reduce by factoring:

$$F = A \bar{B} C + A B (C + \bar{C})$$

Reduce by Law of Complements and Law of Intersection:

$$F = A \bar{B} C + AB$$

328

Reduce by factoring:

$$F = A(\overline{B} \, C + B)$$

Reduce by Law of Absorption $\overline{B} \, C + B = B + C$:

$$F = A(B + C)$$

Expand by multiplying:

$$F = A \, B + A \, C$$

As can be seen, a significant reduction in the equation takes place. This minimization step is very important in the design of digital circuitry since it is obvious that it requires less circuitry to implement the reduced version than the original equation developed directly from the truth table.

Using Boolean algebra is sometimes a very time-consuming and burdensome process for large and complex equations. An equation may have to be rearranged and regrouped several times before a minimized result can be achieved. Additionally, Boolean algebra procedures do not *always* lead to optimum minimized equations. Some methods of circuit reduction do not show themselves in the equation reduction procedure because of the subtility of some logic circuits. For this reason, Boolean algebra has its limitations and other forms of circuit minimization have been developed to quickly and conveniently provide the maximum amount of minimization possible. One such technique is the use of Karnaugh maps.

KARNAUGH MAPS

A Karnaugh map is a method of graphically minimizing logic equations. The equations that define a digital logic function can be arranged to form an illustration or "map" which will permit easy simplification. The Karnaugh map is merely an alternative to Boolean algebra for minimizing logic expressions. It is preferred over Boolean algebra since it makes the reduction process faster, easier, and more efficient. Karnaugh mapping completely eliminates the necessity for using Boolean algebra and permits the translation of a logic function directly from the truth table to the simplified form. Therefore, it is not always necessary to first write equations from the truth table with this method.

Karnaugh maps efficiently replace Boolean logic equations in the sum-of-products form. As discussed earlier, these equations are derived from the truth table. Each of the product terms in the equation is called a *minterm*. Furthermore, each minterm is the product of the various input variables called *literals*. All possible input combinations are listed in the truth table defining the logic function. For a two-input logic circuit, for example, there are four possible input combinations: 00, 01, 10, 11. Therefore, if the input literals are given the designations X and Y, respectively, then their minterms will be : $\overline{X}\overline{Y}$, $\overline{X}Y$, $X\overline{Y}$, and XY.

The product terms are often written simply as the letter m followed by a subscript equal to the decimal number of the binary number being represented by that minterm. For example, the product term AB represents the input states 11. The minterm designation, therefore, would be m^3. The product terms, the binary and decimal equivalents, and the minterm designations for the 2-input logic circuit are shown in Table 8-2.

A Karnaugh map takes this information and translates it directly into a graphical format. A Karnaugh map for a two-input logic circuit is shown in Fig. 8-1. There are four possible product terms, since there are two input variables. Each product term (minterm) is represented by a square (or cell) in the map.

To illustrate how the equation and the map are related, several examples will now be converted from the equation to the map and vice-versa.

Consider the Boolean equation: $C = \overline{A}B + A\overline{B}$. This is the equation for the exclusive OR circuit. It contains two product terms of the two variables, A and B. To plot this equation on the Karnaugh map, simply place a binary 1 in the cells which represent the product terms in the equation as shown in Fig. 8-2. The cells can be identified by referring to the designations on the top and side of the map. Above the map are the designations A and $\overline{A}$, which

Table 8-2. Logical Product of the Minterm Designations of Two Literals.

Decimal	Binary A B	Product term	Minterm designation
0	0 0	$\overline{A}$ $\overline{B}$	M_0
1	0 1	$\overline{A}$ B	M_1
2	1 0	A $\overline{B}$	M_2
3	1 1	A B	M_3

330

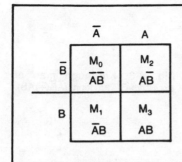

Fig. 8-1. Karnaugh map of two variables.

correspond to the two vertical columns. Likewise, to the left of the map are the designations B and $\overline{B}$, which correspond to the two horizontal rows. The product term corresponding to a specific cell is identified by finding the coordinates of the cell by the letter designations which define the term by reading up and to the left of the cell and forming the product term by combining these literals.

A known equation was translated into a Karnaugh map in this example. The Karnaugh map, however, can also be developed directly from the truth table. By observing the input states corresponding to the binary 1 outputs, the product terms can be translated and then be plotted on the map.

Refer to the map shown in Fig. 8-3 as an example of translating the equivalent Boolean equation from a Karnaugh map. To write the output expression corresponding to this map, first develop a minterm for each cell containing a binary 1. Then, these minterms can be ORed together to form a sum-of-products Boolean equation. The map in Fig. 8-3 defines the exclusive NOR function. This equation can also be written using minterm designations:

$$C = m^0 + m^3$$

Fig. 8-2. Karnaugh map of exclusive-OR function: ($A\overline{B} \oplus \overline{A}B$).

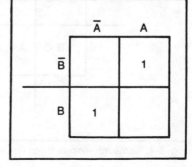

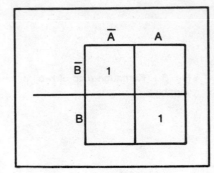

Fig. 8-3. Karnaugh map of exclusive-OR function: ($\overline{A}\overline{B} \oplus AB$).

The Karnaugh map for a three-variable logic circuit is shown in Fig. 8-4. There are eight possible input combinations, since there are three input variables. Each input state is represented by a cell in the map. The designated minterm for each cell is shown. Table 8-3 shows the relationships among the product terms, their binary and decimal equivalents, and the minterm designations. The columns and rows in the map of Fig. 8-5 are designated by the literals corresponding to the inputs. The two vertical columns on the right are designated A, while the two vertical columns on the left are designated $\overline{A}$. Input variable, C, designates a different form of these columns. The two center columns represent C while the two outside columns represent $\overline{C}$. The two horizontal rows of four cells each are designated B and $\overline{B}$. In this map, it can be seen that it requires *three* input designations to define the coordinates of each cell. The minterm represented by each cell, therefore, can be deter-

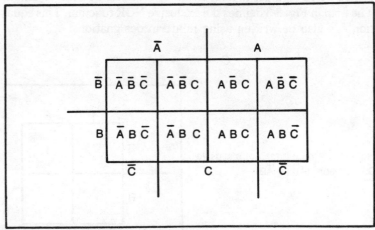

Fig. 8-4. Karnaugh map of three variables.

332

Decimal	Binary A B C	Product term	Minterm designation
0	0 0 0	$\overline{A}$ $\overline{B}$ $\overline{C}$	M_0
1	0 0 1	$\overline{A}$ $\overline{B}$ C	M_1
2	0 1 0	$\overline{A}$ B $\overline{C}$	M_2
3	0 1 1	$\overline{A}$ B C	M_3
4	1 0 0	A $\overline{B}$ $\overline{C}$	M_4
5	1 0 1	A $\overline{B}$ C	M_5
6	1 1 0	A B $\overline{C}$	M_6
7	1 1 1	A B C	M_7

mined by simply writing a product term comprised of the three
literals designating the cell in its row and column position.

The method of recording a given Boolean equation in the Karnaugh map for three variables is similar to that for two variables. Consider the equation:

$$C = A\,\overline{B}\,C + A\,\overline{B}\,\overline{C} + \overline{A}\,B\,C$$

Each three = variable term is designated by a binary 1 in the appropriate cell as shown in Fig. 8-6.

The Karnaugh map in Fig. 8-7 shows how to write an equation from the map. The minterms represented by the cells where binary 1s appear are logically ORed (summed) together to produce the final equation:

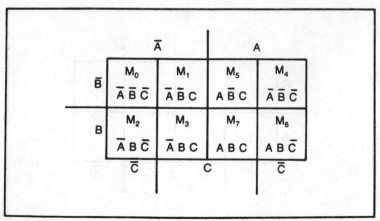

Fig. 8-5. Karnaugh map of three minterm designations for three literals.

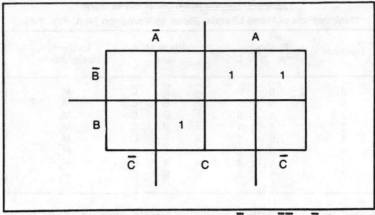

Fig. 8-6. Karnaugh map of the equation: $C = A\overline{B}C + A\overline{B}\overline{C} + \overline{A}BC$.

$$M = \overline{A}\,\overline{B}\,\overline{C} + \overline{A}\,B\,\overline{C} + A\,\overline{B}\,\overline{C} + A\,B\,C$$

In minterm form, the above equation is:

$$M = m_0 + m_2 + m_4 + m_7$$

The same concepts can be applied to logic expressions involving four variables. All sixteen possible combinations of four-input variables, all product terms and their binary and decimal equivalents, are shown in Table 8-4.

Figure 8-8 shows a four-variable Karnaugh map. Each cell in the map represents one of the four-variable minterms. The pro-

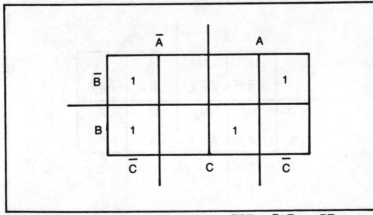

Fig. 8-7. Karnaugh map of the equation: $M = \overline{A}\overline{B}\overline{C} + \overline{A}B\overline{C} + A\overline{B}\overline{C} + ABC$

Table 8-4. All possible Combinations of Four Literals, and Associated Minterm Designations.

Decimal	Binary				Product term				Minterm
	A	B	C	D					
0	0	0	0	0	$\bar{A}$	$\bar{B}$	$\bar{C}$	$\bar{D}$	M_0
1	0	0	0	1	$\bar{A}$	$\bar{B}$	$\bar{C}$	D	M_1
2	0	0	1	0	$\bar{A}$	$\bar{B}$	C	$\bar{D}$	M_2
3	0	0	1	1	$\bar{A}$	$\bar{B}$	C	D	M_3
4	0	1	0	0	$\bar{A}$	B	$\bar{C}$	$\bar{D}$	M_4
5	0	1	0	1	$\bar{A}$	B	$\bar{C}$	D	M_5
6	0	1	1	0	$\bar{A}$	B	C	$\bar{D}$	M_6
7	0	1	1	1	$\bar{A}$	B	C	D	M_7
8	1	0	0	0	A	$\bar{B}$	$\bar{C}$	$\bar{D}$	M_8
9	1	0	0	1	A	$\bar{B}$	$\bar{C}$	D	M_9
10	1	0	1	0	A	$\bar{B}$	C	$\bar{D}$	M_{10}
11	1	0	1	1	A	$\bar{B}$	C	D	M_{11}
12	1	1	0	0	A	B	$\bar{C}$	$\bar{D}$	M_{12}
13	1	1	0	1	A	B	$\bar{C}$	D	M_{13}
14	1	1	1	0	A	B	C	$\bar{D}$	M_{14}
15	1	1	1	1	A	B	C	D	M_{15}

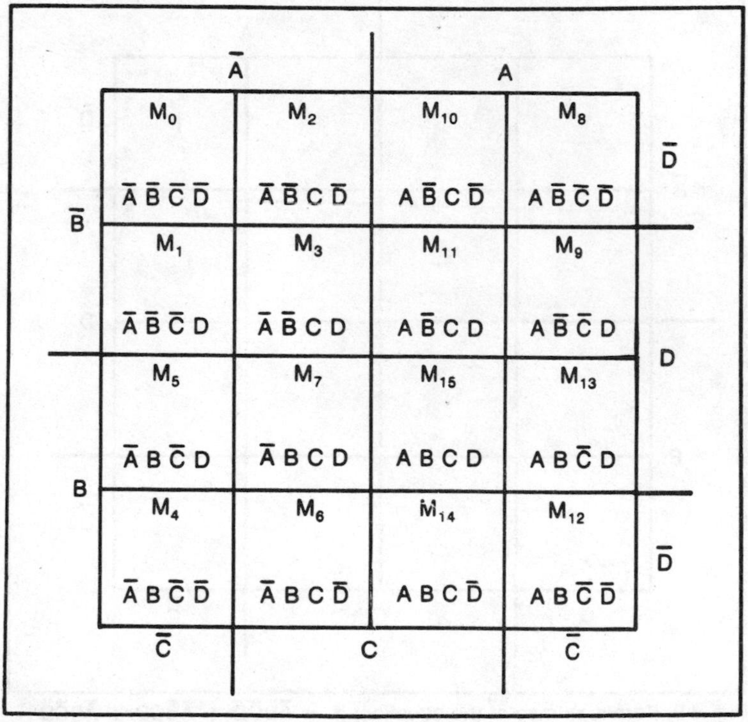

Fig. 8-8. Karnaugh map of four variables.

cedure for recording a sum-of-products equation and for writing an equation from the map are similar to that of the previously-discussed maps. For example, Fig. 8-9 shows the map representing the equation:

$$X = \overline{A}\,\overline{B}\,\overline{C}\,\overline{D} + \overline{A}\,\overline{B}\,C\,D + \overline{A}\,B\,\overline{C}\,\overline{D} + A\,\overline{B}\,\overline{C}\,\overline{D} + A\,\overline{B}\,C\,D$$
$$(X = m_0 + m_3 + m_4 + m_8 + m_{11})$$

The Boolean equations for the BCD invalid code detector circuit, discussed earlier in this chapter, can be written from the truth table as:

$$F = A\,\overline{B}\,C\,\overline{D} + A\,\overline{B}\,C\,D + A\,B\,\overline{C}\,\overline{D} + A\,B\,\overline{C}\,D + A\,B\,C\,\overline{D}$$
$$+ A\,B\,C\,D$$
$$(F = m_{10} + m_{11} + m_{12} + m_{13} + m_{14} + m_{15})$$

Figure 8-10 shows how to place these terms on the Karnaugh map.

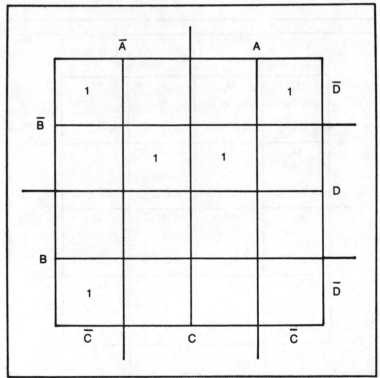

Fig. 8-9. Karnaugh map of the equation: $X = \overline{A}\overline{B}\overline{C}\overline{D} + \overline{A}\overline{B}CD + \overline{A}B\overline{C}\overline{D} + A\overline{B}\overline{C}\overline{D} + A\overline{B}CD$.

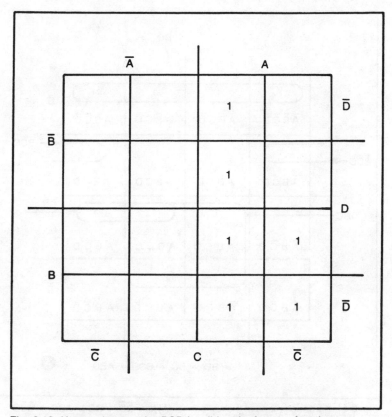

Fig. 8-10. Karnaugh map of a BCD invalid code detector function.

CIRCUIT MINIMIZATION WITH KARNAUGH MAPS

The reduction of logic equations using Boolean algebra is mostly by implementing the Law of Complements ($X + \overline{X} = 1$). The minterms can be grouped to permit factoring out common variables by first writing the logical equation in the sum-of-products form. This method usually produces Law of Complements expressions for at least one of the input variables. Therefore, the expression will be simplified by the elimination of at least one of the input variables from the group of minterms from which it is factored. Almost all of the reduction resulting from the implementation of Boolean algebra is a result of factoring variables using the Law of Complements. The Karnaugh map efficiently implements this technique in a graphical form.

By examining the four-variable Karnaugh maps in Figs. 8-11(A) and (B), it can be seen that adjacent cells (or adjacent minterms)

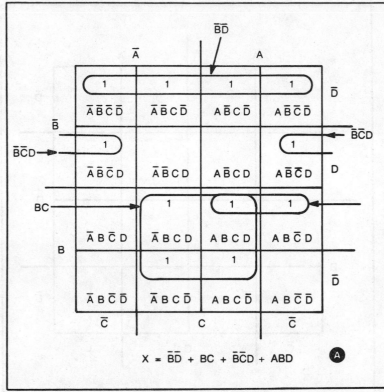

$$X = \overline{B}\overline{D} + BC + \overline{B}\overline{C}D + ABD$$

Fig. 8-11. Karnaugh maps of the equations: (A) X = $\overline{B}\overline{D}$ + BC + ABD + $\overline{B}\overline{C}D$, and (B) X = C$\overline{D}$ + A$\overline{C}$ + $\overline{B}$D.

differ by only *one* of the input variables. That is, only a single variable will change from one cell to an adjacent cell in any direction. For example, in moving from the upper cell to the lower cell containing the binary 1 minterms in the map of Fig. 8-12, notice how only the B variable changes from $\overline{B}$ to B; the A and C variables *do not* change. Therefore, these adjacent minterms specify a reduction that can be performed. This can be seen more plainly by writing the Boolean equation for the recorded minterms. Assume that the function of Y is the sum-of-product equations of these two minterms. The equation from the map of Fig. 8-12, therefore, is:

$$Y = A\,\overline{B}\,C + A\,B\,C$$

Now, by using Boolean Algebra:

338

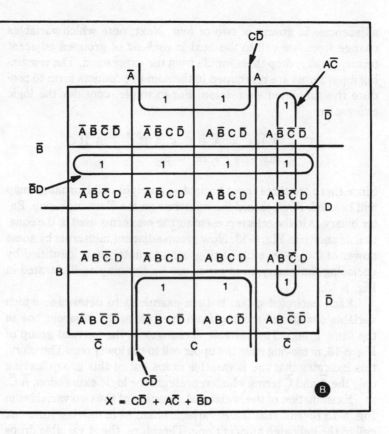

The Karnaugh map showing cells labeled with minterms, with groupings $C\bar{D}$, $A\bar{C}$, $\bar{B}D$, $C\bar{D}$.

$$X = C\bar{D} + A\bar{C} + \bar{B}D$$

$$
\begin{aligned}
Y &= A\,\bar{B}\,C + A\,B\,C \\
Y &= A\,C(B + \bar{B}) \\
Y &= A\,C(1) \\
Y &= A\,C
\end{aligned}
$$

See how AC was factored out of each minterm leaving the expression equal to $(B + \bar{B})$. The expression is greatly simplified since the term $(B + \bar{B})$ is equal to 1. The literal, B, simply drops out, leaving the expression $Y = AC$. Karnaugh map minimization is based on this concept.

The basic procedure for Karnaugh map minimization of a logic equation is as follows. First, map the expression by inserting a binary 1 in each cell representing the minterms in the sum-of-products logic equation. Then, identify the horizontal and vertical adjacencies in groups of two or four. Next, note which variables change from one cell to the next in *each set* of grouped adjacent terms. Finally, drop these inputs from the expression. The remaining input terms are regrouped in the sum-of-products form to produce the simplified expression. For example, consider the logic expression:

$$Y = \overline{A}\,\overline{B}\,\overline{C} + \overline{A}\,\overline{B}\,C + \overline{A}\,B\,\overline{C} + A\,\overline{B}\,C$$
$$Y = m_0 + m_1 + m_2 + m_5$$

Since there are three input variables, an eight-cell Karnaugh map will be used. First, record the minterms on the Karnaugh map. Enter binary 1s in the cells representing the minterms used in the equation as shown in Fig. 8-13. Now group adjacent minterms by some power of 2 (2, 4, 8, etc). Each group of minterms is identified by enclosing the binary 1s in an ellipse on the map as illustrated in Fig. 8-13.

Each encircled group is then examined to determine which variable changes in moving from one cell to the adjacent one in the same group. The variable *B* changes in the vertical group of Fig. 8-13, in moving from the upper cell to the lower one. Therefore, this indicates that the B variable drops out of this group leaving only the $\overline{A}$ and $\overline{C}$ terms which represents the logic expression, $\overline{A}\,\overline{C}$.

Examination of the horizontal grouping of the two variables in Fig. 8-13 reveals that the *A* variable changes in moving from one cell to the indicated adjacent one. Therefore, the *A* variable drops

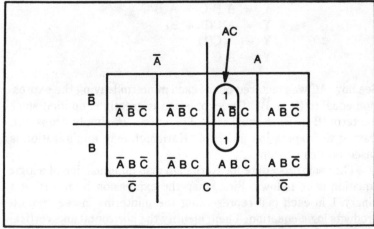

Fig. 8-12. Karnaugh map illustrating how adjacent cells differ by only one literal.

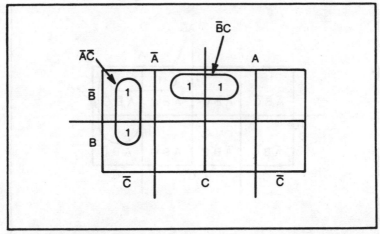

Fig. 8-13. Minimizing the expression Y = m0 + m1 + m2 + m5.

out leaving only the $\overline{B}$ and C variables. A new and shorter minterm is developed from the variables that *have not* changed once the variable that *does* change is identified. A product term of the variables that don't change is formed. These shorter product terms for each group are then ORed (summed) to produce the reduced expression. Therefore, the reduced expression from the Karnaugh map of Fig. 8-13 is:

$$Y = \overline{A}\,\overline{C} + \overline{B}\,C$$

The ability to implement a Karnaugh map to produce a minimized equation results from the skill with which the minterms are properly grouped and with which all of the adjacencies or combinations of adjacencies are recognized. Another two examples of mapping logic equations for practice are given in Fig. 8-14(A) and (B). The Boolean equation of Fig. 8-17A is:

$$X = A\,\overline{B}\,C + A\,\overline{B}\,\overline{C} + A\,B\,\overline{C}$$

The three minterms are recorded in the appropriate cells of the Karnaugh map by the insertion of binary 1s. The redundant input variables are identified by grouping the adjacent minterms. Note how the minterm, $A\overline{B}\overline{C}$, is used twice. It should be pointed out that any given minterm may be used as many times as needed to form adjacent minterm groups of two or four, etc.

The redundant input variables are determined by noting which

341

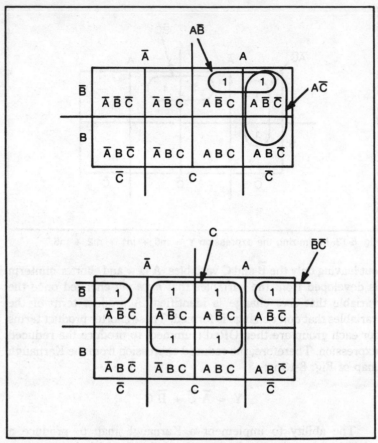

Fig. 8-14. Two examples of using Karnaugh maps to reduce three-variable logic equations.

variable changes from one cell to another within the newly formed groups. The horizontal group of two indicates the change of variable $\overline{C}$. The C variable, therefore, drops out. The new product term is then comprised of the variables that did not change; in this case, $A\ \overline{B}$.

Next, examination of the vertical group of two reveals the redundant variable to be B. The A and $\overline{C}$ variables do not change. Therefore, they represent the new product term, $A\ \overline{C}$, for the minimized expression. The new product terms are finally logically summed or ORed to produce the output expression:

$$X = A\ \overline{B} + A\ \overline{C}$$

342

As can be seen, the newly-formed minimized expression is far more efficient and economical to implement than was the original.

Another example of minimizing a three-variable Boolean equation is illustrated in Fig. 8-14B. This equation is:

$$X = \overline{A}\,\overline{B}\,\overline{C} + \overline{A}\,\overline{B}\,C + \overline{A}\,B\,C + A\,\overline{B}\,\overline{C} + A\,\overline{B}\,C + A\,B\,C$$
$$(X = m_0 + m_1 + m_3 + m_4 + m_5 + m_7)$$

Groups of two or four adjacent minterms are encircled, as shown. The largest grouping possible is desirable, since the larger the grouping, the greater the reduction that will be possible. Moving from one cell to the other in the group of four, note that *both* the A and B variables change. Moving vertically, only the B variables change, while moving horizontally changes the A variables as well. The only input variable that does not change is the C variable. Therefore, *both* the A and B variables can be factored out and dropped from the equation. The remaining four-bit grouping represents only the input variable C and, therefore, we have achieved a substantial circuit minimization. This four-cell grouping denotes that the output expression will be affected *solely* by the variable C *regardless* of the A or B input states.

The unique characteristics of a Karnaugh map are illustrated by the grouping formed by the minterms $\overline{A}\,\overline{B}\,\overline{C}$ and $A\,\overline{B}\,\overline{C}$. Note that between these two minterm cells only the A variable changes. These two cells, therefore, can be considered to be adjacent. Another way of looking at the Karnaugh map is to assume the left edge is adjacent to the right edge. Similarly, the top edge can be assumed to be adjacent to the bottom edge. The Karnaugh map, therefore, can be thought of as being a three-dimensional sphere rather than a flat map. Thus all cells are adjacent on all four sides to other ones. This adjacency results in the expression $\overline{B}\,\overline{C}$ since these variables are common to both cells with only the A variable changing states and, therefore, being dropped from the equation. The minimized final output expression is:

$$X = \overline{B}\,\overline{C} + C$$

The above two examples illustrate the power of the Karnaugh map. Logic expressions can quickly be reduced to their minimum form with a little practice in mapping and grouping minterms. The Karnaugh map provides a visual means of recognizing patterns of minterm groupings so that input variable redundancies can easily

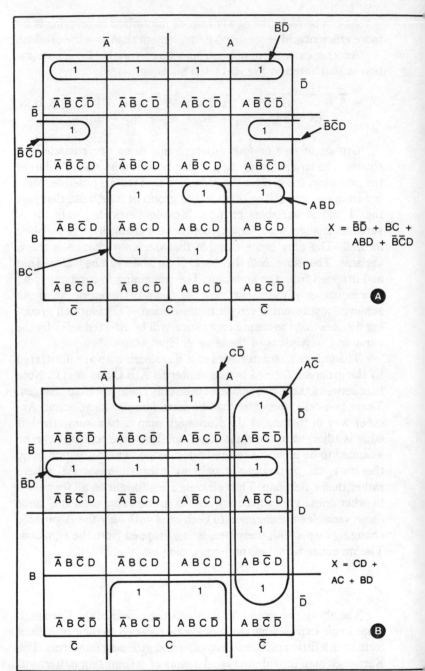

Fig. 8-15. Examples of Karnaugh maps for four-variable logic equations.

344

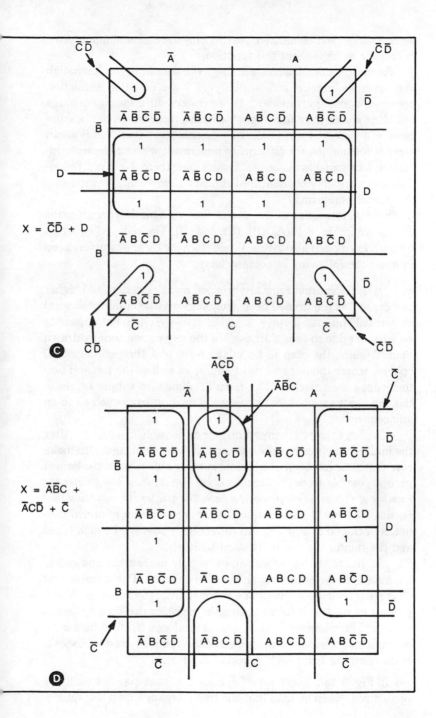

$X = \overline{C}\overline{D} + D$

$X = \overline{A}\overline{B}C + \overline{A}C\overline{D} + \overline{C}$

be established and eliminated, leaving only the essential input terms necessary to implement the function.

As more input variables are used, the benefit of the Karnaugh map in speeding up and simplifying logic equation reduction becomes increasingly evident. Since sixteen different input states can be produced from four-input variables, these states can be combined in a variety of ways to form logic equations. Standard Boolean algebra techniques are difficult to implement with expressions involving four-variable minterms. By mapping them, however, redundancies can readily be identified almost automatically by grouping the related minterms.

Several examples of the use of four-variable Karnaugh maps are shown in Fig. 8-15(A), (B), (C), and (D). The reduced equation for each example is also given. When studying these examples, keep in mind the following important facts:

1. Adjacent minterms are grouped by pairs, quads, and higher powers of 2 as required. These groupings may be either horizontal or vertical and may involve adjacent cells which do not appear to be adjacent due to the "flatness" of the two-dimensionally-drawn map. Assume the map to be in the form of a three-dimensional sphere, where the left and right edges, as well as the top and bottom edges are adjacent. The term "redundant" simply refers to the one input variable that changes in moving from one cell to an adjacent one.

2. Try to use as many minterms as possible in a group. After the initial groupings have been made, go over them again, to make sure that none has been overlooked in being able to form the largest groups possible from the smaller ones. Remember: *the greater the number of minterms encircled at a time, the greater the reduction that results*. There will be occasions, however, where a minterm cannot be included in a group. No reduction is possible in such cases and the minterm must be treated by itself.

3. In each group of variables, simply move from one cell to the adjacent one, noting which variable changes. The variable that changes is redundant and can be dropped from the minterm. A new product expression is formed using the variables that do not change.

4. The minimized expression is produced by forming a sum-of-products expression comprised of the reduced product expressions resulting from each group of minterms.

In Fig. 8-15C, there is one special case that may not easily be recognized. Keep in mind that the true Karnaugh map is a sphere.

Therefore, the four corner cells can also be considered to be adjacent. This can be seen more easily by examining the change of variables when moving from one corner cell to another. As can be seen, in moving from corner to corner, both the A and B variables change. The $\overline{C}$ and $\overline{D}$ variables, however, do not change, and are common to these cells. This permits the reduction of this group to the two-variable term, $\overline{C}\,\overline{D}$. In the center of this map note also the group of eight minterms. Since the A, B, and C variables all change from one cell to another, the only variable that doesn't change is D. This group of variables, therefore, represents simply the input variable D.

Finally, another special case which may occur is when all cells in a map are marked. The entire function represented by this map, therefore, is simply a binary 1.

SUMMARY OF KARNAUGH MAP USE

Below is a list summarizing the rules and procedures for using Karnaugh maps in the reduction and minimization of logic equations:

1. Study the logic equations or truth table for the function to be minimized. Construct a Karnaugh map containing the number of cells equal to 2 raised to the power equal to the number of input variables.

2. Map the minterms directly from the truth table, if provided. There is no need to translate the truth table into a Boolean equation. If a Boolean equation is provided, however, you can plot the minterms in the map from the equation.

3. Cluster the minterms in the map in groups of pairs, quads, or eights. Attempt to include each minterm in the largest possible group to ensure a minimized reduction. Each minterm can be used as many times as necessary to form group. Each group should be identified by encircling it.

4. Note which input variables change when moving from one cell to an adjacent one. The variables that change are redundant and can be dropped from the expression. Alternately, the variables within each group that *do not change* can be identified and used to form a product expression that will appear in the final equation.

5. Finally, write the reduced output expression by ORing all the product terms developed from each group.

Figure 8-16 shows the Karnaugh map used in reducing the

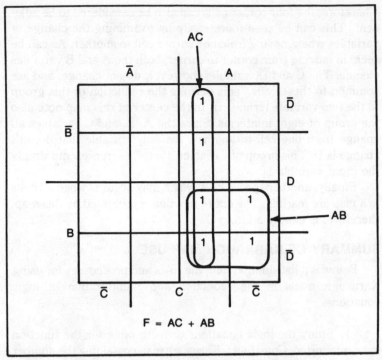

Fig. 8-16. Karnaugh map for the BCD invalid code detector.

Boolean expression for the BCD invalid code detector. The two groups of four variables are identified. The reduced equation, F = AB + AC, is much simpler than the equation written earlier from the truth table.

"Don't Care" States

In some design situations, all combinations of the input variables will not occur. For example, a design may call for the use of only seven of 16 possible input states where a four-variable input circuit is identified. By the application of the circuit, the input combinations that can never occur can easily be determined. There are various combinations of input states in other situations which will not affect the operation of the circuit and, therefore, the circuit "won't care" whether or not they occur. It is sometimes useful to identify these "don't care" states since they can be of value in minimizing the logic expression via a Karnaugh map. The "don't care" states can be plotted on the map along with the minterms specified by the truth table or the Boolean equation. In most cases, as you will find, they will aid in the reduction of the circuitry required to implement the desired function.

Assume that a design calls for four-input variables and the output function is indicated by the equation:

$$M = \overline{A}\,\overline{B}\,C\,D + \overline{A}\,\overline{B}\,C\,\overline{D} + A\,\overline{B}\,C\,D + A\,B\,C\,\overline{D} + A\,B\,C\,D$$

Figure 8-17 shows how to plot this function on a Karnaugh map. The variables are grouped to reduce the amount of circuitry required to implement this function as can be seen by the reduced equation:

$$M = \overline{A}\,\overline{B}\,C + \overline{B}\,C\,D + A\,B\,C$$

In the design process, it was determined that there are four "don't care" states: A B C D, A B C D, A B C D, and A B C D. These four "don't care" states can be plotted on the Karnaugh map represented by an X as shown in Fig. 8-17B. These "don't care" Xs can be grouped with the 1s to form larger groups to produce even further minimization. As before, the more minterms that can be included within a group, the more reduction of circuitry there will be in the final product. As can be seen from this example, three groups of four can now be formed. The resulting equation becomes:

$$M = \overline{A}\,C + C\,D + B\,C$$

This equation is much simpler than either the original or the reduced version without the use of the "don't care" states. When designing a combinational logic circuit, every attempt should be made to identify and include the "don't care" states in the Karnaugh map since they generally lead to significantly more circuit reductions.

IMPLEMENTING LOGIC EQUATIONS

The next step in designing a digital circuit is the selection of circuitry to implement the design. The basic goal is to perform the desired function with a minimum of components and the lowest possible cost. This will also reduce power consumption, size, weight, and increase reliability, as well.

The four practical methods to implement a combinational logic function with integrated circuits are:

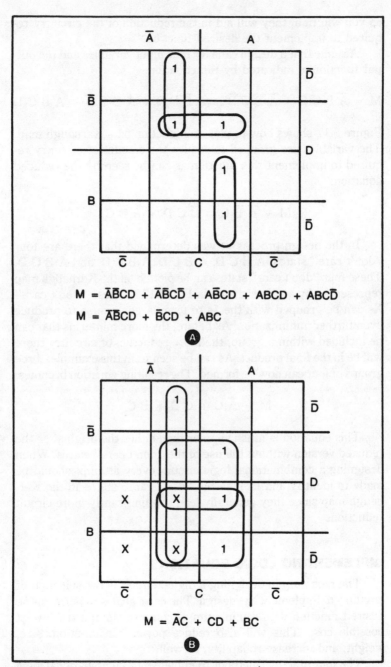

$$M = \overline{A}\overline{B}CD + \overline{A}\overline{B}C\overline{D} + A\overline{B}CD + ABCD + ABC\overline{D}$$
$$M = \overline{A}\overline{B}CD + \overline{B}CD + ABC$$

Ⓐ

$$M = \overline{A}C + CD + BC$$

Ⓑ

Fig. 8-17. Examples fo the use of "don't care" states in minimizing logic equations.

1. SSI
2. MSI
3. ROM
4. PLA

Each of these approaches has its own benefits and limitations. Each of these methods of implementation will be discussed in the following sections. In evaluating these methods, the BCD invalid code detector will be used as an example.

SSI IMPLEMENTATION

The use of SSI logic gates is the most direct method of logic equation implementation. The individual, basic NAND and NOR gates comprise the circuit. This literal approach should be used only when the function is simple. Some of the other techniques should be used, however, when larger and more complex functions are needed.

To illustrate the use of SSI implementation in the BCD invalid code detector circuit, consider the original Boolean equation:

$$F = A \overline{B} C \overline{D} + A \overline{B} C D + A B \overline{C} \overline{D} + A B \overline{C} D + A B C \overline{D} + A B C D$$

Figure 8-18A shows how this expression is readily implemented with SSI logic circuits. A 4-input logic gate is required for each product term. Three *7420*, dual 4-input TTL gates can be used. One gate will be used for each minterm expression in the equation. The output function, *F*, will then be produced by ORing all the product terms together. A 6-input OR gate is required, since there are six terms. The 7430 8-input TTL OR gate can be used for this purpose. Since two of these inputs will not be needed. They can be connected to any of the other inputs. The 4-input variables must come from a source where both the normal and complement signals are available. Figure 8-18B shows how to generate the complement signals from the normal outputs if the complements are not available. A standard 7404 TTL hex inverter containing six inverters can be used, even though only four will be needed. As can be seen, implementing this function using SSI circuitry requires a minimum of four, and possibly five, integrated circuit packages and, therefore, the circuit will take a considerable amount of time, space, and cost to produce. It is unwise to implement the BCD in-

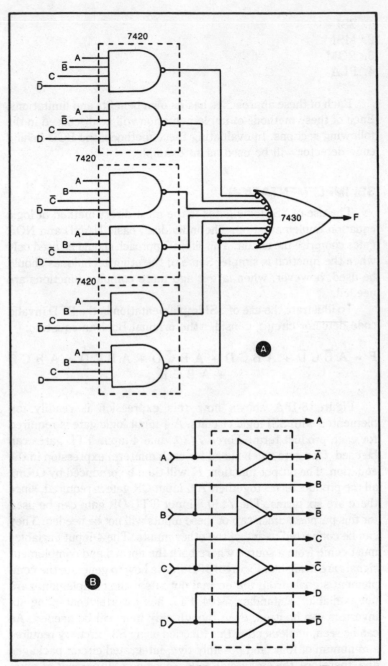

Fig. 8-18. (A) SSI implementation of a BCD invalid-code detector. (B) A method of generating complementary input signals using a 7404 hex inverter IC.

valid code detector circuit as shown in this example since, by the use of the Karnaugh map, circuit minimization can reduce the original equation to the amplified expression:

$$F = A C + A B$$

Figure 8-19 illustrates how to implement this reduced logic equation with SSI circuitry. Only three two-input logic gates are required. This means that a single standard 7400 quad two-input NAND gate can be used to implement this expression. This reduces the package count, power consumption, and printed circuit board design time as well as the size, weight and cost of the circuit. The value of minimizing logic expressions by using a Karnaugh map is quite evident in this example.

MSI IMPLEMENTATION

There are numerous MSI functional circuits which can be used to implement combinational logic circuit designs. While these circuits are designed to perform common combinational logic functions, they can often be adapted to perform other functions to provide a simplified, low cost method of implementing a logic expression. When designing digital circuits, MSI ICs should thoroughly be considered as a viable alternative to SSI devices.

The decoder and multiplexer (data selector) are the two most useful MSI circuits for implementing logic equations. A decoder (or 1-of-N detector) accepts a number of logic inputs and recognizes

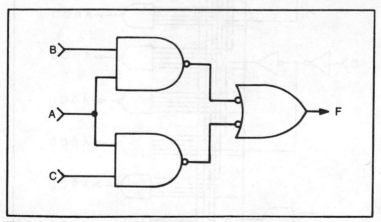

Fig. 8-19. A BCD invalid code detector circuit using a minimum number of SSI components.

353

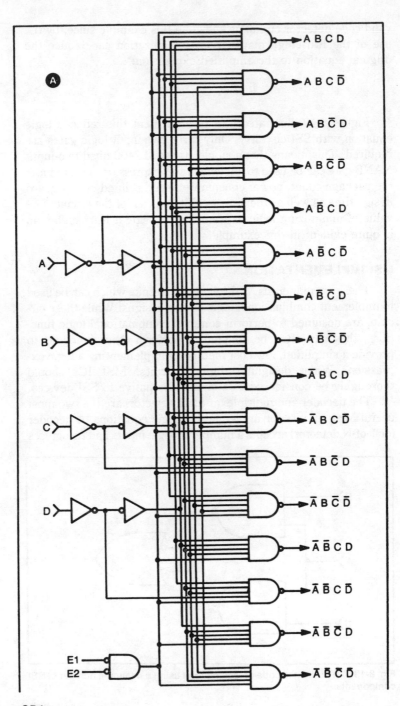

354

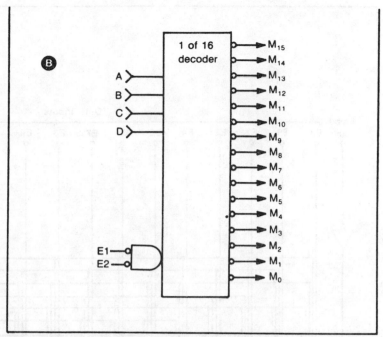

Fig. 8-20. (A) Logic diagram of an MSI decoder. (B) Block diagram of the decoder.

all possible combinations of the input states. This is accomplished by using AND or NAND gates to detect each of the possible input conditions. A 1-of-16 decoder circuit is shown in Fig. 8-20(A). It accepts four inputs, which are subsequently decoded by NAND gates to produce 16 outputs.

The 74154 TTL decoder is a typical version of this type of decoder. It is packaged in a 24-pin dual-inline package. It can be seen from this illustration that this decoder is basically a minterm generator. All sixteen possible states are generated within the single integrated circuit, eliminating the necessity to interconnect external SSI gates and inverters. This circuit generates active low outputs. Inverters can be used on each output, if active high outputs are required. Furthermore, all sixteen gates are enabled when inputs E1 and E2 are low. The block diagram used to represent this MSI decoder is shown in Fig. 8-20(B). To simplify the drawing of this circuit only the inputs and outputs are shown. Minterm numbers are used to designate the outputs.

The multiplexer (or data selector) is another MSI circuit widely used to implement combinational logic functions. A typical

355

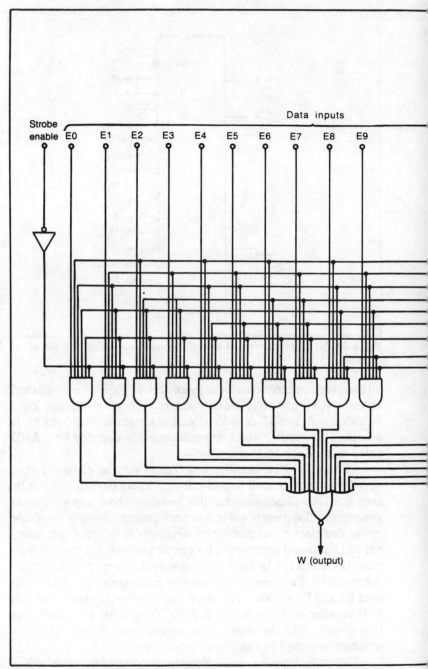

Strobe enable

Data inputs

E0 E1 E2 E3 E4 E5 E6 E7 E8 E9

W (output)

Fig. 8-21. (A) Logic diagram of the 7415 TTL MSI multiplexer (data selector).

356

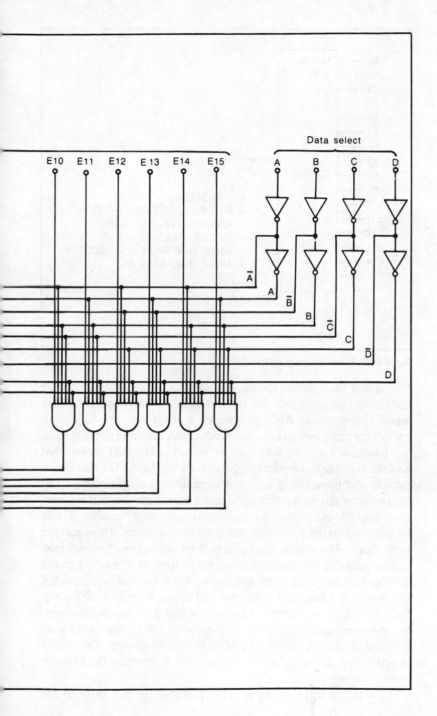

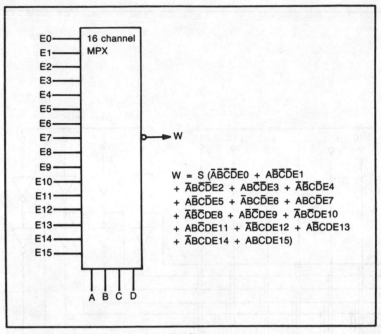

$$W = S (\overline{A}\overline{B}\overline{C}\overline{D}E0 + A\overline{B}\overline{C}\overline{D}E1$$
$$+ \overline{A}B\overline{C}\overline{D}E2 + AB\overline{C}\overline{D}E3 + \overline{A}\overline{B}C\overline{D}E4$$
$$+ A\overline{B}C\overline{D}E5 + \overline{A}BC\overline{D}E6 + ABC\overline{D}E7$$
$$+ \overline{A}\overline{B}\overline{C}DE8 + A\overline{B}\overline{C}DE9 + \overline{A}B\overline{C}DE10$$
$$+ AB\overline{C}DE11 + \overline{A}\overline{B}CDE12 + A\overline{B}CDE13$$
$$+ \overline{A}BCDE14 + ABCDE15)$$

Fig. 8-21B. Block diagram of the 7415.

16-channel multiplexer circuit is shown in Fig. 8-21. Any one of the sixteen input signals can be routed to the single output. Each input is applied to an AND gate which is enabled by the 4-bit input code. This input code selects the input which is routed to the output.

Examination of the data selector circuit in Fig. 8-21 reveals that all four-variable minterms are generated by the AND gates in the circuit, which are ORed together to produce a single output. The data selector circuit itself implements a logic equation that is a sum of all possible minterms. An additional fifth input variable, E, can be accommodated by connected it to one or more of the sixteen input lines. Any one of the sixteen 4-bit minterms, for example, can be added to the output by the application of a binary 1 to the appropriate data input. The associated input line can be connected to binary 0 if a minterm is not needed in the output. A fifth input code bit can be implemented by connecting it (or its complement) to the appropriate data inputs. A single strobe or enable line or lines can also be used to enable or inhibit the entire circuit. The output is active low but an inverter can be used to provide the complement, if needed.

The use of an MSI decoder or a data selector as a BCD invalid code detector can readily be illustrated in the following example.

Figure 8-22 shows the 74154 1-of-16 MSI decoder configured to implement the BCD invalid code detector function. Each of the six four-variable minterms is defined and generated by the decoder. The proper decoder outputs are then fed to a TTL NOR gate to produce the output function. Two integrated circuit packages are required to implement this method. Since MSI integrated circuits cost considerably more than do SSI circuits, this implementation is not the most desirable approach, nor does it produce the most efficient design.

Figure 8-23 shows how the BCD invalid code detector can be implemented with a single 74150 16-channel data selector. Binary 1s (+5 volts) are applied to the six higher-order inputs, which enable the gates to generate the proper minterms. The remaining inputs are connected to binary 0 (ground) to inhibit those minterms from being applied to the output. Even though this implementation results in the use of only a single integrated circuit package, this MSI device is much larger and more expensive than the simple SSI circuit developed earlier.

Although the implementation of an MSI decoder nor a data selector did not lead to an efficient design for the example problem, there are many instances where these devices will afford the most efficient design. Since every design is different, evaluation

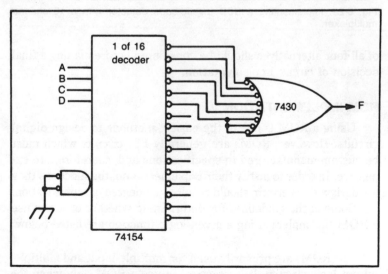

Fig. 8-22. Implementation of a BCD invalid-code detector with a 1-of-16 MSI decoder.

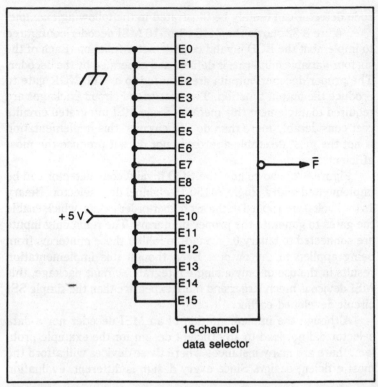

Fig. 8-23. Implementing a BCD invalid-code detector with a 16 channel multiplexer.

of all four alternatives should be considered before making a final decision of circuit implementation.

ROM IMPLEMENTATION

Using a ROM is one of the easiest methods to design digital circuits. However, ROMs are generally LSI circuits which must be custom-manufactured to specifications and, therefore, are expensive. In order to justify their implementation, the functions they are designed to perform should require that degree of sophistication.

Some of the guidelines for determining whether or not to use a ROM for implementing a given logic function are listed below:

1. ROMs are primarily used for multiple-input and multiple-output logic circuits. It is practical to use a ROM only when the number of inputs and outputs are four or more. A ROM is not a

good choice, therefore, for a BCD invalid code detector, even though it has *four* inputs, since it has only a *single* output. Much of a ROM's capabilities would be wasted in this application.

2. ROMs are most desirable in applications where all possible input combinations are specified by the logic design. For example, in a four-input-variable circuit, a ROM is economical only when all or most of the input states are used.

The use of a ROM should be considered if the circuit being designed has at least four inputs and four outputs. Evaluate the design by studying the truth table to see if it meets the criteria indicated above. If it does, the ROM can be implemented directly from the truth table as the input signals specify the ROM's address states while the output states specify the contents of memory at each address location. No further design procedure is necessary with ROMs.

PLA IMPLEMENTATION

The last alternative available in implementing combinational logic circuits is the use of the *programmable logic array*. This LSI device is primarily used for implementing large, complex logic functions. These devices do not become practical until the complexity of the design reaches a very high level. Since this book is devoted to *basic* integrated circuits, no further discussion concerning PLAs will be presented.

MULTIPLE-OUTPUT COMBINATIONAL CIRCUITS

So far, all of the applications discussed involve circuits with single outputs. There are many applications, however, requiring multiple outputs as well as multiple inputs. All of the design procedures previously discussed can be applied to combinational logic circuits with multiple outputs—only minor variations are required.

The methods of defining the problem and stating the design objectives are similar. The type and number of inputs and the type and number of outputs should be completely specified. Then, the problem statement is converted into a truth table which will completely define the operation of the circuit. The total number of states which can exist will be determined by the number of inputs. Based on the inputs, all of the outputs required by the application must be defined. This merely means that a separate column in the truth table must be created for each output of the circuit. A binary 1 is recorded in each column adjacent to the set of input conditions necessary to produce that output. Be sure to note the states which *won't* occur or which have no meaning for the application. These "don't care" states can greatly aid the reduction and minimization of the circuit as previously discussed. Once the truth table has been completed, the circuit to be designed will be completely defined.

Next, write a separate Boolean equation for each output by examining the truth table. Minimize these equations with the use of a Karnaugh map for each. The final design will be implemented from these minimized equations.

There are several important points to consider when choosing the integrated circuits to implement to the final design. First, depending upon the complexity of the design, ROMs should be considered first, since they will generally result in the simplest and easiest circuits. Next, MSI logic circuits should be considered if ROMs are too complex or sophisticated for the application. For many common functions, standard MSI circuits already exist making circuit design unnecessary. Finally, SSI circuits should be considered only for multiple-output circuits of minimum complexity.

When implementing multiple-output functions with SSI circuits, it is good practice to examine the minimized output equations derived from the Karnaugh maps to determine whether common product terms exist. If the same product term happens to occur in the output expressions more than once, it is necessary to generate that term only one time. This will further reduce the amount of circuitry required.

DESIGN EXAMPLES

Virtually any logic design problem can be solved using the previously-described techniques, although there will be many variations because of the wide range of practical applications. The skill of any designer can only be developed through practice. Therefore, the following examples are provided to illustrate the many ways in which the design procedures can be used. They are intended to give the serious digital designer the necessary experience to achieve competence. For good exercise and to test your understanding, try to solve each of the following examples on your own before studying the given solutions.

A 2-OF-4 DETECTOR

The circuit will have four inputs: A, B, C, and D. It will produce a binary 1 output, F, whenever any *two* of the inputs are binary

1. (Develop a truth table for the circuit, write the output equation, minimize the equation, and select a method for implementing it.)

Solution. Table 8-5 shows the truth table for this circuit. There are sixteen possible input combinations which can occur with four inputs. The design requirements state that the output, F, will be binary 1 *only* when any two of the four inputs are also binary 1. By examining the truth table, it can be seen where these six conditions occur. These states are indicated by a binary 1 in the output column, F.

Although you can go directly from the truth table to a Karnaugh map for simplification of this function, it is generally good practice to write the logic equation from the truth table first. It will take little time and aids the designer in better visualizing the function. The equation as derived from the truth table is:

$$F = \overline{A}\,\overline{B}CD + \overline{A}\,B\overline{C}D + \overline{A}\,BC\overline{D} + A\overline{B}\,\overline{C}D + A\overline{B}C\overline{D} + AB\overline{C}\,\overline{D}$$

$$(F = m_3 + m_5 + m_6 + m_9 + m_{10} + m_{12})$$

Next, plot the function on a Karnaugh map using either the logic equation or the truth table as shown in Fig. 8-24. Mark a binary 1 in the cells identified by the minterms specified by the truth table or the equation. As can be seen, the variables are widely spaced and separated and there are no two minterms that can be paired

	Inputs			Output
A	B	C	D	F
0	0	0	0	0
0	0	0	1	0
0	0	1	0	0
0	0	1	1	1
0	1	0	0	0
0	1	0	1	1
0	1	1	0	1
0	1	1	1	0
1	0	0	0	0
1	0	0	1	1
1	0	1	0	1
1	0	1	1	0
1	1	0	0	1
1	1	0	1	0
1	1	1	0	0
1	1	1	1	0

Table 8-5. Truth Table for 2-of-4 Detector.

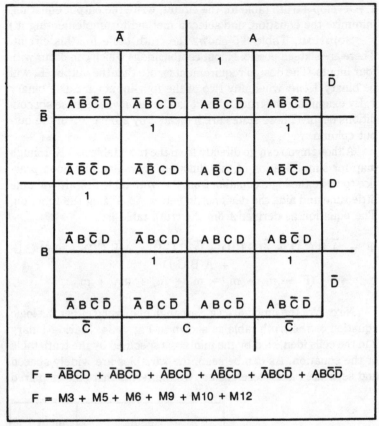

$$F = \overline{A}\overline{B}CD + \overline{A}B\overline{C}D + \overline{A}BC\overline{D} + A\overline{B}\overline{C}D + A\overline{B}C\overline{D} + AB\overline{C}\overline{D}$$

$$F = M3 + M5 + M6 + M9 + M10 + M12$$

Fig. 8-24. Karnaugh map for the 2-of-4 detector.

together. Since there is absolutely no simplification of this logic function possible, it must be directly implemented.

Since only a single output is specified, the use of a ROM is quickly ruled out. The method of implementation, therefore, will be either by SSI or MSI integrated circuitry. The designer's job now is to evaluate the alternatives and select the best method of implementation.

The 2-of-4 detector circuit can be implemented in several ways. Figure 8-25A illustrates how to directly implement the equation with SSI logic gates. The six input products are formed with three 7420 dual four-input NAND gates. The output sum is produced by a 7430 eight-input OR gate. The 7404 hex inverter, shown in Fig. 8-25B, may be needed to generate the complements of the signals if they are not normally available. A total of five integrated circuit

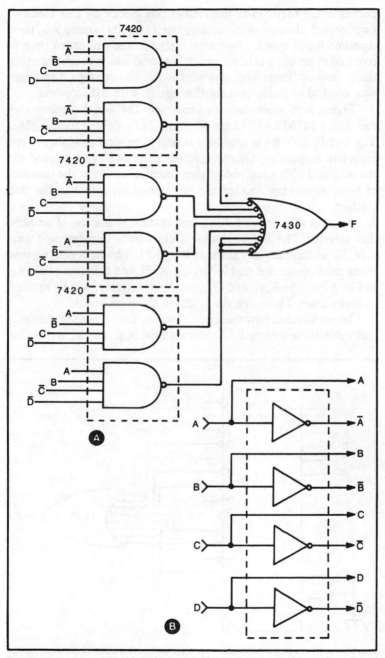

Fig. 8-25. (A) 2-of-4 detector. (B) Method of generating complementary input signal using a 7404 hex inverter.

packages are required to implement this circuit by this method. Even though the cost of these integrated circuits is quite low, they consume much space. Moreover, a significant amount of time is required to lay out a printed circuit board on which to interconnect these devices. Therefore, it is worthwhile to investigate an alternate method of implementing this circuit with MSI devices.

Figure 8-26 shows how to implement the 2-of-4 detector circuit with a 74154 1-of-16 decoder and a 7430 eight-input OR gate. The 1-of-16 decoder is used as a minterm generator while the appropriate outputs are ORed together in the 7430 gate to produce the output, F. This method of implementation offers the benefits of being somewhat smaller and simpler to lay out than the SSI method.

Another alternative for implementation is the use of an MSI data selector. The 2-of-4 detector circuit can be implemented with a 74151 multiplexer as shown in Fig. 8-27. The data select gates in the multiplexer are enabled by the A, B, and C inputs as shown in Fig. 8-28. The B, C, and D inputs, respectively, will be applied to these lines. These are the LSBs of the 4-bit words.

To understand how the circuit works, first consider the decimal value of the three least significant bits, B, C, and D, of the 4-bit

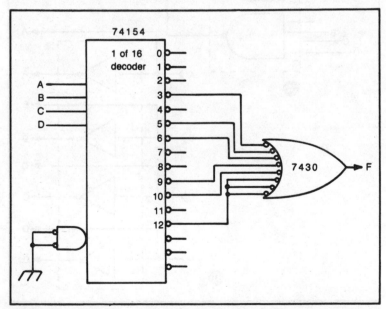

Fig. 8-26. Implementation of a 2-of-4 detector circuit with a 1-of-16 decoder and eight-input gate.

366

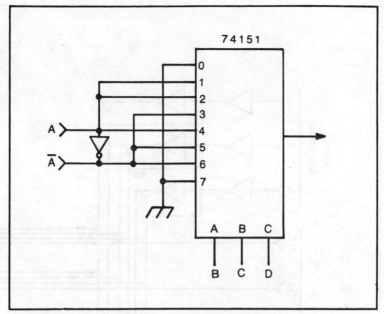

Fig. 8-27. MSI data selector used as 2-of-4 decoder.

words and analyze the truth table to determine which inputs of the multiplexer to use. Disregard the A input (MSB) at this time. Examination will reveal that six of the sixteen possible input combinations will be used. The decimal values of the B-C-D input for each output, F, are 3, 5, 6, 1, 2, and 4. The unused input states are decimal 0 and 7 ($\overline{B}\,\overline{C}\,\overline{D}$ and B C D). Since these two states will not be used, the 0-input and 7-input of the multiplexer are connected to ground, which will disable them. The remaining six inputs are connected to either A or $\overline{A}$ in order to form the complete 4-bit product terms. The external inverter shown in Fig. 8-27 may or may not be required depending on the availability of the $\overline{A}$ input signal.

It can be seen that the simplest and easiest method of implementing the 2-of-4 detector circuit is with the 74151 multiplexer integrated circuit. It provides a complete design within a single integrated circuit package with a minimum of printed circuit board design and layout time. However, since the multiplexer is about twice as expensive as all of the integrated circuits comprising the SSI version combined, the designer will have to decide which version best satisfies the requirements. In most cases, the extra design time and larger, more complicated printed circuit board layout for the SSI version will offset the greater cost of the 74151 multiplexer.

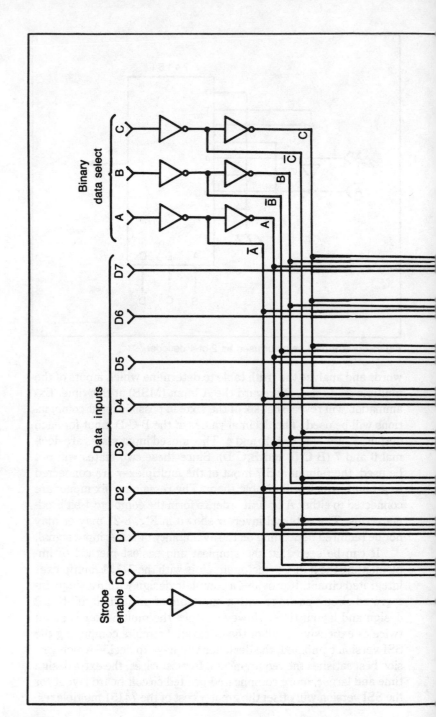

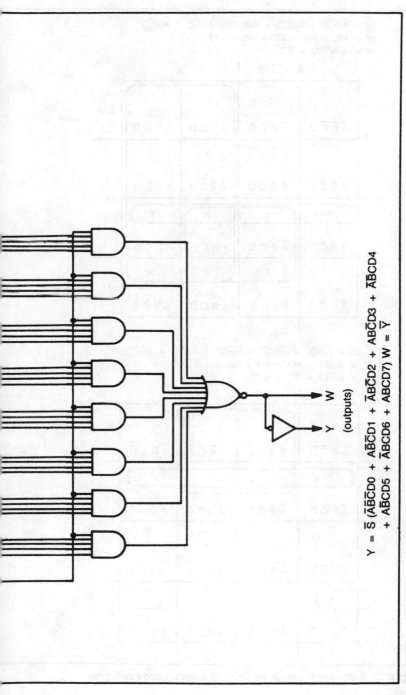

$Y = \overline{S} \ (\overline{A}\overline{B}\overline{C}D0 + A\overline{B}\overline{C}D1 + \overline{A}B\overline{C}D2 + AB\overline{C}D3 + \overline{A}\overline{B}CD4$
$+ A\overline{B}CD5 + \overline{A}BCD6 + ABCD7) \ W = \overline{Y}$
(outputs)

Fig. 8-28. 74151 TTL data selector.

369

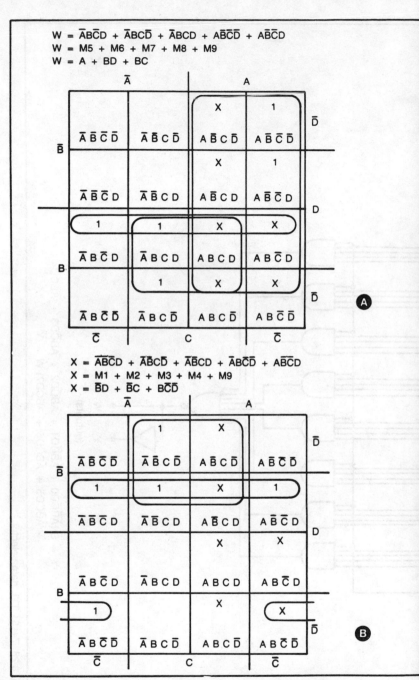

Fig. 8-29. Karnaugh maps for the BCD to excess-3 code converter.

370

$Y = ABCD + \bar{A}BCD + \bar{A}B\bar{C}\bar{D} + \bar{A}BCD + A\bar{B}\bar{C}\bar{D}$
$Y = CD + \bar{C}\bar{D}$

$Z = \bar{A}\bar{B}\bar{C}\bar{D} + \bar{A}BC\bar{D} + \bar{A}B\bar{C}D + \bar{A}BCD + A\bar{B}\bar{C}\bar{D}$
$Z = \bar{D}$

371

A PARALLEL 8241 BCD TO
4-BIT EXCESS-3 CODE CONVERTER

Design a code converter circuit to translate the 8421 BCD code into the 4-bit excess-3 code using parallel inputs and parallel outputs. (*Hint:* Since the 8421 BCD code is used for the inputs, the six invalid states can be considered "don't care" states.)

Solution. The first step in any design is to develop a truth table. In this case four input lines will be required, since the inputs are the 8421 BCD code. They can be labeled A, B, C, and D. Also, four output lines will be required, since the excess-3 code is comprised of four bits. They can be labeled W, X, Y, and Z. Table 8-6 shows the truth table for this circuit.

After the truth table has been developed, the next step is to write the Boolean equations for each of the output bits. This is accomplished by examining where the positions of binary 1s occur in each output column. A sum-of-products expression can be writ-

Table 8-6. Truth Table for BCD-to-Excess 3 Code Converter.

Inputs 8421 BCD				Outputs XS3			
A	B	C	D	W	X	Y	Z
0	0	0	0	0	0	1	1
0	0	0	1	0	1	0	0
0	0	1	0	0	1	0	1
0	0	1	1	0	1	1	0
0	1	0	0	0	1	1	1
0	1	0	1	1	0	0	0
0	1	1	0	1	0	0	1
0	1	1	1	1	0	1	0
1	0	0	0	1	0	1	1
1	0	0	1	1	1	0	0
1	0	1	0				
1	0	1	1		Don't		
1	1	0	0		care		
1	1	0	1		states		
1	1	1	0				
1	1	1	1				

ten with each of the appropriate minterms involved. For this circuit, the output equations are:

$$W = \overline{A}\,B\,\overline{C}\,D + \overline{A}\,B\,C\,\overline{D} + \overline{A}\,B\,C\,D + A\,\overline{B}\,\overline{C}\,\overline{D} + A\,\overline{B}\,\overline{C}\,D$$
$$X = \overline{A}\,\overline{B}\,\overline{C}\,D + \overline{A}\,\overline{B}\,C\,\overline{D} + \overline{A}\,\overline{B}\,C\,D + \overline{A}\,B\,\overline{C}\,\overline{D} + A\,\overline{B}\,\overline{C}\,D$$
$$Y = \overline{A}\,\overline{B}\,\overline{C}\,\overline{D} + \overline{A}\,\overline{B}\,C\,D + \overline{A}\,B\,\overline{C}\,\overline{D} + \overline{A}\,B\,C\,D + A\,\overline{B}\,\overline{C}\,\overline{D}$$
$$Z = \overline{A}\,\overline{B}\,\overline{C}\,\overline{D} + \overline{A}\,\overline{B}\,C\,\overline{D} + \overline{A}\,B\,\overline{C}\,\overline{D} + \overline{A}\,B\,C\,\overline{D} + A\,\overline{B}\,\overline{C}\,\overline{D}$$

The next step is to map the equations using a 16-cell Karnaugh map for each output. Each output can be mapped directly from the truth table or from the Boolean equations. Be sure to include the "don't care" states which can be identified by "X"s. These don't care states can be combined or grouped with the binary 1s on the map to help reduce the equations.

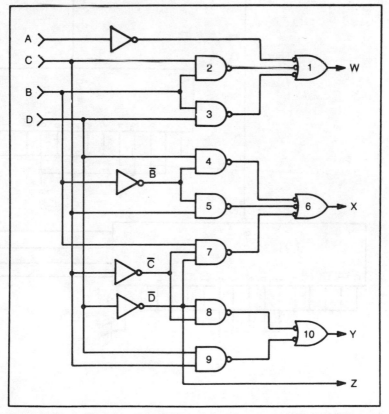

Fig. 8-30. Implementation of the BCD to excess-3 code converter with SSI components.

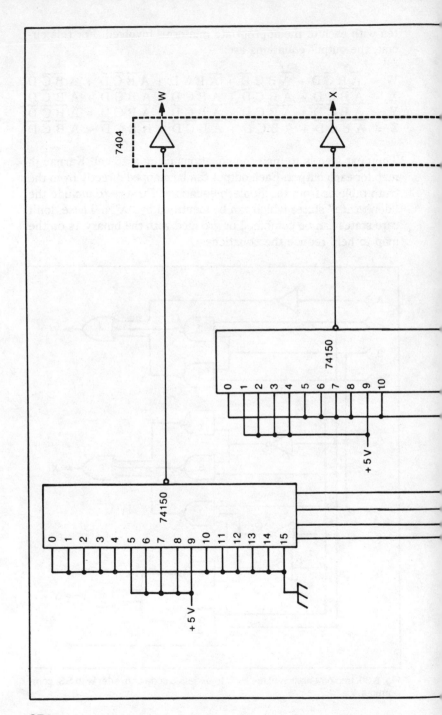

374

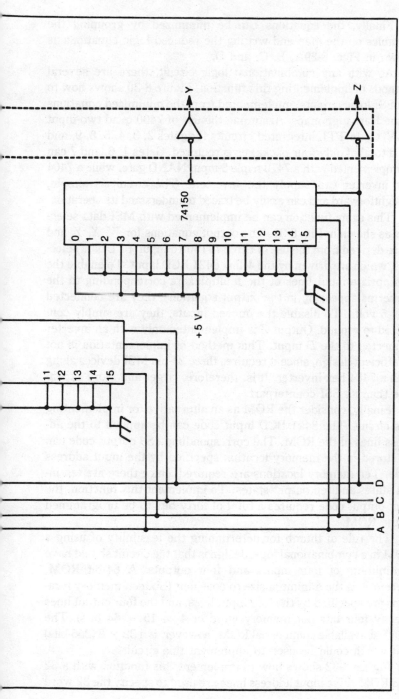

Fig. 8-31. Implementation of the BCD to excess-3 code converter with MSI data selectors.

Finally, the equations can be minimized by grouping the variables on the map and writing the reduced logic equations as shown in Figs. 8-29A, B, C, and D.

As with any combinational logic circuit, there are several methods of implementing this function. Figure 8-30 shows how to use SSI logic circuits, implemented from the minimized equations of the Karnaugh maps. Assuming the use of 7400 quad two-input NAND gate TTL integrated circuits for gates 2, 3, 4, 5, 8, 9, and 10, a total of only four packages is required. Gates 1, 6, and 7 can be implemented with a 7410 triple 3-input NAND gate, while a 7404 hex inverter can supply the inverters. The circuit is simple, straightforward and can easily be traced to understand its operation.

This same function can be implemented with MSI data selectors as shown in Fig. 8-31. The output equations for W, X, Y, and Z are derived from the use of three 74150 16-input TTL data selectors, which are driven by the 4-line 8421 BCD input. To enable the appropriate input lines of the multiplexers corresponding to the minterms appearing in the output equations, they are connected to $+5$ volts. To disable the unused inputs, they are simply connected to ground. Output Z is implemented only with an inverter connected to the D input. This method of implementation is not an efficient design, since it requires three 24-pin MSI devices along with a 7404 hex inverter. It is, therefore, larger and more expensive than its SSI counterpart.

Finally, consider the ROM as an alternative for implementing this circuit. The 8421 BCD input code can be applied to the address lines of the ROM. The corresponding $XS3$ output code can be stored in the memory location specified by the input address code. Ten memory locations are required, since there are ten input states and ten output states. To implement this function, the 4-bit output code requires a total of forty bits to be programmed in the ROM.

The rule of thumb for determining the feasibility of using a ROM in a combinational logic design is that the circuit should have a minimum of four inputs and four outputs. A 64-bit ROM, therefore, is the minimum size to consider. (Sixteen memory locations are specified by the four input lines, and the four output lines specify four bits per memory word or $4 \times 16 = 64$ bits). The smallest available commercial ROM, however, is a 32×8 (256-bits) unit which could be used to implement this circuit.

Figure 8-32 shows how to implement this function with a 32 $\times$ 8 ROM. Five input address lines are used to specify the 32-word

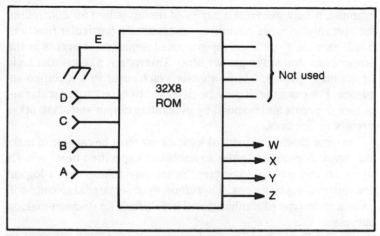

Fig. 8-32. Using a ROM to implement the BCD to excess-3 code converter.

memory. In this application, the fifth input, E, is not required, and can simply be connected to ground. The BCD input code is applied to the A, B, C, and D input lines. Since each memory location can hold eight bits, these are eight output lines, even though only four of them are required for this application. To correspond with the desired output code, they are labeled: W, X, Y, and Z. The XS3 code will be stored in the memory of the ROM when it is manufactured.

A significant amount of memory is wasted with this arrangement since only 40 of the possible 256 bits are used. The cost of this circuit can be very low, however, particularly if it is to be used in a high-volume application.

After due consideration, the two most desirable methods of implementing this circuit are SSI or ROM; which is best depends upon whether the unit is to be produced in small quantities or is to go into large-scale production. The SSI implementation is the approach with the lowest unit cost, but does require four integrated circuit packages and associated printed circuit design. The ROM method is more expensive but requires less space. The ROM method should carefully be considered depending upon the quantities needed and the size and space limitations of the design.

SEQUENTIAL LOGIC CIRCUIT DESIGN

A sequential logic circuit is a circuit designed to perform a sequence of logical operations occurring over a period of time. For example, it may generate a series of timing pulses for controlling the operation of other circuits to "automate" a particular function. It will execute a specified programmed sequence of events in the proper order and at the proper time. Alternately, a sequential logic circuit may "process" logic signals which occur in a specified sequence. For example, it may be designed to detect a particular sequence of events and respond by generating output signals to other circuits or displays.

In some cases, a sequential logic circuit must be capable of making logical decisions in order to execute its specified functions. Of course, combinational logic circuits are used to implement logical decision-making functions. Therefore, most sequential circuits will contain some type of combinational logic circuit for decision-making purposes.

The ability of a sequential logic circuit to store data is its key feature. A sequential circuit must have some type of memory for it to be able to properly perform its sequence in generating a desired sequence of output pulses. The primary element in any sequential logic circuit is the flip-flop.

A sequential logic circuit responds differently with various inputs applied to it. It generates specific output pulses depending upon its function, the states of its inputs and the current state of its stored memory.

A general block diagram of a sequential logic circuit is illustrated in Fig. 8-33. The state of the circuit is determined by the flip-flop memory which is the heart of the circuit. Clock pulses are generally used to control the flip-flops. The combinational logic cir-

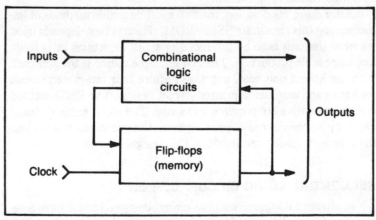

Fig. 8-33. Block diagram of a sequential logic circuit.

cuits are driven by the flip-flop outputs as well as by various other input signals. In turn, the combinational logic outputs drive the flip-flops as well as other external circuits, if needed.

The total *number* of *different* states in which a sequential logic circuit can exist is determined by the number of flip-flops in the circuit. These states are *defined* by a particular binary code, which is stored in the flip-flops. The state of the sequential logic circuit will change as the inputs are applied and the clock pulses occur, which will cause the flip-flops to be set or reset. The states of the flip-flops can be interpreted as a special form of binary code which subsequently controls the combinational logic circuits to cause the correct sequence of events to occur, and to generate the proper sequence of output pulses.

The most common forms of sequential logic circuits are counters and shift registers. Standard binary and BCD counters are comprised of flip-flops with, in some cases, combinational logic. A standard counter or shift register can generally be implemented to meet the requirement for a sequential logic circuit. There are, however, many applications where special sequential circuits can be of benefit. Unusual applications and special functions are readily implemented with special forms of sequential logic circuits. Special sequential logic circuits often result in a more efficient design, and operation at higher speed when unique codes and sequences are required.

The process by which the circuit changes from one state to another is the most common way of classifying sequential logic circuits. The transition of states can occur either *synchronously* with the application of an external clock pulse or *asynchronously*—without the need for an enabling clock pulse. The speed of operation is a direct function of the clock frequency in a synchronous sequential circuit—the states of the circuits change in step with the clock pulses. In asynchronous circuits, a state change occurs as a result of a previous change. This means that their operating speed is a direct function of the propagation delay times within the components comprising the circuit, and the rate of occurrence of the external signals. Very high operating speeds can be obtained with asynchronous circuits, since most integrated circuit logic circuitry intrinsically has very short propagation delays. However, because of unequal propagation delays of various gates and circuit paths, unreliable operation can occur. False triggering and invalid states can also cause asynchronous circuits to operate incorrectly. Since asynchronous circuit design requires careful analysis of all possible fault conditions which may occur and provision of a means of correcting these faults, the design of these circuits becomes more difficult. Synchronous circuits are generally easier to design, implement and control. They are, therefore, recommended over asynchronous circuit designs. Emphasis in this section will be on the design and implementation of synchronous sequential circuits using J-K flip-flops.

Design Procedure

Most sequential logic circuits are usually some form of counter which will sequence through a number of states in response to applied inputs. The flip-flops in the counters will set and reset to generate the output pulses according to a specific count sequence necessary for the intended application. Such sequential circuits can be frequency dividers, which have a required number of states, or counters which can implement a specific code. These counters are commonly referred to as *sequencers* or *controllers* when they are used for control purposes. Although a wide variety of different code types can be implemented for control purposes, most sequencers use cyclical codes, where only a single flip-flop in the counter changes state at a time.

In the design procedure described in this chapter the use of synchronous circuits employing J-K flip-flops will be assumed. This is the most commonly-used approach, and will result in the most reliable and versatile design.

The design procedure for sequential logic circuits is:

1. State the problem and completely define the design objectives.

2. From the problem definition, develop a *State Table*.

3. From the State Table, develop Karnaugh maps for the flip-flop inputs.

4. From the Karnaugh maps, write the input logic equations for the flip-flops.

5. From the logic equations, draw the complete logic diagram.

6. Using standard integrated circuits, implement the final design.

Defining the Problem

Defining the objective is the first step in designing a sequential logic circuit. A complete and concise description of the func-

380

tion to be performed should be written, with the exact operations to occur stated. There is no standard method of expressing the logic functions to be performed. However, it is most important to include all possible conditions. The characteristics of the input and output signals should be specified in order to determine the number of states the circuit must assume.

The inputs and outputs of the circuits can be expressed in many different ways. They may be expressed as the logic waveforms which define the sequence of functions to be performed. They may be logic levels which occur at specific times causing certain operations to take place. Or, they may be expressed in a *truth table* or *state table*. In a state table, the input and output signals are shown in terms of 1s and 0s which show the sequence of changes at each of the steps defined in the problem.

The number of states in which the circuit can exist will generally be decided by specifying the input and output signals and writing a description of the function to be performed. The number of circuit states will generally be determined by the number of steps in the sequence of operations needed to occur. The number of flip-flops required for the memory section will be determined by the number of states the circuit must be able to assume. The flip-flops will define a binary word, while the sequence of the steps designates *how* the flip-flops change state. The code sequence may be any one of a number of special codes including the standard binary code, XS3, Gray, etc. Additionally, any binary sequence can be chosen and implemented depending upon the required application.

Developing a State Table

A state table, completely defining all the states in the circuit, should be developed after determining the number of states required by the application. The state table is simply a truth table which expresses the outputs of the flip-flops in the circuit for each of the states required by the application. The number of flip-flops can be calculated by knowing the number of states required. For example, an application requiring seven states will need a 3-bit counter since $2^3 = 8$. (Note that one of the eight states won't be used).

A state table for an application requiring seven states is shown in Table 8-7. The seven states, numbered 0 through 6, have been specified by the application. The eighth state, number 7 with a binary output 100, is not used but included in the table and labeled "not used." The binary code for each state has no relationship to the decimal state assigned to it. Therefore, the flip-flop outputs are

Table 8-7. Static State Table for 7-State Counter. (Compare with Table 8-8).

State	Flip-flop outputs A	B	C	
0	0	0	0	
1	1	1	0	
2	0	1	0	
3	1	0	1	Recycle
4	0	0	1	
5	0	1	1	
6	1	1	1	
7	1	0	0	Not used

simply treated as a bit pattern rather than a binary number.

The state table in Table 8-7 is interpreted by observing the flip-flop states as the circuit changes (or increments) from one step to the next. In this example, after the sixth state (binary output 111) occurs, the next clock pulse causes the circuit to recycle back to the initial zero state.

Another method of constructing a state table is illustrated in Table 8-8. In this table, an additional column labeled $t + 1$, is included. In the column labeled t, the states of the flip-flop outputs are shown *before* the application of a clock pulse. In the column labeled $t + 1$, the states of the flip-flop outputs are shown *after* the occurrence of a clock pulse. The information provided in this

Table 8-8. Dynamic State or Flow Table for 7-State Counter. Output States after the Clock Pulse (t + 1) and Prior to the Pulse (t) are Indicated.

State	t A	B	C	t + 1 A	B	C
0	0	0	0	1	1	0
1	1	1	0	0	1	0
2	0	1	0	1	0	1
3	1	0	1	0	0	1
4	0	0	1	0	1	1
5	0	1	1	1	1	1
6	1	1	1	0	0	0
7	1	0	0	Not used		

table is exactly the same as the one shown in Table 8-7. The only difference is the format of the table.

Tables 8-7 and 8-8, illustrate only one of many possible special codes which may occur as the result of developing a sequential circuit for a unique application. The code could have been derived from the desired flip-flop output states at each step in the circuit. Or, it could have been developed by observing the output waveforms which were specified by the original application requirements. Examination of the tables reveals that no recognizable code sequence exists. It is merely a random code which meets the particular application.

The most desirable approach for most sequential circuit applications, where a special counter or sequencer is required, is to implement a circuit where only a single flip-flop changes state at a time. An example of such a code is the Gray code. Such circuits can be made to operate much faster than other types of counters. False triggering or spurious undesirable output pulses ("glitches") will not be caused by the unequal propagation delays in the various circuit components which would occur when multiple flip-flops simultaneously change state. The various counter states, decoded by gates, can produce very short-duration pulses equal in time to the difference between the propagation delay changes in the various flip-flops, which could cause false triggering. By changing the state of only a single flip-flop at a time, these pulses are virtually eliminated. Additionally, it is desirable to use a synchronous circuit in which all the flip-flops are stepped at the same precise time in order to help minimize glitches. There are many different codes in which only one bit of a word changes from one state to the next. The Gray code is only one of them.

In developing a special code for a counter, another useful guideline is to set the initial state of all the flip-flops to 0. Most circuits will have a reset state from where all operations initiate. This state is easily identified when it is made equal to 0. To generate this initial condition, the direct *clear* inputs on most J-K flip-flops can all be tied together and brought low. This common line can also be manually controlled by a pushbutton or a special circuit which will automatically bring it low upon initial application of power.

DEVELOPING A KARNAUGH MAP FOR A COUNTER

Using a Karnaugh map is another method of showing the states of a special counter. Each cell of the map depicts a specific state. The decimal number corresponding to each state may be written within the respective cell, which will indicate the binary code produced by the circuit. The sequence of flow, as defined by the state table, can be indicated by drawing arrows on the map from cell to cell. A visual representation of the states of the sequential circuit is then produced by the Karnaugh map. A Karnaugh map plotting the seven-state counter defined in the state tables of Tables 8-7 and 8-8 is shown in Fig. 8-34.

The Karnaugh map can aid in the selection of a suitable cyclical code, where only a single bit will change from one state to the next. Only one variable will change when moving from one cell to any adjacent cell within a Karnaugh map. To create a special code of this nature, therefore, all that is necessary is to choose an initial starting place (usually 0), and then move to as many adjacent cells as required by the application to generate the special code.

Two examples of how the Karnaugh map can be used to develop a special code are shown in Fig. 8-41. The initial starting point in both cases is 000 or $\overline{A}\ \overline{B}\ \overline{C}$. Since the counter in each example has six states, only six of the eight cells will be used. Note how the state changes after the sixth state back to the initial state. It is important to remember that the Karnaugh map can be considered a sphere, with all edges considered to be adjacent, as well.

This same technique can be used in developing sequencers for *any* number of states—It is not always possible to create a code where only a single bit changes from one state to the next. For example, in counters with odd number of states, more than one bit will have to change in recycling to the initial state. Figure 8-36 il-

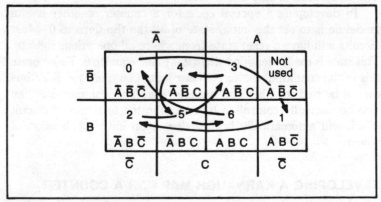

Fig. 8-34. Karnaugh map for the seven-state counter.

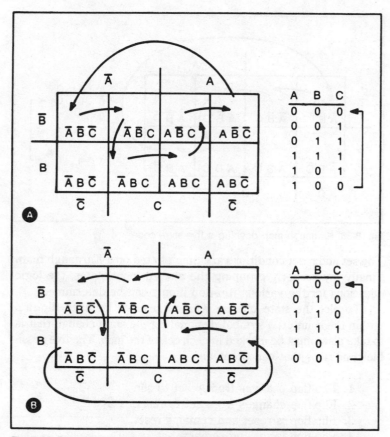

Fig. 8-35. Two examples of Karnaugh maps defining six-state cyclical counters.

lustrates how a 5-state code changes only a single bit at a time until it has to recycle back to its initial state. In recycling from its fifth state (110) to its initial state (000), two bits must change. This condition is generally not detrimental, and in the instances where it is important, an even number of states can be introduced. The extra or unneeded "dummy" state would not be used by the application, but would serve only as a means of recycling the counter.

In designing a counter or sequencer, the most important application of a Karnaugh map is in the determination of the input states to the flip-flops required to produce the special code. Certain states must be applied to the J and K inputs to cause the flip-flops to set and reset in the desired code sequence. These inputs are determined by examining the state table and indicating which flip-flop must be set or reset in changing from one state to the next.

385

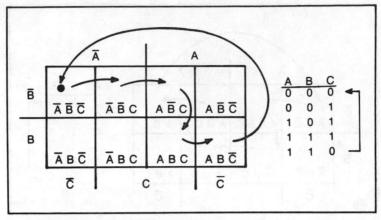

Fig. 8-36. Karnaugh map defining a five-state code.

The set and reset conditions are then plotted on a Karnaugh map. Finally, by properly grouping the plotted input states, the logic equations for the various flip-flop inputs can be determined.

To plot the state change Karnaugh maps for each flip-flop within the counter, a symbol designating the state change that is to take place must be marked in each cell of the map. The five possible conditions that can occur are:

1. Flip-flop changes from reset to set.
2. Flip-flop changes from set to reset.
3. Flip-flop is reset and remains reset.
4. Flip-flop is set and remains set.
5. Don't care.

The five symbols used to represent the five conditions just described are:

1 Flip-flop changes from reset to set.
/ Flip-flop is set and remains set.
0 Flip-flop changes from set to reset.
O Flip-flop is reset and remains reset.
X A "don't care" state exists or input conditions don't occur.

Figure 8-37 summarizes the state changes and their respective symbols. The column on the left shows the symbol used to indicate the state change. The column labeled t represents the state of the flip-flop prior to the application of a clock pulse. The column labeled *t + 1* indicates the state of the flip-flop following the occurrence of a clock pulse. To determine how each flip-flop changes from one state to the next, the state table must be analyzed, with the state changes then plotted on a Karnaugh map. Each flip-flop of the counter must be plotted on a separate Karnaugh map.

The state change that must take place in the output variable associated with the Karnaugh map in moving from one state to the next is designated by the symbol plotted in each cell of the map. For example, if flip-flop *A* is presently reset, as indicated by its condition in the cell, and must change state (set) to transfer to the next state in the succeeding cell, a "1" will be written in that cell. *The symbol in a cell represents the state change that must take place to move to the next state!* This can be illustrated by developing a Karnaugh map for the flip-flops in the special seven-state counter previously discussed. The maps for this circuit are shown in Fig. 8-38, B, and C.

In each cell, the symbol designating the state change that will take place in going from the current state is recorded. Verification of the correct symbol in each case can be accomplished by using the state tables in Table 8-7 and 8-8 as a reference. For example, consider state *2* of the *B* flip-flop. This state is defined by the code 010 ($\overline{A}$ B $\overline{C}$), located in the lower left corner of the Karnaugh map. In going from this state to the next state, *3*, which is defined by the code 101 (A $\overline{B}$ C), the *B* flip-flop will change from set to reset. Therefore, in cell, $\overline{A}$ B $\overline{C}$, the symbol designating this condition, 0, must be recorded.

After the Karnaugh maps are completely plotted for each flip-flop, they will be used to develop the J and K input logic equations. This is accomplished by grouping together the various terms in the maps in groups of pairs, quads, eights, etc. in a method, similar to that used in minimizing combinational equations. When group-

Fig. 8-37. Four symbols used to represent state changes of flip-flops.

State change symbol	t	t + 1
1	0	1
/	1	1
0	1	0
O	0	0

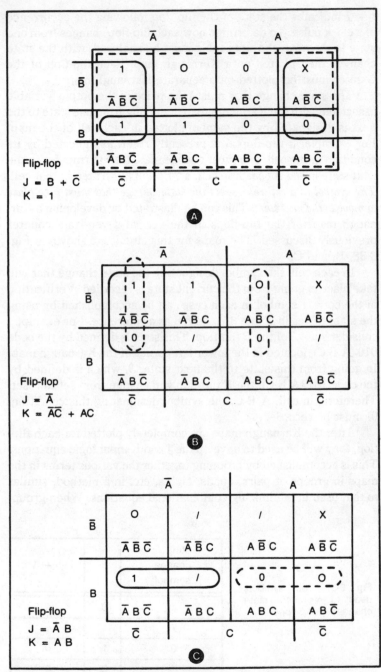

Fig. 8-38. Karnaugh maps of flip-flops in a seven-state counter.

388

ing variables together in the Karnaugh maps, there are some special rules that must be followed. These are:

J INPUT EQUATION:

1 Each "1" cell MUST be accounted for in the J equation.
/ Optional
0 Optional
O Must NOT be used
X Optional

K INPUT EQUATION:

1 Optional
/ Must NOT be used
0 Each "0" cell must be accounted for in the K equation.
O Optional
X Optional

All *1* terms marked in the cells of the Karnaugh map must be considered in developing the J input equation. In other words, each *1 must* be used in some way to account for all the necessary input states. Conversely, each cell marked *O* MUST NOT be used. All other symbols can be used in the same way as "don't care" states are used in any other Karnaugh map.

All *0* terms marked in the cells of the Karnaugh map must be considered in developing the K input equation. Conversely, the "/" cells *must not* be used. All other symbols can be used in the same way as "don't care" states are used in any other Karnaugh map.

The proper groupings of both the J and K input equations are shown in the Karnaugh maps of Figure 8-38(A), (B), and (C). The *J* input equations are identified by the groups marked with solid lines. The *K* inputs are identified by the dashed lines. These Karnaugh maps are read the same way as the ones for combinational equations. Simply determine which variable *does not* change from one cell to a succeeding one within the group, and create a product term from them. Finally, OR together all the terms from all the groups. The equations which correspond to the *J* and *K* input states are designated adjacent to each map. The correct grouping of variables can be verified by using the rules previously given.

A special case exists in the Karnaugh map of flip-flop A in that all eight cells are valid for the *K* input. Therefore, a single large group of eight cells can be formed to represent the input term for the K input of the A flip-flop. In the case where all terms can be grouped together, a binary 1 condition is indicated.

Drawing the Logic Diagram

A logic diagram can be drawn for a counter or sequencer after knowing the number of flip-flops required and the equations for the J and K inputs for each. Please note that this section deals *strictly* with *J-K flip-flops* and *synchronous* counters. The logic diagram of a seven-state counter is illustrated in Fig. 8-39. Note how the T inputs are all tied together and connected to a common clock input bus. All *clear* inputs are tied together, permitting the provision of a common reset input to the entire counter, if desired. The remaining circuitry represents the logic gates implementing the respective J and K input equations for each flip-flop. Gates *1* through *4* are positive NAND gates (type 7400), while gates *5* and *6* are positive NOR gates (type 7402). The J-K flip-flops can be implemented with two 7476 dual J-K flip-flop integrated circuits. The final circuit is a counter which will sequence itself in the defined code with a minimum amount of hardware.

Two more design examples will be presented to further illustrate the design procedure for sequential logic circuits. They will illustrate how a counter can be designed for any number of states and to sequence in any bit pattern desired. Equally easy to design are special codes or arbitrary sequences.

TWO-BIT GRAY CODE COUNTER

Once the problem is stated and completely specified, a state table is developed. The 2-bit Gray code counter state table is shown in Table 8-9. The states are labeled 0 through 3, which represent the four possible states that can exist with two bits. Since this is a Gray code counter, note how only one bit changes at a time in going from one state to another, including the recycle transition.

Next, plot the state changes for each flip-flop on a Karnaugh map. This is accomplished by examining the state changes that must occur in each flip-flop when moving from one state to the next. They are then plotted in the appropriate cells on the Karnaugh map. The symbol designating the transition which must occur to move to the next state must be plotted in each cell.

The Karnaugh maps for the A and B flip-flops with their appropriate state changes plotted are shown in Fig. 8-40(A) and (B).

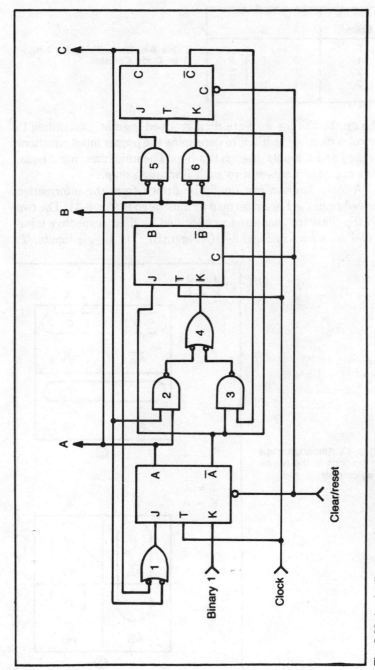

Fig. 8-39. Logic diagram of a seven-state counter.

State	A	B	
0	0	0	Recycle
1	0	1	
2	1	1	
3	1	0	

Table 8-9. State Table for 2-bit Gray-Code Counter.

The symbols in the map are then grouped together, according to the rules discussed earlier, to determine the proper input equations for the J and K inputs on each flip-flop. The minimized input equations are shown adjacent to each Karnaugh map.

A logic diagram can finally be drawn from the information derived from the Karnaugh map as illustrated in Fig. 8-41. The two J-K flip-flops are connected as specified by their respective input equations shown in Figs. 8-41(A) and (B). The toggle inputs, T,

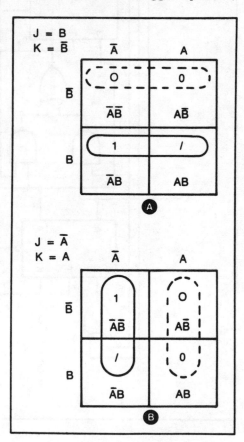

Fig. 8-40. Karnaugh maps for flip-flops in the two-bit Gray counter.

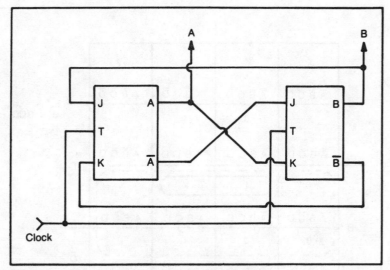

Fig. 8-41. Logic diagram of the two-bit Gray counter.

of the flip-flops are tied together and connected to a common clock
input since this is a synchronous circuit.

EXCESS-3 CODE BCD COUNTER

From the definition of the problem, it can be determined that
a ten-state counter is required. A BCD counter is a decade counter
having ten states. The standard XS3 code is specified and,
therefore, is defined. A state table can readily be developed as
shown in Table 8-10. Note that in the XS3 code the initial state,
0, is 0011. From this point the counter increments is the standard

	Outputs			
State	A	B	C	D
0	0	0	1	1
1	0	1	0	0
2	0	1	0	1
3	0	1	1	0
4	0	1	1	1
5	1	0	0	0
6	1	0	0	1
7	1	0	1	0
8	1	0	1	1
9	1	1	0	0

Table 8-10. State Table
for Excess-3 Counter.

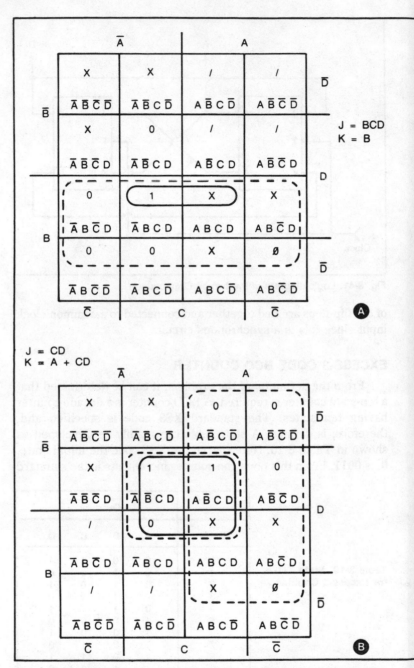

Fig. 8-42. Karnaugh maps defining the excess-3 counter. (J equals solid line and K equals broken line.)

$$J = AB + D$$
$$K = D$$

	$\bar{A}$		A	
	X	X	0	0
$\bar{B}$	$\bar{A}\bar{B}\bar{C}\bar{D}$	$\bar{A}\bar{B}C\bar{D}$	$A\bar{B}C\bar{D}$	$A\bar{B}\bar{C}\bar{D}$
	X	0	0	1
	$\bar{A}\bar{B}\bar{C}D$	$\bar{A}\bar{B}CD$	$A\bar{B}CD$	$A\bar{B}\bar{C}D$
	1	0	X	X
B	$\bar{A}B\bar{C}D$	$\bar{A}BCD$	$ABCD$	$AB\bar{C}D$
	0	/	X	1
	$\bar{A}B\bar{C}\bar{D}$	$\bar{A}BC\bar{D}$	$ABC\bar{D}$	$AB\bar{C}\bar{D}$
	$\bar{C}$	C		$\bar{C}$

Row side labels (right): $\bar{D}$, D, D, $\bar{D}$

C

$$J = K = 1$$

	$\bar{A}$		A	
	X	X	1	1
$\bar{B}$	$\bar{A}\bar{B}\bar{C}\bar{D}$	$\bar{A}\bar{B}C\bar{D}$	$A\bar{B}C\bar{D}$	$A\bar{B}\bar{C}\bar{D}$
	X	0	0	0
	$\bar{A}\bar{B}\bar{C}D$	$\bar{A}\bar{B}CD$	$A\bar{B}CD$	$A\bar{B}\bar{C}D$
	0	0	X	X
B	$\bar{A}B\bar{C}D$	$\bar{A}BCD$	$ABCD$	$AB\bar{C}D$
	1	1	X	1
	$\bar{A}B\bar{C}\bar{D}$	$\bar{A}BC\bar{D}$	$ABC\bar{D}$	$AB\bar{C}\bar{D}$
	$\bar{C}$	C		$\bar{C}$

Row side labels (right): $\bar{D}$, D, D, $\bar{D}$

D

binary code sequence until the tenth state (1100) is reached when the counter recycles back to 0011.

Next, translate the flip-flop transitions from the state table into the symbols to plot on the Karnaugh maps. Figure 8-42(A), (B), (C) and (D) show the four 16-cell Karnaugh maps used to plot the state changes for each flip-flop. Six of the sixteen states will not be used and, therefore, can be treated as "don't care" states, since only a ten-state counter is being designed. These six "don't care" states are 0000, 0001, 0010, 1101, 1110, and 1111. An "X" is placed in the appropriate "don't care" cell of each of the four Karnaugh maps.

The transitions of each flip-flop from one state to the next are analyzed and plotted on their respective Karnaugh map. Develop the input equations for each flip-flop using the rules governing the grouping of symbols within the Karnaugh maps. The appropriate groupings for this application are shown in Fig. 8-42 along with the resulting logic equations for the J and K inputs. The J input groupings are designated with solid lines while the K input groupings are designated with dashed lines.

Finally, the logic diagram is drawn from the input equations derived from the Karnaugh maps. One method of implementing this circuit is illustrated in Fig. 8-43. The J and K inputs to each flip-flop are specified by their respective input equations. Standard SSI logic packages can be employed for the gating. A synchronous circuit is formed by connecting all the T inputs together and feeding them with a common clock.

DESIGN VARIATIONS

The sequential circuits we have discussed are special counters which can have any number of states and any code sequence. All of these circuits have only a single input: a clock. There are, however, other sequential circuits that use external signals for controlling the counter. These external inputs are used to determine precisely when a counter or sequencer steps from one state to the next. These external inputs can be incorporated in the design procedure by merely including the input variables with the J and K input expressions. The J and K inputs of the various flip-flops must have the appropriate input signals as determined by the count sequence of the counter in order to cause a circuit to change from one state to the next. If an external input signal is to have control of the change from one state to a succeeding one, then that external signal becomes one of the product terms in the equations for the J and K inputs on each of the applicable flip-flops.

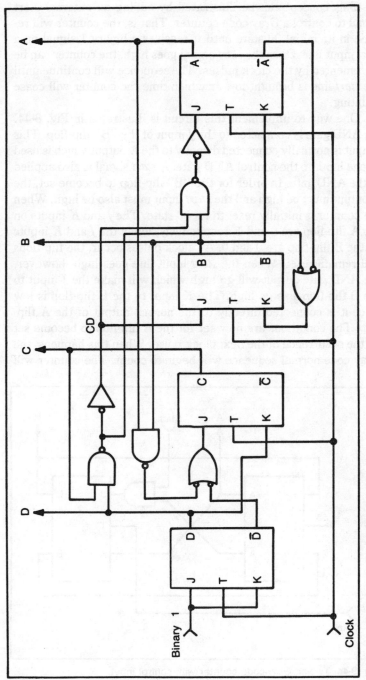

Fig. 8-43. Excess-3 BCD counter circuit.

This concept can be illustrated by adding an external start signal to control a Gray code counter. That is, the counter will remain in its initial 00 state until it receives a binary 1 signal on a *start* input line. Once the *start* signal goes high, the counter can be incremented by the clock pulses. The sequence will continue until the *start* line is brought low at which time the counter will cease counting.

One way to implement this circuit is illustrated in Fig. 8-44. An AND gate is connected to the *J* input of the "B" flip-flop. This J input is normally connected directly to the $\overline{A}$ output which is used as one input to the control AND gate. A *start* signal is also applied to the AND gate. In order for the "B" flip-flop to become set, the $\overline{A}$ output must be high and the *start* input must also be high. When the counter is initially reset to its 00 state. The *J* and *K* inputs on the A flip-flop are 0 and 1, respectively, while the *J* and *K* inputs on the B flip-flop are 0 and 0. As clock pulses occur, the flip-flops will remain reset. When the *start* input line goes high, however, the AND gate output will go high which will make the J input to the B flip-flop also go high. The K input to the B flip-flop is low since it is connected directly to the normal output of the A flip-flop. The conditions are now set for the B flip-flop to become set on the occurrence of the next clock pulse. When this happens, the Gray code normal sequence will begin to count. The counter will

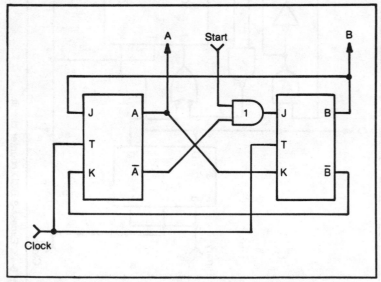

Fig. 8-44. Two-bit Gray-code counter with control input.

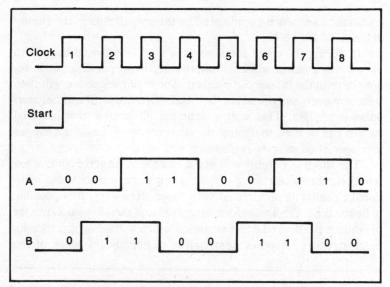

Fig. 8-45. Timing diagram of the two-bit Gray-code counter.

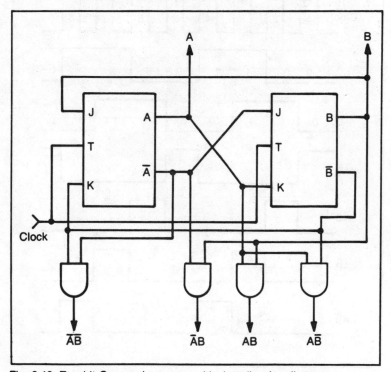

Fig. 8-46. Two-bit Gray-code counter with decoding for all states.

399

continue to sequence as indicated by the waveforms in the timing diagram of Fig. 8-45.

If, during the count sequence, the *start* line should happen to go low, the counter will continue to run the proper Gray code sequence until the 00 state is reached. The count sequence will then stop, however, and remain in the reset (00) state until another *start* pulse is applied. This simple example illustrates how external signals can be used to control the occurrence of the state changes in a special counter or sequencer.

The flip-flop outputs will often be able to directly control external circuits when using a special sequencer circuits. No additional circuitry is required in such cases. However, it is possible to define the control waveforms required and *then* design a counter to produce the desired count sequence which will subsequently minimize circuitry. Another approach is to decode the state of the

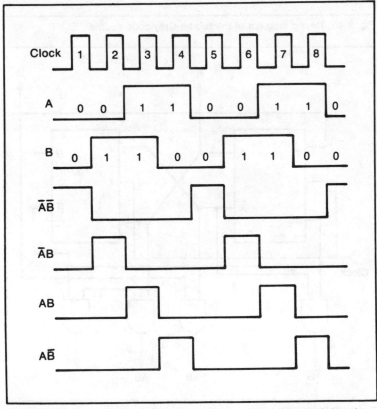

Fig. 8-47. Timing diagram for the two-bit Gray-code counter and decoder.

special counter to obtain a sequence of timing pulses. AND gates can be connected to the outputs of the flip-flops to recognize each unique state the counter produces. These decoder output gates can then be used to control the sequence of operations in external circuits.

How all four states of the 2-bit Gray code counter are decoded is shown in Fig. 8-46. The output signals produced by the decoder gates are illustrated in Fig. 8-47. As the counter steps from one state to the next one, a sequence of timing pulses is generated. The external circuits are controlled by these timing pulses. To create the necessary timing pulses in some applications, all states must be decoded. However, only specific states may be required in other applications which can minimize the number of necessary decoder gates. MSI decoder circuits can be used for 3-bit and 4-bit counters to reduce the amount of circuitry required to decode the desired states.

Appendix

Appendix

Appendix

Design A Digital Die

The purpose of this Appendix is to give you practice in designing digital integrated circuitry. The problem presented here combines both combinational and sequential logic design. Keep in mind that there is no single "perfect" way of designing or implementing a given circuit. For most applications, many methods are suitable.

Many games use dice to randomly select a number. It is possible to design and construct digital dice which simulate the marks on the dice with LEDs. Figure A-1 illustrates the arrangement of LEDs labeled T through Z. The numbers 1 through 6 will be represented in the standard die format when the appropriate LEDs are illuminated. The objective of this design is to develop the circuitry necessary to randomly select a number from 1 through 6 and display it. Assume that each of the LEDs is driven by a saturated pnp transistor switch as shown in Figure A-2A. The type of transistor and the values of R1 and R2 are not critical, with the exception that the value of resistor R2 must be such that the transistor will saturate, and the LED illuminate upon the application of a binary 1 level input to the resistor. An open-collector TTL inverter may replace the transistor, as indicated in Fig. A-2B.

In starting this design, a helpful starting point would be to assume that the random nature of the circuit is derived from a high-speed clock oscillator. When the oscillator is enabled, the logic circuit will be rapidly stepped through the necessary states. The intermittent pressing of a control pushbutton for the clock oscillator

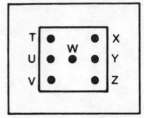

Fig. A-1. Arrangement of spots on a die, with spots identified.

will "pseudo-randomly" determine when the clock starts and stops and at what state the die circuit will be in when it begins and when it ends. This pseudo-random technique will produce sufficiently random results for fair die operation.

The complete circuit can be broken down into four basic sections. These are:

1. A clock circuit
2. A 6-state counter
3. A code converter
4. The LED display

These sections are shown properly interconnected in the simplified block diagram of Fig. A-3.

A six-state counter is required for the sequential circuit, since there are six possible combinations of illuminated LEDs. A clock

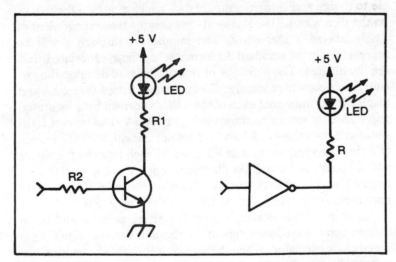

Fig. A-2. (A) Discrete component LED driver circuit. (B) TTL open-collector inverter LED driver.

406

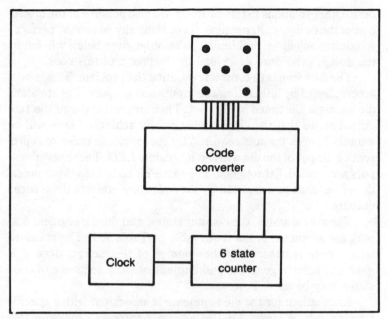

Fig. A-3. Simplified block diagram of the digital die.

circuit is used to step the counter. The speed of the clock should be high enough to prevent the user from being able to control the outcome. If the clock is too slow, the user can observe the individual state changes and stop the clock at a desired state. Any frequency above approximately 50 Hz should be satisfactory.

A specific binary code is generated by the six-state counter. This code can be almost any desired sequence of binary states. To represent the six states, a three-bit counter will be required. Since a three-bit counter will produce a maximum of $2^3 = 8$ states, two of these states won't be required and can be considered as "don't care" states.

The output of the six-state counter drives a code converter in which the code developed by the six-state counter is converted into the proper logic output signals to drive the LEDs in the display. This is a two-part design problem as can be seen from Fig. A-3. A six-state counter must first be designed and then an appropriate code converter. The die display has already been specified as well as the driver circuit as shown in Fig. A-2. The clock circuit can be any astable free-running multivibrator with a pushbutton switch employed to start and stop it.

One possible solution to this design problem will be presented here. Other solutions to this problem are also possible at the discretion of the designer. Remember there is usually no single "perfect" solution to any given problem! The solution given below will follow the design procedure described in Chapter 8 of this book.

The first step is to completely define the problem. This is best accomplished by illustrating the inputs and outputs. The standard die format is illustrated in Fig. A-4. These represent the six discrete output states that the circuit must finally achieve. There will be a total of seven outputs required by the circuit in order to represent each spot of the die with an individual LED. These seven outputs are labeled T through Z. The three-bit code from the counter, therefore, must be converted by the code converter into these seven outputs.

The six die states, the counter states, and the die segment outputs are all shown in the truth table of Table A-1. The standard binary code is chosen for the counter of this design since it is generally easy to generate and implement. Any sequence of code states may be used, however.

Each output for the die segments is associated with a specific counter state. A binary 1 in the column T through Z indicates that the associated LED will be turned on. This truth table can be verified by referring to the die formats in Fig. A-4. The design problem, therefore, is completely defined in the truth table of Table A-1. Note that the 110 and 111 states for the counter are not used and can, therefore, be considered as "don't care" states.

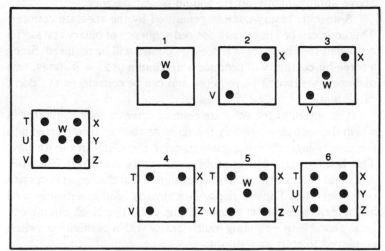

Fig. A-4. The six possible "sides" of the digital die.

Die state	State of counter			Die segments						
	A	B	C	T	U	V	W	X	Y	Z
1	0	0	0	0	0	0	1	0	0	0
2	0	0	1	0	0	1	0	1	0	0
3	0	1	0	0	0	1	1	1	0	0
4	0	1	1	1	0	1	0	1	0	1
5	1	0	0	1	0	1	1	1	0	1
6	1	0	1	1	1	1	0	1	1	1
	1	1	0	} Don't care						
	1	1	1							

To implement a six-state counter which steps in the standard binary code shown in the truth table is the first part of the design. By using Karnaugh maps as shown in Fig. A-5, the design can be developed. A separate Karnaugh map for each flip-flop is used. The appropriate symbols used to indicate the state change as specified by the counter state table are inserted into their respective cells. The various cells can then be properly grouped to specify the J and K inputs. The input equations for each J-K flip-flop are developed from the completed Karnaugh maps. The proper equations for each flip-flop are shown in Fig. A-5 and can be implemented with J-K flip-flops and SSI logic gates.

The next step is to design a code converter which will translate the six-state binary code into the proper output code specified by the die segments as shown in Table A-1. This is accomplished by writing the equation for each of the outputs, T through Z, and then implementing them. However, it is desirable to initially study the truth tables to determine any simplifications the tables may suggest. Upon careful examination, it can be concluded that outputs T and Z, U and Y, and V and X are equal. The output equations and, therefore, the resulting respective circuits are the same for each of the equal outputs. This means the total number of output equations can be reduced from seven to only four. For circuit minimization, the designer can now proceed directly to the Karnaugh maps which are shown in Fig. A-6A, B, C, and D. The "don't care" states are designated with the symbol "X." In these maps, each output expression is minimized and the minimum output equation for each die segment is given.

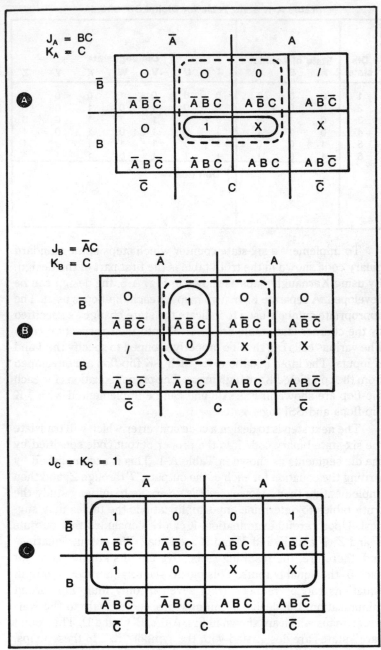

Fig. A-5. Karnaugh maps defining six-state counter. (J is denoted by a solid line and K is denoted by a broken line.)

410

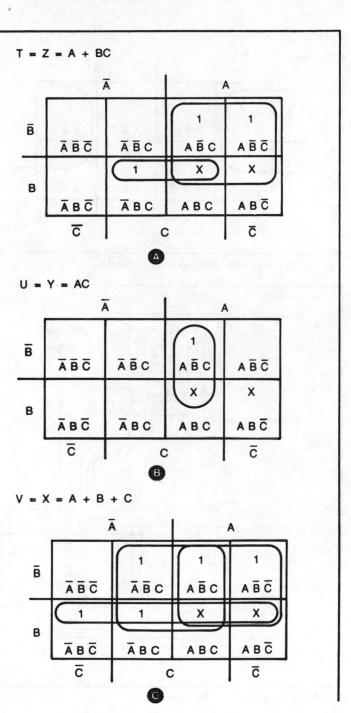

T = Z = A + BC

A

U = Y = AC

B

V = X = A + B + C

C

411

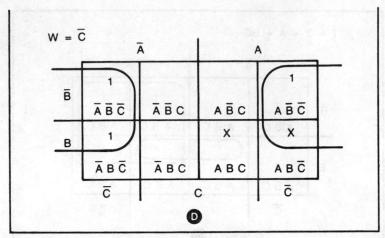

Fig. A-6. Karnaugh maps defining code converter.

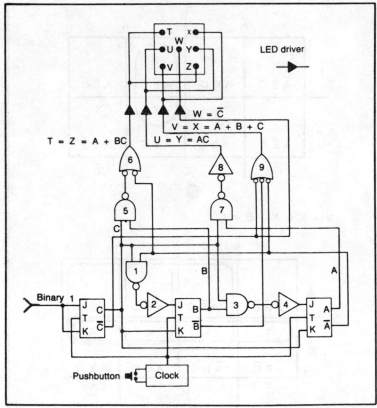

Fig. A-7. Logic diagram of the digital die.

412

The complete logic diagram for the circuit is shown in Fig. A-7. The six-state counter is implemented with J-K flip-flops, A, B, and C. To implement the logic inputs specified by the counter design, gates *1* and *3* and inverters *2* and *4* are used. Gates *5, 6, 7,* and *9* and inverter *8* are used to implement the logic equations for the code converter. Each solid triangle represents an LED driver circuit as shown in Fig. A-2.

Index

Index

417

418

Other Bestsellers From TAB

Other Bestsellers From TAB